Reader's Digest

BEAT
HIGH BLOOD
PRESSURE
COOKBOOK

Control your blood pressure and enjoy great food

Published by the Reader's Digest Association Limited
London • New York • Sydney • Montreal

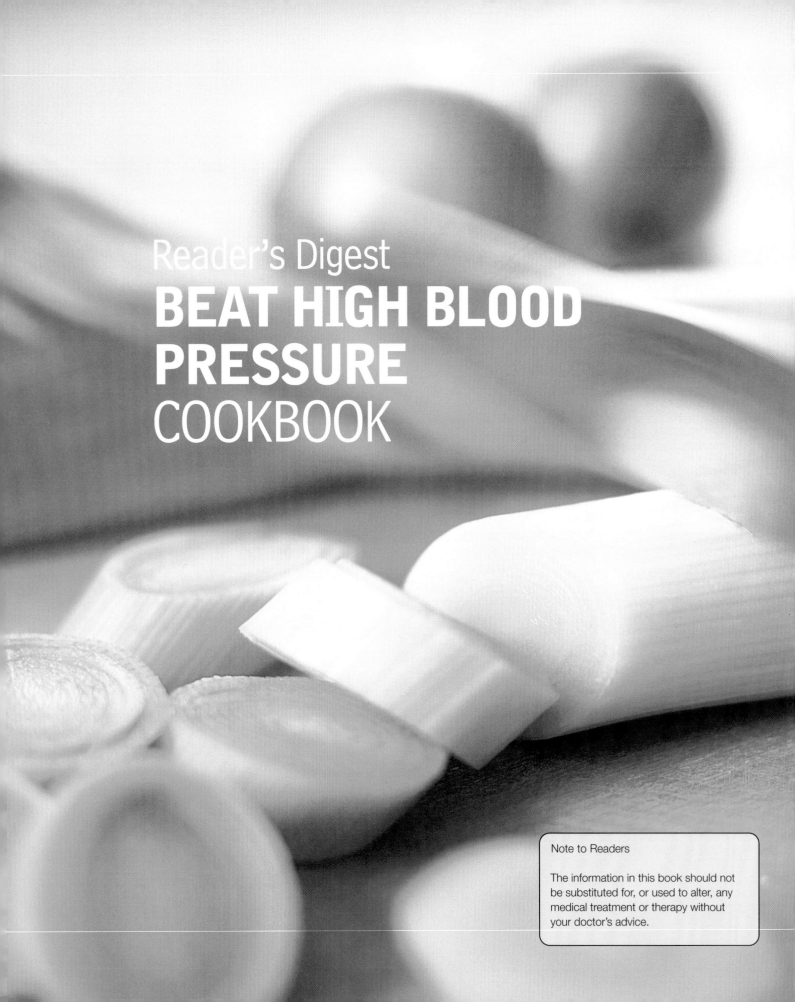

Reader's Digest
BEAT HIGH BLOOD PRESSURE
COOKBOOK

Introduction

Working on the *Beat High Blood Pressure Cookbook* has been a great education for everyone involved. First it was a case of understanding the role of food in managing high blood pressure – a role much greater than any of us had previously realised. Then it was a question of selecting the most appropriate recipes and making sure that they were as delicious and varied as possible. That is the challenge – and pleasure – of putting together a cookbook with two goals: to offer wonderfully tasty meals and to provide a plan to defeat one of the most serious health concerns of our times.

We hope you agree that we have succeeded in both. The recipes in the *Beat High Blood Pressure Cookbook* were chosen for taste, easy preparation and cooking, and accessible ingredients. Thumb through the pages and we are certain your mouth will water at what you see. This is great everyday food – popular dishes with a fresh twist, fun and easy to prepare, and oh-so-delicious. Even if you completely ignore the health sections of the book, we're certain you will still find this one of the freshest and most useful cookbooks in your kitchen.

But as much as we at Reader's Digest love great food, we are also passionate about health. And we believe and hope that we have put together a powerful and effective, all-natural plan for beating high blood pressure. The Beat High Blood Pressure Plan is based on a highly respected US dietary strategy for reducing high blood pressure — the so-called DASH, or Dietary Approaches to Stop Hypertension. We have translated this for a British public and expanded it to include a lifestyle programme that includes many other elements that research has proved can significantly reduce blood pressure.

Based on the science now available, it is fair to assume that you may be able to reduce your blood pressure by as much as 10 per cent – and quickly – by following our Beat High Blood Pressure plan. The key is enjoying a low-salt diet with dishes as delicious as those you'll find in the following pages. Add plenty of potassium-rich fruit and vegetables as this magic mineral has been shown scientifically to help reduce high blood pressure. Stay active and keep your weight in check. People who follow these tenets have achieved not only significantly lower blood pressure but also lower cholesterol and greater energy as well. And imagine the morale-boosting effect of achieving such important health goals.

High blood pressure has become a major threat to the UK's health. But unlike other serious diseases, it is mostly caused – and controlled – by diet and basic life choices. With the *Beat High Blood Pressure Cookbook*, we've tried to make the right choices as easy and delectable as possible. Try these recipes, follow the plan, and you, too, can join the ranks of those who have beaten the silent but deadly disease of high blood pressure. And what a pleasure it will have been.

Cortina Butler
EDITOR-IN-CHIEF, READER'S DIGEST BOOKS

CONTENTS

The recipes

9 Breakfast & brunch

39 Starters & snacks

59 Meat

77 Poultry

101 Seafood

117 Vegetarian

155 Main dish salads

189 Side dishes

221 Soups & stews

241 Sweet things

Defining blood pressure 274

Eat to beat high blood pressure 282

Beyond food 292

The Beat High Blood Pressure Plan 297

Four weeks of great eating 302

The Daily Tracker 310

Health glossary 311

Index 313

Breakfast & brunch

High-vitality milk shake, 10

Banana and apricot smoothie, 11

Banana and mango shake, 12

Strawberry-yoghurt smoothie, 13

Fruity muesli, 14

Sweet couscous, 16

Pepper and potato omelette, 17

Mushroom and herb omelette, 18

Potato, sweetcorn and pepper frittata, 20

Zesty Cheddar and asparagus quiche, 21

Breakfast sausage burgers, 22

Whole-grain griddle cakes with fruit and yoghurt, 23

Pecan waffles with maple, pear and blackberry sauce, 24

Multi-grain waffles with apple-raspberry sauce, 25

Blueberry swirl brunch cake, 26

Orange, raisin and walnut bread, 28

Parmesan and spring onion puffs, 29

Blueberry muffins with lemon glaze, 30

Cherry and oat muffins, 32

Spicy apple muffins, 33

Peaches and cream bread, 34

Maple and toasted walnut bread, 35

Herb and Cheddar scones, 36

Corn bread, 38

The recipes

Starters & snacks

Double-cheese pizza bites, 40

Roast pepper pinwheels, 42

Beef satay with ginger dipping sauce, 43

Little chicken salad rolls, 44

Portobello pizzas, 46

Heavenly devilled eggs, 47

Sausage-stuffed chestnut mushrooms, 48

Chicken dumplings with sesame dipping sauce, 50

Parmesan breadsticks, 51

Guacamole with a kick, 52

Hot crab dip, 53

Crudités with three dips, 54

Spicy root vegetable wedges with creamy mustard dip, 56

Pitta crisps with hummus, 57

Spiced fruits, nuts and seeds, 58

Meat

Sizzling beef fajitas, 60

Succulent meat loaf, 62

Roast beef hash, 63

Stir-fried beef salad with mango, 64

Seared sirloin with garden vegetables, 66

Fusilli and meatballs, 67

Pesto-coated pork chops, 68

Cidered pork with red cabbage, 70

Lamb curry, 71

Fragrant lamb with spinach, 72

Leg of lamb with double mint sauce, 74

Veal Marsala, 75

Veal escalopes with lemon-garlic sauce, 76

Poultry

Citrus-grilled chicken breasts with melon salsa, 78

Chicken with apples, 80

Basmati chicken pilaf, 81

Poached chicken breasts in vegetable and herb sauce, 82

Greek chicken pitta pockets, 83

Sautéed chicken with caramelised onions, 84

Chicken and cashew pancakes, 86

Chicken en papillote with carrots and courgettes, 87

Country Captain chicken, 88

Moroccan chicken with couscous, 90

Chicken with rosemary and orange sauce, 92

Orange-glazed poussins, 93

Chicken jamboree, 94

Chicken and apricot casserole, 95

Turkey piccata, 96

Turkey escalopes with fruity sauce, 98

Turkey Stroganoff, 99

Spicy turkey chilli with spaghetti, 100

THE RECIPES

Seafood

Poached salmon with cucumber-dill sauce, 102

Lemon-glazed plaice fillets, 103

Sole en papillote, 104

Scallop and cherry tomato sauté, 106

Crispy tuna steaks in citrus sauce, 107

Spaghettini with seafood, 108

Classic grilled Dover sole, 110

Steamed fish with ginger and sesame, 111

Sauté of king prawns, 112

Grilled salmon with pepper and sweetcorn relish, 114

Fish baked on a bed of broccoli, sweetcorn and red pepper, 115

Summer salmon and asparagus, 116

Vegetarian

Baked rice with wild mushrooms and cheese, 118

Spanish rice, 119

Rice pilaf with dried fruits and almonds, 120

Bulghur wheat with spring vegetables, 122

Sunny risotto with carrots, 124

Barley pilaf with herbs, 125

Quinoa pilaf with cherries and walnuts, 126

Millet with spinach and pine nuts, 127

Kasha with onions and mushrooms, 128

Lentil risotto, 130

Wild rice with walnuts, 131

Nutty lemon barley, 132

Cracked wheat pilaf with tomato, onions and basil, 133

Refried bean burritos, 134

Tuscan-style baked polenta, 136

Chickpea and vegetable eggah, 137

Three beans and rice, 138

Spicy lentil dhal, 139

Falafel pittas, 140

Lentils with macaroni, 141

Saffron couscous with peppers, 142

Braised vegetables with falafel and yoghurt sauce, 144

Green pasta with white beans, 145

Persian-style squash couscous, 146

Penne primavera, 148

Noodles with roast vegetables, 149

Tagliatelle with mushroom medley, 150

Cold sesame noodles and vegetables, 152

Spaghetti with chickpeas and spicy tomato sauce, 153

Linguine with no-cook sauce, 154

Main dish salads

Oriental chicken salad, 156

Barley, black bean and avocado salad, 158

Warm sesame chicken salad, 159

Curry chicken and rice salad, 160

Marinated duck and kasha salad, 162

Crab and grapefruit salad, 163

Mango chicken salad, 164

Indian-style rice with turkey, 166

Marinated duck salad with bulghur, 167

Pork and pear salad with pecans, 168

Garden pasta salad, 169

Roast beef and rice salad, 170

Tabbouleh with goat's cheese, 172

Tropical beef and rice salad, 173

Lemony lentil and vegetable salad, 174

Turkey salad with red cabbage, 175

Fresh artichoke and crab salad, 176

Sweet-and-sour duck salad, 178

Steakhouse salad, 179

Peachy cottage cheese salad, 180

Prawns with dill dressing, 181

Sweetcorn and whole grain salad, 182

Avocado and prawn cups, 184

Creamy turkey salad with grapes and pecans, 185

Apple and date salad, 186

Pasta salad with cucumber salsa, 187

Warm kasha and seafood salad, 188

Side dishes

Asparagus with confetti vinaigrette, 190

Country-style mashed potatoes, 191

Orange-glazed carrots, 192

Mangetout with apples and ginger, 194

Pan-roasted new potatoes with garlic, 195

Sesame stir-fried asparagus and peas, 196

Balsamic baked tomatoes with Parmesan crumbs, 197

Lemony sugarsnap peas, 198

Curried mushrooms, peas and potatoes, 200

Crispy cauliflower with Parmesan and almonds, 201

Tex-Mex sweetcorn pudding, 202

Squash and aubergine casserole, 203

Sweetcorn fritters, 204

Sweet-and-sour cabbage, 206

Boston baked beans, 207

Black-eyed beans with sweet peppers, 208

Vegetable stir-fry with spicy garlic sauce, 209

Spicy red cabbage parcels, 210

Indian style okra with potatoes, 212

Braised cabbage, apple and caraway, 213

Stuffed jacket-baked potatoes, 214

Brussels sprouts and potatoes with caraway-mustard sauce, 215

Avocado salad with raspberries, 216

Hot cabbage and grape coleslaw, 218

Oriental sprouted salad, 219

Crunchy nut coleslaw, 220

Soups & stews

Asparagus and pea soup, 222

Cream of courgette soup, 223

Cool blueberry soup, 224

Peach soup with almonds, 226

Cream of leek and potato soup, 227

Mediterranean roasted vegetable soup, 228

Cheddar cheese and broccoli soup, 229

Old-fashioned chicken noodle soup, 230

New England clam chowder, 232

Soup of leafy greens and herbs, 233

Minestrone with meatballs, 234

Beefy mushroom and barley soup, 236

Tomato and lentil soup, 237

Chickpea soup with asparagus, 238

Moroccan vegetable tagine, 239

Speedy two-bean chilli, 240

Sweet things

Frozen pineapple and berry slush, 242

Mango, peach and apricot fizz, 244

Tomato and citrus blush, 245

Fruit boats with orange glaze, 246

Far Eastern fruit salad, 247

Raspberry frozen yoghurt, 248

Ambrosia, 250

Flamed pineapple, 251

Apple crumble, 252

Fruit with apricot-chocolate cream, 253

Fresh plum tartlets, 254

Chequerboard cherry pie, 256

Banana custard tart, 257

Daffodil cake, 258

Cappuccino cake, 259

Oaty chocolate chip cookies, 260

Pecan biscuits, 262

Chocolate snacking cakes, 263

Lemon angel cake with strawberries, 264

Ginger and pear upside-down cake, 265

Lemon mousse with strawberries, 266

Blueberry bavarian, 268

Chewy muesli bars, 269

Old-fashioned glazed gingerbread, 270

Chocolate-nut meringues, 271

The recipes

It's good food time.

In front of you are hundreds of recipes for healthy

dishes that are easy to prepare, featuring fresh

ingredients and wonderful flavours.

Each dish has been chosen for its taste and

the nutrients it contains, such as potassium,

that help to maintain healthy blood pressure.

So enjoy cooking, enjoy the food and stay well.

Breakfast & brunch

High-vitality milk shake

This satisfying 'breakfast in a glass' makes a great energising start to the day. It is ideal for people in a hurry or those who aren't keen on eating in the morning.

Preparation time **5 minutes**   *Serves 2*

350ml (12fl oz) skimmed milk, chilled

225g (8oz) plain low-fat yoghurt

juice of 1 large orange

1 large banana, sliced

1 tsp clear honey

1 tbsp wheatgerm

1 Place all the ingredients in a blender or food processor and process for a couple of minutes until smooth and creamy.

2 Pour into two tall glasses and enjoy immediately, while the milk shake is still frothy.

Some more ideas

Berry shake Use 175g (6oz) strawberries instead of banana. Raspberries are good too, or try the chopped flesh of 1 mango.

• Replace the wheatgerm with 1 tbsp ground sunflower seeds (grind them in a clean coffee grinder or with a pestle and mortar).

• Use low-fat vanilla frozen yoghurt instead of plain yoghurt.

Health points

• The addition of wheatgerm boosts the content of vitamin E and B vitamins in this recipe, and orange juice provides vitamin C, so this is truly a 'high vitality' drink.

Each serving provides

Key nutrients 220kcals, 1g fat (of which 0g is saturated fat), 13g protein, 35g carbohydrate, 160mg sodium (0.4g salt), 1.1g fibre

Good source of potassium (877mg)

Banana and apricot smoothie

Milk shakes used to be dense in calories and low in nutrients. Today fruity smoothies have reinvented how we use the blender. 'Shakes' are now fresher and lighter, made with fruit and yoghurt, or fruit juice and milk, and bursting with nutrients.

Preparation time **10 minutes**   *Serves 4*

2 large bananas, thickly sliced

1 can (about 400g) apricot halves in natural juice

225g (8oz) plain low-fat bio yoghurt

4 tsp chopped fresh mint

1 tbsp honey

250ml (8fl oz) orange juice

sprigs of fresh mint to garnish

1 Put the bananas, apricots and their juice, yoghurt, mint and honey into a food processor or blender, and blend to a smooth purée, scraping down the sides of the container once or twice. If you like your smoothies cold, add a few ice cubes to the mix. The blending will take longer as the blades pulverise the ice. Add the orange juice and blend briefly until mixed.

2 Pour the smoothie into tall glasses and garnish with sprigs of mint. Serve immediately.

Some more ideas

Strawberry and banana smoothie Instead of apricots use 225g (8oz) strawberries. Reserve 4 strawberries and blend the remainder with the bananas and yoghurt (there is no need to add honey or mint). Mix in apple juice in place of the orange juice. Stir in the grated zest and juice of 1 lime. Pour into glasses and garnish each one with a reserved strawberry skewered on a cocktail stick and placed across the top of the glass.

Peach and cinnamon smoothie Blend 1 can (about 400g) peaches in natural juice with 1 tbsp caster sugar, ½ tsp ground cinnamon, and the bananas and yoghurt. Add skimmed milk in place of the orange juice. Sprinkle the top of each smoothie with a little extra cinnamon.

Health points

• These drinks are completely additive-free, unlike many shop-bought versions.

Each serving provides

Key nutrients 156kcals, 1g fat (of which 1g is saturated fat), 5g protein, 35g carbohydrate, 59mg sodium (0.15g salt), 1.5g fibre

Useful source of potassium (646mg)

Banana and mango shake

A thick banana-flavoured milk shake with a tropical touch, this will certainly appeal to children and adults alike. It is filling, nourishing and quick – as appropriate for dessert as it is for breakfast.

Preparation time **5 minutes**   *Serves 2*

½ ripe mango

1 small ripe banana, sliced

125ml (4fl oz) skimmed milk

125ml (4fl oz) orange juice

2 tsp lime juice

1 tsp caster sugar

2 heaped tbsp vanilla frozen yoghurt

sprigs of fresh mint to garnish

1 Peel the skin from the mango and cut the flesh away from the stone. Chop the flesh roughly. Put into a blender with the banana.

2 Add the milk, orange juice, lime juice, sugar and frozen yoghurt, and blend on maximum speed for 30 seconds or until mixed and frothy.

3 Pour into glasses and serve immediately, garnished with sprigs of mint.

Some more ideas

• Use soya milk instead of cow's milk; omit the frozen yoghurt or use soya ice cream.

• Substitute a ripe peach for the mango half.

• For a shake rich in fibre, use 115g (4oz) pitted prunes instead of the mango, and lemon instead of lime juice.

Health points

• Milk is an excellent source of several important nutrients, such as protein, calcium and phosphorus (important for strong bones and teeth), and many of the B vitamins, particularly B_1, B_2, B_6 and B_{12}.

• Bananas are a good source of potassium, which helps regulate blood pressure as well as being vital for muscle and nerve function. They are also naturally sweet.

• Mangoes are rich in carotenoid compounds and vitamin C, both antioxidants that protect the body against damage by free radicals.

Each serving provides   Key nutrients 121kcals, 0.6g fat (of which 0.2g is saturated fat), 4g protein, 27g carbohydrate, 48mg sodium (0.12g salt), 1.5g fibre

Useful source of potassium (464mg)

Strawberry yoghurt smoothie

This refreshing drink is perfect for summer, when strawberries are plentiful and full of flavour and vitamins. It takes only a few minutes to prepare, so it is ideal as a nourishing start to the day or as a snack-in-a-glass at any time.

Preparation time **5 minutes**   *Serves 4*

450g (1lb) ripe strawberries, hulled

grated zest and juice of 1 large orange

225g (8oz) plain low-fat yoghurt

1 tbsp caster sugar, or to taste *(optional)*

To garnish

4 small strawberries

4 small slices of orange

1 Put the strawberries in a food processor or blender and add the grated orange zest, orange juice and yoghurt. Blend to a smooth purée, scraping down the sides of the container once or twice. Taste the mixture and sweeten with the sugar, if required.

2 For a really smooth consistency, press through a sieve to remove the strawberry seeds.

3 Pour into glasses. Garnish with small strawberries and slices of orange, both split so they sit on the rim of the glass.

Some more ideas

Apricot yoghurt smoothie
Use dried apricots to make a smoothie with an extra charge of beta-carotene and fibre. Gently simmer 200g (7oz) ready-to-eat dried apricots in 900ml (1½ pints) of strained Earl Grey tea for about 30 minutes or until tender. Cool, then pour the apricots and liquid into a blender. Add the orange zest and juice and yoghurt, and blend until smooth. Taste and sweeten with sugar, if required.

• Add a sliced banana to the strawberries. This will thicken the texture of the smoothie and will also add natural sweetness, so taste before adding sugar. You may not need any.

Health points

• Strawberries contain higher levels of vitamin C than any other berries. And, despite their sweetness, 115g (4oz) of strawberries contain fewer than 32kcals!

photo, page 15

Each serving provides   Key nutrients 85kcals, 1g fat (of which 0.3g is saturated fat), 4g protein, 17g carbohydrate, 56mg sodium (0.14 salt) 1g fibre

Useful source of potassium (360mg)

Fruity muesli

This breakfast cereal was invented over a century ago by Dr Bircher-Benner at his clinic in Zürich to improve children's diets. Soaking the cereal – here using milk – makes it easier to eat and digest.

Preparation time **10 minutes, plus overnight soaking**   *Serves 4*

115g (4oz) rolled oats

115g (4oz) sultanas

250ml (9fl oz) skimmed milk

1 apple

2 tsp lemon juice

25g (1oz) hazelnuts, roughly chopped

15g (½oz) pumpkin seeds

1 tbsp sesame seeds

100g (3½oz) strawberries, chopped

4 tbsp plain low-fat yoghurt

4 tsp honey

1 Place the oats and sultanas in a large bowl and add the milk. Stir to mix evenly, then cover and place in the refrigerator. Leave to soak overnight.

2 The next day, just before eating, grate the apple, discarding the core. Toss the apple with the lemon juice to prevent browning.

3 Stir the hazelnuts, pumpkin seeds and sesame seeds into the oat mixture, then stir in the grated apple and strawberries.

4 To serve, divide the muesli among four cereal bowls, and top each with a spoonful of yoghurt and honey.

Some more ideas

Mango muesli Soak the rolled oats in buttermilk instead of milk. Just before eating, stir in 25g (1oz) roughly chopped almonds and 20g (¾oz) sunflower seeds, then add 1 roughly mashed banana and 1 chopped mango. Serve the muesli topped with plain low-fat bio yoghurt.

Health points

• Hazelnuts are a particularly good source of vitamin E and most of the B vitamins, apart from B_{12}. Like most other nuts, they have a high fat content; however, this is mostly the more beneficial monounsaturated fat.

• By making your own cereal, you know exactly what's in it and what's not! High levels of sodium, fat and sugar are missing from this nutritious cereal recipe.

Each serving provides   Key nutrients 315kcals, 9g fat (of which 1g is saturated fat), 9g protein, 53g carbohydrate, 58mg sodium (0.14g salt), 4g fibre

Useful source of potassium (687mg)

Fruity muesli *p14*

Strawberry yoghurt smoothie *p13*

Sweet couscous *p16*

Pepper and potato omelette *p17*

Sweet couscous

Couscous isn't just an accompaniment. It can be used for both savoury dishes and for sweet ones, such as this quickly made, delicious hot cereal that uses both dried and fresh fruit.

Preparation and cooking time **about 20 minutes**   *Serves 4*

225g (8oz) couscous

85g (3oz) raisins

85g (3oz) ready-to-eat pitted prunes, chopped

finely grated zest of 1 small orange

750ml (1¼ pints) skimmed milk

To serve

2 nectarines, sliced

8 tbsp virtually-fat-free fromage frais

1 Put the couscous in a bowl with the raisins, prunes and orange zest, and stir to mix thoroughly.

2 Pour the milk into a saucepan and bring just to the boil. Pour the hot milk over the couscous mixture, stirring well, then cover with foil. Leave to soak for about 10 minutes or until the couscous is plumped up and all the milk has been absorbed.

3 Spoon the couscous into bowls and top with sliced nectarines and fromage frais. Serve immediately.

Some more ideas

• Instead of raisins and prunes, use other dried fruit such as dried pears or peaches.

• Use the finely grated zest of 1 small pink grapefruit or lemon rather than orange zest.

Health points

• Prunes are a great source of fibre, vitamins, minerals and phytochemicals. They are also known to have a natural laxative effect.

photo, page 15

Each serving provides   **Key nutrients** 316kcals, 1.5g fat (of which 0.3g is saturated fat), 14g protein, 66g carbohydrate, 109mg sodium (0.27g salt), 2.5g fibre

Useful source of potassium (835mg)

Pepper and potato omelette

Here, a light-textured omelette is folded around red and green peppers and potatoes. Because egg whites replace some of the whole eggs, the omelette is very low in fat.

Preparation time **10 minutes**   Cooking time **18 minutes**   *Serves 2*

1 medium red-skinned potato, chopped (about 115g/4oz)

1 medium onion, chopped

75g (2¾oz) chopped green pepper

75g (2¾oz) chopped red pepper

2 medium eggs

3 medium egg whites

½ tsp Tabasco sauce

salt to taste

2 slices wholemeal bread, toasted

1 Preheat the oven to 200°C (400°F, gas mark 6). Coat a 20cm (8in) ovenproof nonstick frying pan with cooking spray or a teaspoon of olive oil and set over a medium heat. Add the potato and sauté for 5 minutes or until soft.

2 Stir in the onion and green and red peppers. Sauté for a further 5 minutes or until soft. Remove the pan from the heat and transfer the vegetables to a plate. Coat the pan again with oil or cooking spray and return to the heat.

3 Whisk together the eggs, egg whites, Tabasco sauce and salt in a medium bowl. Pour into the hot pan and cook until the base is set, lifting up the edge with a heatproof rubber spatula to let the uncooked egg flow underneath.

4 Spoon the vegetables over half of the omelette and fold it over the filling. Transfer the pan to the oven and bake for 3 minutes or until the omelette is completely set. Cut the omelette in half and serve with toast.

Some more ideas

• Add 115g (4oz) finely diced skinless, boneless chicken breast to the recipe. Sauté it with the onions and peppers in step 2.

• Make a soufflé omelette. Whisk the egg whites until stiff and fold them into the beaten whole eggs and Tabasco in step 3. The omelette will seem much bigger, but there is no change in calories!

Health points

• This omelette is a delicious way to get one of your daily servings of vegetables. When vegetables are used as an omelette filling, even finicky eaters will enjoy them.

photo, page 15

Each serving provides   **Key nutrients** 255kcals, 8g fat (of which 1g is saturated fat), 18g protein, 30g carbohydrate, 375mg sodium (0.94g salt), 5g fibre

Useful source of potassium (600mg)

Mushroom and herb omelette

An omelette is the ultimate impromptu meal, prepared quickly and easily from a few simple ingredients. This delicious version is filled with garlicky mushrooms. Serve as a lunch or supper with a green salad and warm, crusty bread.

Preparation time **5 minutes**   Cooking time **10 minutes**   *Serves 1*

2 large eggs

1 tsp chopped fresh chervil

1 tsp chopped fresh tarragon

1 tsp snipped fresh chives

1 tbsp water

salt and pepper to taste

55g (2oz) mushrooms, sliced

1 garlic clove, crushed

15g (½oz) unsalted butter

1 Crack the eggs into a bowl, then add the chervil, tarragon, chives, water and pepper to taste. Beat just enough to break up the eggs. Take care not to overbeat, as this will spoil the texture of the omelette. Set aside while preparing the mushrooms.

2 Heat an 18cm (7in) omelette pan or nonstick frying pan. Add the sliced mushrooms and garlic, and cook gently for 3–4 minutes or until the mushrooms have softened and released their juices. Turn up the heat a little and continue cooking for about 1 minute or until the mushroom juices have evaporated. Tip the mushrooms into a small bowl and set aside. Wipe the pan clean with kitchen paper.

3 Heat the pan over a high heat for a few seconds until hot. Add the butter and melt it, tilting the pan to coat the bottom. Pour in the egg and herb mixture. Cook for about 1 minute, stirring gently with a wooden spatula and pulling the cooked egg from the edge towards the centre to let the liquid egg flow on to the pan.

4 When the omelette holds together, stop stirring and cook for about 30 seconds or until the underside is golden brown. The top surface should be just setting.

5 Scatter the mushrooms along the middle third of the omelette. Using the spatula, fold an outside third of the omelette into the centre, over the mushrooms, then fold the opposite third over that. Quickly slide the folded omelette on to a warmed plate and serve immediately.

Some more ideas

Tomato and basil soufflé omelette Separate the eggs and beat the yolks with 1 tsp water, 2 tbsp torn fresh basil leaves, 4 deseeded and diced plum tomatoes and pepper to taste. Whisk the egg whites until stiff. Stir a spoonful into the egg yolk and tomato mixture, then carefully fold in the rest of the whites with a metal spoon. Preheat the grill to moderate. Melt 2 tsp butter in the omelette pan and pour in the egg and tomato mixture. Cook over a low heat for 2–3 minutes or until the underside of the omelette is lightly browned. Place the pan under the grill and cook for 2–3 minutes or until the top is golden brown and puffed up. Carefully fold the omelette in half, then slide on to a warmed plate and serve immediately.

Health points

• Chives are mild-flavoured miniature versions of the spring onion. They are believed to stimulate the appetite.

Each serving provides   Key nutrients 267kcals, 23g fat (of which 9g is saturated fat), 17g protein, 0.3g carbohydrate, 185mg sodium (0.46g salt), 0.6g fibre

Mushroom and herb omelette *p18*

Potato, sweetcorn and pepper frittata *p20*

Zesty Cheddar and asparagus quiche *p21*

Breakfast sausage burgers *p22*

Potato, sweetcorn and pepper frittata

Known in Italy as a frittata, or in Spain as a tortilla, a flat omelette can be served hot or at room temperature, at any meal. Take a tip from Spanish tapas bars and serve it, cut into bite-size pieces, instead of salty or high-fat snacks with drinks.

Preparation time **10 minutes**   Cooking time **about 20 minutes**   *Serves 4*

675g (1½lb) potatoes, peeled, quartered lengthwise, and thinly sliced across

1 red, yellow or orange pepper, deseeded and chopped

2 tbsp olive oil

1 onion, halved and thinly sliced

250g (9oz) frozen sweetcorn, thawed

6 eggs

4 tbsp finely chopped parsley

pepper to taste

1 Put the potatoes in a saucepan of boiling water. Bring back to the boil, then reduce the heat to a simmer. Add the chopped peppers and simmer for 3 minutes. Drain well, then cover and keep hot.

2 Heat a 25cm (10in) nonstick frying pan over a high heat. Add the oil to the pan and swirl it around. When the oil is hot, reduce the heat to medium. Add the onion and sauté, stirring often, for about 3 minutes or until softened.

3 Add the potatoes and pepper and the sweetcorn. Continue sautéing, stirring and turning the vegetables, for about 8 minutes or until the potatoes are tender. Remove the pan from the heat.

4 In a large bowl, beat the eggs with the parsley and pepper to taste. Use a slotted spoon to add the vegetables to the eggs, stirring them in thoroughly. (If any vegetables have stuck to the bottom of the pan, thoroughly clean and dry the pan before heating it with an additional 1 tbsp oil; however, this should not be necessary with a reliable nonstick pan.)

5 Replace the pan, with the oil remaining from cooking the vegetables, over a moderate heat. When the pan is hot, pour in the egg mixture, spreading out the vegetables evenly. Cook the frittata, shaking the pan frequently, for 3–4 minutes or until the edges are set and the top is beginning to look set.

6 Meanwhile, preheat the grill to the hottest setting. Place the frittata under the grill and cook for 2 minutes or until the top is just set. Pierce the top of the frittata with a knife to check that it is cooked through.

7 Remove the pan from under the grill and leave the frittata to set for 2 minutes, then slide it on to a serving plate. Serve hot or at room temperature, cut into wedges.

photo, page 19

Some more ideas

Fennel and courgette frittata
Replace the pepper, onion, and sweetcorn with 1 bulb of fennel, thinly sliced; 85g (3oz) mushrooms, thinly sliced; and 1 courgette, cut in half length-wise and thinly sliced across. Sauté these vegetables in the hot oil for 3 minutes before adding the partly cooked potatoes.

Pepper and potato frittata
Use 3 peppers (any colour) and 2 onions; omit the sweetcorn.

Health points

• Sweetcorn is a useful source of dietary fibre and vitamins A, C and folate. Although some vitamins are lost in canned sweetcorn, they are retained in the frozen vegetable.

• Potatoes and peppers both contribute vitamin C to this dish.

Each serving provides   Key nutrients 361kcals, 14.5g fat (of which 3g is saturated fat), 18g protein, 44g carbohydrate, 143mg sodium (0.36g salt), 4g fibre

Useful source of potassium (800mg)

Zesty Cheddar and asparagus quiche

How do you get the rich taste of a classic quiche with a fraction of the fat? One technique: make the case with thinly sliced potatoes. It's a heart-smart substitute for traditional shortcrust!

Preparation time **30 minutes**   Cooking time **45 minutes**   *Serves 6*

1 tbsp plain dried breadcrumbs

225g (8oz) small new potatoes, peeled and very thinly sliced

450g (1lb) asparagus, trimmed

pepper to taste

100g (3½oz) reduced-fat Cheddar cheese, grated

3 spring onions, sliced

1 can (about 410g) evaporated skimmed milk

3 medium eggs

1 teaspoon dry mustard

1 Preheat the oven to 200°C (400°F, gas mark 6). Coat a 23cm (9in) flan dish with cooking spray or a teaspoon of olive oil and sprinkle with the breadcrumbs. Beginning in the centre, arrange the potato slices in the dish, in slightly overlapping circles up to the rim. Lightly coat with cooking spray or oil and press down gently. Bake for 10 minutes.

2 Set 8–12 asparagus spears aside. Cut the remaining spears into 2.5cm (1in) pieces.

3 Sprinkle the potato case one-third of the cheese. Cover with the asparagus pieces, then sprinkle with the spring onions and another third of the cheese. Arrange the whole asparagus spears on top.

4 Beat together the evaporated milk, eggs, mustard and salt and pepper to taste. Pour into the dish and sprinkle with the remaining cheese. Bake for about 35 minutes or until a knife inserted in the centre of the filling comes out clean.

Some more ideas

• This versatile recipe tastes great with broccoli spears and chopped broccoli in place of the asparagus.

• You can change the cheese to reduced-fat mozzarella.

Health points

• One large egg has 6g of protein as well as vitamin E, folate, B vitamins and iron.

photo, page 19

Each serving provides   **Key nutrients** 220kcals, 10g fat (of which 4.5g is saturated fat), 18g protein, 17g carbohydrate, 258mg sodium (0.65g salt), 2g fibre

Useful source of potassium (633mg)

Breakfast sausage burgers

For a satisfying Sunday brunch, you can't beat homemade sausage burgers. By making them with turkey breast and some secret ingredients, the fat content falls to less than a gram a piece!

Preparation time **10 minutes**   Cooking time **6 minutes**   *Serves 12*

450g (1lb) skinless, boneless turkey breast

115g (4oz) cooked brown or basmati rice

4 tbsp puréed prunes

1 tbsp Dijon mustard

½ tsp dried sage

½ tsp dried rosemary, crumbled or finely chopped

1 Cut the turkey breast into large chunks. Place in a food processor and pulse until coarsely minced.

2 Transfer the minced turkey to a mixing bowl. Add the rice, prune purée, mustard, sage and rosemary, and stir just to combine.

3 Shape the mixture into 12 burgers about 5cm (2in) in diameter. Spray the grill pan with cooking spray or coat it with olive oil. Preheat the grill to moderate.

4 Place the burgers on the grill pan and grill for about 3 minutes on each side or until cooked through.

Some more ideas

• For easier mornings, make the sausage burgers the night before. Keep them, on a plate covered with cling film, in the refrigerator. Add an extra 30 seconds or so per side to the cooking time to compensate for the fact that the burgers are chilled.

• You can substitute minced chicken breast or lean minced pork for the turkey.

Health points

• Puréed prunes are great for healthy cooking. They replace the fat in this recipe, and can also be used as a substitute for butter, margarine or other fat when baking.

photo, page 19

Each serving provides   Key nutrients 83kcals, 0.5g fat (of which 0g is saturated fat), 10g protein, 10g carbohydrate, 35mg sodium (0.14g salt), 0.3g fibre

Whole-grain griddle cakes with fruit and yoghurt

Wheatgerm, rolled oats and wholemeal flour make these delicious griddle cakes high in fibre as well as iron and B vitamins. Raspberries or blueberries bring vitamin C to the nutritional party.

Preparation time **10 minutes**   Cooking time **15 minutes**   *Makes 16*

140g (5oz) wholemeal flour

20g (¾oz) rolled oats

1 tbsp wheatgerm, preferably toasted

2 tbsp soft light brown sugar

2 tsp baking powder

225ml (8fl oz) semi-skimmed milk

300g (10½oz) plain low-fat yoghurt

2 egg whites

225g (8oz) raspberries or blueberries

1 In a large bowl, mix together the flour, oats, wheatgerm, sugar and baking powder. In another bowl, beat the milk with 115g (4oz) of the yoghurt and the egg whites. Add to the flour mixture and stir quickly to moisten the dry ingredients.

2 Spray a nonstick griddle or frying pan with cooking spray or coat with a teaspoon of olive oil and heat until hot. (Do not use cooking spray near flame.) Use 2 tablespoons of batter for each griddle cake. Ladle into the hot pan, cooking 3 or 4 griddle cakes at a time.

3 When bubbles show on the surface, lift the cakes with a spatula. If browned underneath, turn over and cook until the other side is golden brown.

4 Transfer the griddle cakes to heated plates and serve with the berries and remaining yoghurt.

Some more ideas

• Try 100g (3½oz) buckwheat flour in place of the wholemeal flour.

• Replace one-third of the wholemeal flour with cornmeal (maize meal) or polenta.

Health points

• Batters for griddle cakes or drop scones usually contain vegetable oil or melted butter. Here milk and yoghurt provide the moisture, which makes the griddle cakes significantly lower in fat.

• You can store the griddle cakes in the freezer, then thaw quickly in the microwave or toaster, to enjoy as a change from breakfast cereal.

Each griddle cake provides   **Key nutrients** 85kcals, 1g fat (of which 0.5g is saturated fat), 4.5g protein, 15g carbohydrate, 139mg sodium (0.35g salt), 2g fibre

Pecan waffles with maple, pear and blackberry sauce

Crisp, crunchy waffles, so popular in France, Belgium and North America, are a lovely treat for breakfast or brunch. You will need a waffle iron that can be used on the hob, or an electric waffle maker.

Preparation time **20 minutes** Cooking time **10–15 minutes** *Makes 4*

125g (4½oz) plain flour

1 tsp baking powder

½ tsp ground cinnamon

1 tbsp caster sugar

1 large egg, separated

200ml (7fl oz) skimmed milk

15g (½oz) butter, melted

15g (½oz) pecan nuts, finely chopped

For the sauce

1 large, ripe dessert pear

4 tbsp maple syrup

50g (1¾oz) pecan nut halves

100g (3½oz) blackberries

1 First make the maple and fruit sauce. Cut the pear lengthways into quarters and cut out the core, then cut the pear into fine dice. Put into a small heavy saucepan and add the maple syrup. Warm gently, then remove the pan from the heat. Stir in the pecan nut halves and the blackberries. Set aside while making the waffles.

2 Heat and lightly oil the waffle iron or maker according to the manufacturer's instructions.

3 Meanwhile, make the waffle batter. Sift the flour, baking powder, cinnamon and sugar into a mixing bowl. Make a well in the centre and add the egg yolk and milk. Gently whisk the egg yolk and milk together, then gradually whisk in the flour to make a thick, smooth batter. Whisk in the melted butter, then stir in the finely chopped pecans.

4 Whisk the egg white in a separate bowl until stiff. Pile it on top of the batter and, using a large metal spoon, fold it in gently.

5 Spoon a small ladleful (3–4 tbsp) of batter into the centre of the hot waffle iron or maker, then close the lid tightly. After about 2–3 minutes, open the waffle iron: the waffle should be golden brown on both sides and should come away easily from the iron.

6 Lift the cooked waffle from the iron using a round-bladed knife. Keep warm while cooking the rest of the waffles.

7 Just before all the waffles are ready, gently warm the fruit sauce, then pour into a sauceboat or serving bowl. Serve with the warm waffles.

Some more ideas

Parmesan waffles Omit the cinnamon, sugar and pecans from the batter. Instead, sift the flour with a good pinch each of black pepper and cayenne pepper, and salt to taste. Add 2 tbsp freshly grated Parmesan cheese before folding in the egg white. Omit the fruit sauce.

• To keep waffles warm, spread them in a single layer on a rack in an oven set to its lowest temperature.

• Use walnuts instead of pecans, and either maple syrup or clear honey in the sauce.

Health points

• The pectin in pears is a good source of soluble fibre, which helps to lower blood cholesterol levels.

photo, page 27

Each serving (1 waffle) provides Key nutrients 360kcals, 16g fat (of which 3g is saturated fat), 8g protein, 48g carbohydrate, 180mg sodium (0.4g salt), 3.5g fibre

Useful source of potassium (369mg)

Multi-grain waffles with apple-raspberry sauce

The robust flavour of these waffles, made with wholemeal and buckwheat flours and linseed, is complemented by a sweet, tangy fruit sauce. The yield here is based on using a waffle iron or maker with two 10cm (4in) squares.

Preparation time **10 minutes**   Cooking time **15 minutes**   *Makes 8*

4 tbsp linseeds

4 tbsp wholemeal flour

4 tbsp buckwheat flour

4 tbsp plain white flour

2 tsp soft light brown sugar

2 tsp baking powder

1 medium egg, separated

225ml (8fl oz) buttermilk

2 medium egg whites

For the sauce

175ml (6fl oz) apple juice

2 dessert apples, cut into 1cm (½in) chunks

½ tsp vanilla extract

125g (4½oz) fresh raspberries

1 To make the sauce, bring the apple juice to the boil in a frying pan over a high heat and cook for 1 minute. Add the apples and simmer for 4 minutes or until just tender but still firm. Remove from the heat and leave to cool to room temperature. Stir in the vanilla extract and raspberries.

2 Place the linseeds in a mini food processor or spice grinder and grind to a coarse meal. Transfer to large bowl and add the wholemeal flour, buckwheat flour, plain white flour, brown sugar, baking powder and salt. Stir to mix well.

3 Combine the egg yolk and buttermilk in a small bowl. Whisk the 3 egg whites in a large bowl until stiff peaks form. Make a well in the centre of the dry ingredients and stir in the egg yolk mixture. Gently fold in the egg whites.

4 Heat a nonstick waffle iron or maker and spray it with cooking spray or oil it lightly with oilive oil. Spoon the batter into the iron, spreading it gently. Close and cook for about 2 minutes or until golden brown and crisp. Serve the waffles warm with the apple-raspberry sauce.

Some more ideas

• You can make the waffles partially or completely in advance. For the former, mix the dry ingredients and freeze in a resealable plastic bag. Just before cooking, add the eggs and buttermilk as instructed in the recipe. Or prepare and cook the waffles, then cool them and wrap in foil. Refrigerate or freeze. At serving time, toast in a toaster or under the grill. You can also make the sauce in advance.

• Use fresh blueberries in place of raspberries.

Health points

• Linseed oil is a rich source of omega-3 fatty acids, which help reduce the risk of heart disease and stroke. To make the linseeds' oil and fibre available to the body, the seeds need to be ground.

photo, page 27

Each serving (1 waffle) provides   Key nutrients 172kcals, 6g fat (of which 1g is saturated fat), 7g protein, 24g carbohydrate, 193mg sodium (0.49g salt), 3g fibre

Blueberry swirl brunch cake

This moist and tender cake is bursting with juicy berries. Brown sugar and cinnamon make it so melt-in-the-mouth delicious you won't believe it's so low in calories and fat.

Preparation time **20 minutes**   Cooking time **40 minutes**   *Serves 16*

375g (13oz) fresh or frozen blueberries

70g (2½oz) soft light brown sugar

1 tsp ground cinnamon

115g (4oz) butter, softened

200g (7oz) caster sugar

1 medium egg

1 medium egg white

1 tbsp grated lemon zest

350g (12oz) self-raising flour

300ml (10fl oz) semi-skimmed milk

1 Preheat the oven to 180°C (350°F, gas mark 4). Grease and flour a 33 x 23cm (13 x 9in) baking tin. In a small bowl, toss 300g (10½oz) of the blueberries with the brown sugar and cinnamon until the berries are coated.

2 Using an electric mixer at high speed, beat the butter with the caster sugar for about 2 minutes or until light and fluffy. Add the egg and egg white, and beat for 2 minutes. Beat in the lemon zest. Reduce the speed to low. Add the flour alternately with the milk, one-third at a time, stopping the mixer occasionally to scrape the bowl with a rubber spatula. Do not overbeat.

3 Spread half of the cake mixture in the tin and sprinkle with the blueberry mixture. Spoon the remaining cake mixture on top, spreading evenly. Swirl through several times with a knife, then top with the remaining blueberries.

4 Bake for 40–45 minutes or until a skewer inserted in the centre comes out clean. Leave to cool in the tin, set on a wire rack, for 15 minutes. Cut into 16 equal pieces. Serve warm or at room temperature.

Some more ideas

• Fresh raspberries or sliced strawberries work equally well in this recipe.

• Add orange zest in place of lemon zest and add 2 tbsp fresh orange juice to the cake mixture for more citrus flavour.

Health points

• Blueberries are very low in calories and high in vitamin C. They also have high antioxidant properties.

Each serving provides   **Key nutrients** 210kcals, 7g fat (of which 4g is saturated fat), 4g protein, 36g carbohydrate, 146mg sodium (0.37g salt), 1g fibre

Blueberry swirl brunch cake *p26*

Pecan waffles with maple, pear and blackberry sauce *p24*

Multi-grain waffles with apple-raspberry sauce *p25*

Orange, sultana and walnut bread *p28*

Orange, sultana and walnut bread

Inspired by Danish pastries, this bread is sure to become a breakfast or brunch favourite (and no one will suspect it's so low in fat). It's also wonderful with a cup of tea mid-afternoon.

Preparation time **30 minutes plus rising**   Cooking time **20 minutes**   *Serves 16*

500g (1lb 2oz) white bread flour

175g (6oz) caster sugar

1 sachet (7g/¼oz) easy-blend dried yeast

salt to taste

300ml (10floz) semi-skimmed milk

70g (2½oz) butter

1 medium egg, beaten

55g (2oz) walnuts, toasted and finely chopped

35g (1¼oz) sultanas

grated zest of 3 oranges

125g (4½oz) icing sugar, sifted

1–2 tbsp fresh orange juice

1 Mix 225g (8oz) flour, 70g (2½oz) caster sugar, the yeast and salt in a large bowl. Heat the milk and 55g (2oz) of the butter in a small saucepan until lukewarm. Stir into the flour mixture. Stir in the egg. Add another 175g (6oz) flour and stir vigorously for 2–3 minutes or until the dough pulls away from the side of the bowl.

2 Dust a work surface with the remaining flour. Turn out the dough and knead for about 10 minutes or until smooth and elastic, working in enough flour to keep it from sticking. Coat a large bowl with cooking spray or a teaspoon of olive oil and put in the dough; turn to coat. Cover with a damp towel and rest for 10 minutes.

3 Meanwhile, line a baking tray with baking parchment. Toss the walnuts and sultanas with the remaining caster sugar and 1 tablespoon orange zest; set aside. Melt the remaining butter; set aside. Place the dough in the baking tray and pat into a 35 x 23cm (14 x 9in) oval.

4 Brush the dough with the melted butter. Score the dough lengthways into three equal sections without cutting through. Cut the outer sections into strips 7.5cm (3in) long and 2.5cm (1in) wide. Spread the walnut filling down the centre. Fold the strips over the filling and seal the ends well. Cover with a towel. Leave to rise in a warm place for about 45 minutes or until almost doubled in size.

5 Meanwhile, preheat the oven to 190°C (375°F, gas mark 5). Bake the bread for about 20 minutes or until golden. Cool on a wire rack for 15 minutes. Meanwhile, stir the icing sugar with the remaining orange zest and enough orange juice to make an icing that will coat the back of the spoon. Drizzle over the warm bread. Serve warm or at room temperature.

photo, page 27

Some more ideas

• For more fibre, substitute wholemeal bread flour for up to half of the white flour.

• Use dried cranberries or cherries in place of sultanas.

Health points

• By making fruited breads yourself, you can control the amount of fat, salt and sugar they contain.

• Baking from scratch is a great opportunity to add fibre-rich ingredients such as nuts and seeds to bread doughs and cake mixtures.

Each serving provides   **Key nutrients** 257kcals, 7g fat (of which 3g is saturated fat), 5g protein, 47g carbohydrate, 37mg sodium (0.09g salt), 1g fibre

Parmesan and spring onion puffs

It's as easy as 1, 2, 3 to make these puffs! Just measure, mix and bake. A few spoonfuls of Parmesan adds a big boost of flavour, so no one will ever guess you've cut back on the fat.

Preparation time **15 minutes**   Cooking time **25 minutes**   *Makes 12*

140g (5oz) plain flour

3 tbsp freshly grated Parmesan cheese

pepper to taste

2 medium eggs

1 egg white

225ml (8floz) semi-skimmed milk

15g (½oz) butter, melted

2 spring onions, finely chopped

1 Preheat the oven to 220°C (425°F, gas mark 7). Lightly coat a 12-hole bun tin or muffin tray with cooking spray or a teaspoon of olive oil and put into the oven to heat. Mix together the flour, Parmesan and pepper in a medium bowl. Make a well in the centre of the flour mixture.

2 Whisk the eggs, egg white, milk and butter in another bowl until frothy. Pour into the well in the flour mixture and stir just until smooth. Stir in the spring onions.

3 When a drop of water dances and sizzles in the tin, it's hot enough. Spoon in the batter, dividing it evenly among the holes. Bake for 15 minutes. Reduce the oven temperature to 180°C (350°F, gas mark 4) and bake for a further 10 minutes or until golden and puffed up. Immediately remove from the tin and quickly make a small slit in the side of each puff to release the steam. Serve hot.

Some more ideas

• Replace the Parmesan with another grating cheese such as pecorino.

• Add a few dried herbs such as dried thyme or oregano to the batter.

Health points

• By using a strong cheese in small amounts, you can have lots of flavour while keeping the fat and sodium content to a minimum.

• Spring onions, like other members of the onion family, contain allium compounds that may help relieve high blood pressure.

photo, page 31

Each serving (1 puff) provides   Key nutrients 91kcals, 4g fat (of which 2g is saturated fat), 5g protein, 10g carbohydrate, 76mg sodium (0.19g salt), 0.5g fibre

Blueberry muffins with lemon glaze

What makes these muffins extra special is the abundance of berries and the sweet lemon glaze drizzled on top. You can freeze them for up to a month. Take them out of the freezer the night before for a perfect breakfast.

Preparation time **20 minutes**   Cooking time **20 minutes plus cooling**   *Makes 12*

280g (10oz) self-raising flour

100g (3½oz) caster sugar

225ml (8fl oz) semi-skimmed milk

2 medium eggs

85g (3oz) fromage frais

2 tsp vanilla extract

175g (6oz) fresh blueberries

For the glaze

125g (4½oz) icing sugar, sifted

1 tbsp grated lemon zest

1–2 tbsp semi-skimmed milk

1 Preheat the oven to 200°C (400°F, gas mark 6). Lightly coat a 12-hole American-style muffin tray with cooking spray or a teaspoon of olive oil. Mix together the flour and caster sugar in a large bowl. Whisk the milk, eggs, fromage frais and vanilla extract in another bowl until blended.

2 Make a well in the centre of the flour mixture. Pour in the milk mixture and stir with a fork just until blended. Fold in two-thirds of the blueberries.

3 Spoon the mixture into the muffins tins and sprinkle evenly with the remaining blueberries. Bake for about 25 minutes or until a skewer inserted in the centre of a muffin comes out clean. Cool the muffins on a wire rack for 10 minutes.

4 Meanwhile, mix the icing sugar with the lemon zest and enough milk in a small bowl to make a glaze that will coat the back of the spoon. Drizzle the glaze over the muffins.

Some more ideas

• Make these muffins with raspberries or blackberries.

• Change the vanilla extract to almond or orange.

Health points

• Blueberries are one of the best fruit sources of valuable antioxidants. In fact, the very pigments that give blueberries their colour – which are called anthocyanins – help to remove free radicals from the body and may even help to prevent memory loss.

Each serving (1 muffin) provides   Key nutrients 188kcals, 2g fat (of which 1g is saturated fat), 5g protein, 39g carbohydrate, 112mg sodium (0.28g salt), 1g fibre

Blueberry muffins
with lemon glaze *p30*

Parmesan and spring onion puffs *p29*

Cherry and oat muffins *p32*

Peaches and cream bread *p34*

Cherry and oat muffins

Most modern-day muffins should be ashamed – they're oversized, lacking in fibre, loaded with fat and packed with sugar. These tender golden muffins are bundles of whole grains that will please your heart and your palate.

Preparation time **15 minutes**   Cooking time **40 minutes**   *Makes 12*

85g (3oz) rolled oats

100g (3½oz) plain flour

85g (3oz) wholemeal flour

35g (1¼oz) wheatgerm, preferably toasted

6½ tbsp caster sugar

1 tsp baking powder

½ tsp bicarbonate of soda

350ml (12fl oz) buttermilk

3 tbsp olive oil

1 medium egg

grated zest of 2 oranges

115g (4oz) dried cherries

1 Preheat the oven to 190°C (375°F, gas mark 5). Lightly coat a 12-hole American-style muffin tray with cooking sprayor a teaspoon of olive oil; each hole should be about 6cm (2½in) diameter. Spread out the oats in a baking tray and bake for about 10 minutes or until golden brown and crisp, stirring occasionally. Transfer to a large bowl and cool to room temperature.

2 Add the plain and wholemeal flours, wheatgerm, 5½ tablespoons of the sugar, the baking powder and bicarbonate of soda to the oats, stirring to combine. Whisk together the buttermilk, oil, egg and orange zest in a small bowl until blended.

3 Make a well in the centre of the dry ingredients and pour in the buttermilk mixture. Stir just until the dry ingredients are moistened. Fold in the cherries.

4 Spoon the mixture into the muffin tins. Sprinkle the top of each muffin with ¼ teaspoon of sugar. Bake for about 30 minutes or until golden brown and a skewer inserted in the centre of a muffin comes out clean. Remove the muffins from the tray to a wire rack to cool.

Some more ideas

• For muffins with a lemon flavour substitute grated lemon zest for the orange zest.

• Add chopped dates or dried apples to the mixture.

• Instead of dried cherries, use dried cranberries or raisins.

Health points

• These muffins are a good source of fibre, making them a worthy part of the morning meal.

• Using olive oil in the mixture increases the amount of good monounsaturated fat. Most shop-bought muffins have far too much saturated fat.

photo, page 31

Each serving (1 muffin) provides   **Key nutrients** 191kcals, 5g fat (of which 1g is saturated fat), 5g protein, 34g carbohydrate, 129mg sodium (0.32g salt), 2g fibre

Spicy apple muffins

We will bet the Muffin Man never offered such healthy fare! Apple sauce replaces some of the fat, and fresh apples and oats add nutritious fibre. But these are still as delicious as any homemade muffin you can remember.

Preparation time **10 minutes**   Cooking time **20 minutes**   *Makes 12*

240g (8½oz) plain flour

165g (5¾oz) soft light brown sugar

2 sachets (about 40g/1½oz each) apple-flavoured instant porridge

25g (1oz) butter

1 tsp bicarbonate of soda

½ tsp mixed spice

1 jar (about 280g) unsweetened apple sauce

2 tbsp sunflower oil

2 medium eggs

1 large dessert apple, cored and chopped

1 Preheat the oven to 190°C (375°F, gas mark 5). Lightly coat a 12-hole American-style muffin tray with cooking spray or a teaspoon of olive oil. Combine 50g (1¾oz) of the flour, 4 tablespoons of the brown sugar, 1 sachet of porridge and the butter in a small bowl. Rub in with your fingertips until the mixture is crumbly. Set aside.

2 Mix the remaining flour and porridge mix with the bicarbonate of soda, mixed spice and salt in a medium bowl, and make a well in the centre.

3 Stir together the apple sauce, oil, remaining brown sugar and the eggs in another bowl until the brown sugar has dissolved. Pour into the well in the dry ingredients and stir just until combined (do not overmix; the mixture should be lumpy). Stir in the apple.

4 Spoon the mixture into the muffin tins. Sprinkle with the crumble topping. Bake for about 20 minutes or until a skewer inserted in the centre of a muffin comes out clean.

Some more ideas

• Use a pear instead of the apple, and add 75g (2½oz) raisins to the mixture.

• For a denser muffin with even more fibre, you can replace some or all of the plain flour with wholemeal flour.

Health points

• Oats are a nutritional winner. They are high in soluble fibre, B vitamins and vitamin E, as well as heart-healthy minerals. Oats may help to reduce blood cholesterol levels.

photo, page 37

Each serving (1 muffin) provides   Key nutrients 261kcals, 6g fat (of which 2g is saturated fat), 4g protein, 40g carbohydrate, 145mg sodium (0.37g salt), 1.5g fibre

Good source of potassium (101mg)

Peaches and cream bread

Fresh peaches and virtually-fat-free fromage frais combine in this delicious quick bread, which is just as perfect for brunch as it is at teatime.

Preparation time **15 minutes**   Cooking time **1 hour plus cooling**   *Serves 16*

2 medium peaches

215g (7½oz) plain flour

85g (3oz) wholemeal flour

4 tbsp wheatgerm, preferably toasted

150g (5½oz) caster sugar

1 tsp bicarbonate of soda

125g (4½oz) fromage frais

1 medium egg

2 medium egg whites

2 tbsp light olive oil

1 tsp almond essence

1 Preheat the oven to 180°C (350°F, gas mark 4). Lightly coat a 23 x 13cm (9 x 5in) loaf tin with cooking spray or a teaspoon of olive oil.

2 Blanch the peaches in a saucepan of boiling water for 20 seconds; drain. Peel, stone and finely chop the peaches.

3 Combine the plain and wholemeal flours, wheatgerm, sugar and bicarbonate of soda in a large bowl.

4 Mix together the fromage frais, whole egg, egg whites, oil and almond essence in a small bowl. Make a well in the dry ingredients, pour in the fromage frais mixture and stir just until combined. Fold in the peaches.

5 Spoon the mixture into the tin and smooth the top. Bake for about 1 hour or until a skewer inserted in the centre comes out clean. Cool in the tin, on a rack, for 10 minutes, then turn out on to the rack to cool completely before slicing.

Some more ideas

• Try using plums or nectarines in place of peaches. Blanch and peel them the same way.

• If fresh peaches are not in season, you can use canned peaches (in natural juice).

Health points

• Peaches are full of vitamin C – 100g/3½ oz provides 77per cent of the recommended daily intake.

photo, page 31

Each serving provides   **Key nutrients** 135kcals, 3g fat (of which 1g is saturated fat), 4g protein, 25g carbohydrate, 103mg sodium (0.26g salt), 1g fibre

Maple and toasted-walnut bread

This healthy bread has it all: just the right amount of sweetness, a delicious moist crumb, and the toothsome crunch of nuts throughout. The only thing it doesn't have is lots of fat and cholesterol.

Preparation time **15 minutes**   Cooking time **50 minutes plus cooling**   *Serves 16*

285g (10oz) self-raising flour

85g (3oz) butter, softened

250g (9oz) maple syrup

1 egg, lightly beaten

1 can (about 170g) evaporated skimmed milk

1 tsp vanilla extract

55g (2oz) walnuts, toasted and chopped

1 Preheat the oven to 180°C (350°F, gas mark 4). Lightly coat a 23 x 13cm (9 x 5in) loaf tin with cooking spray or a little olive oil. Put the flour into a large bowl and make a well in the centre.

2 Beat the butter in a medium bowl with a wooden spoon until creamy; blend in the syrup. Beat in the egg, and then the milk and vanilla extract. Pour the mixture into the well in the flour and stir just until the flour disappears. (Do not overbeat; a few lumps are fine.) Stir in the walnuts.

3 Scrape the mixture into the loaf tin. Bake for about 50 minutes or until golden brown and a skewer inserted in the centre comes out clean. If the bread browns too fast, loosely cover it with foil (shiny-side up) during the last 15 minutes of baking.

4 Cool in the tin, on a wire rack, for 10 minutes. Turn the bread on to the rack to cool completely.

Some more ideas

• For a different nutty flavour, use toasted pecan nuts or toasted slivered almonds in place of the walnuts.

• This bread is also delicious flavoured with almond essence instead of vanilla extract.

Health points

• There is some evidence to suggest that eating unsalted nuts may help to relieve high blood pressure. Nuts provide healthy monounsaturated fat and are high in fibre. Walnuts are particularly heart-healthy: they contain alpha-linolenic acid, an omega-3 fat that may lower risk for heart attack, and ellagic acid, an antioxidant compound. Store nuts in a cool, dry place, or keep them in the refrigerator for longer-lasting freshness.

photo, page 37

Each serving provides   **Key nutrients** 180kcals, 8g fat (of which 3.5g is saturated fat), 3.5g protein, 25g carbohydrate, 116mg sodium (0.29g salt), 0.7g fibre

Herb and Cheddar scones

Revive the tradition of homemade bread in your house with these fast and easy-to-make brunch scones. There's no rolling out or cutting required, so they go from mixing bowl to oven in just 15 minutes.

Preparation time **15 minutes**   Cooking time **12 minutes**   *Makes 18*

250g (9oz) self-raising flour

1 tbsp snipped fresh chives

1 tsp chopped fresh thyme

¼ tsp bicarbonate of soda

40g (1½oz) butter, cut into pieces

55g (2oz) reduced-fat Cheddar cheese, grated

175ml (6fl oz) buttermilk

1 egg white, lightly beaten

1 Preheat the oven to 230°C (450°F, gas mark 8). Line a baking tray with baking parchment or coat with cooking spray or a teaspoon of olive oil. Mix together the flour, chives, thyme and bicarbonate of soda in a large bowl.

2 Rub in the butter until the mixture resembles coarse crumbs. Stir in half of the cheese. Make a well in the centre and pour in the buttermilk. Mix with a fork until a soft, sticky dough forms.

3 Drop heaping tablespoons of the dough on to the baking tray, making 18 mounds. Brush them with the egg white and sprinkle with the remaining cheese. Bake for 12 minutes or until puffy and golden.

Some more ideas

• Use other herbs instead of chives and thyme. Snipped fresh basil and sage are good choices.

• Try reduced-fat mozzarella or feta cheese as a change from Cheddar.

Health points

• Despite its name, buttermilk is low in fat and it makes an excellent liquid for baking. It makes these scones extra light. If you don't have any buttermilk to hand, you can use sour milk instead: stir 1 tbsp of either vinegar or lemon juice into 225ml (8fl oz) skimmed milk and leave until the milk curdles.

Each serving (1 scone) provides   Key nutrients 75kcals, 2.5g fat (of which 1.5g is saturated fat), 3g protein, 11g carbohydrate, 112mg sodium (0.28g salt), 0.4g fibre

Corn bread *p38*

Spicy apple muffins *p33*

Maple and toasted walnut
bread *p35*

Herb and Cheddar scones *p36*

Corn bread

Warm from the oven, corn bread is just irresistible. This version has sweetcorn kernels added, which makes it even more delicious. It will complement any brunch meal, but especially a spicy omelette.

Preparation time **10 minutes**   Cooking time **20 minutes**   *Serves 16*

1 fresh corn-on-the-cob, or 70g (2½oz) frozen sweetcorn kernels, thawed

140g (5oz) plain flour

100g (3½oz) cornmeal (maize meal) or polenta

1 tbsp baking powder

150ml (5fl oz) semi-skimmed milk

4 tbsp olive oil

1 egg

1 tbsp clear honey

1 Preheat the oven to 220°C (425°F, gas mark 7). Lightly coat an 18cm (7in) square baking tin that is 5cm (2in) deep with cooking sprayor a teaspoon of olive oil. If using fresh corn-on-the-cob, remove the kernels using a sharp knife. Set aside.

2 In a medium bowl, thoroughly mix together the flour, cornmeal and baking powder. In a small bowl, combine the sweetcorn, milk, oil, egg and honey, and beat well to mix.

3 Pour the egg mixture into the flour and cornmeal mixture. Quickly and thoroughly mix together. Pour into the baking tin, scraping any mixture from the sides of the bowl into the tin. Spread the mixture evenly with a spatula.

4 Bake for 20–25 minutes or until lightly browned and a knife inserted in the centre comes out clean. Cut into 4.5cm (1¾in) squares and serve straightaway.

Some more ideas

• To make a Tex-Mex corn bread, add some spices to add a subtle flavour. Use ½ tsp chilli powder (or more to taste) and ¼ tsp ground cumin.

Health points

• Sweetcorn has a surprisingly large mixture of important nutrients. It is particularly rich in folate, which helps reduce the risk of heart disease. It also contains lutein, which is healthy for your eyes. Plus, sweetcorn offers protease inhibitors, which are chemical compounds that may help to prevent cancerous tumours from developing.

photo, page 37

Each serving provides   Key nutrients 100kcals, 4g fat (of which 0.5g is saturated fat), 2.5g protein, 14g carbohydrate, 120mg sodium (0.3g salt), 0.5g fibre

Starters & snacks

Double-cheese pizza bites

These personal-sized pizzas are loaded with fresh tomato slices and topped up with two kinds of cheese, black olives and fresh herbs. A delicious way to welcome your guests.

Preparation time **30 minutes plus rising**   Cooking time **10 minutes**   *Makes 48*

350g (12oz) white bread flour

1 tsp caster sugar

1 sachet (7g/¼oz) easy-blend dried yeast

225ml (8floz) lukewarm water

1 tbsp extra virgin olive oil

pepper to taste

350g (12oz) cherry tomatoes

115g (4oz) fontina or Cheddar cheese, grated

3 tbsp freshly grated Parmesan cheese

12 kalamata olives, pitted and cut into slivers

fresh oregano leaves

1 Mix 115g (4oz) of the flour, the sugar and yeast in a bowl. Stir in the water and oil until blended. Put 200g (7oz) of the remaining flour in a food processor and add the yeast mixture and pulse until blended. With the motor running, add the remaining flour, 1 tablespoon at a time, until a soft dough forms (you will need to process for about 2 minutes).

2 Dust a work surface lightly with flour. Turn out the dough and knead for 1–2 minutes or until smooth. Shape into a ball. Cover with a clean tea towel and rest for 10 minutes.

3 Preheat the oven to 230°C (450°F, gas mark 8). Line two baking trays with baking parchment. Divide the dough into four pieces. Wrap three in cling film and refrigerate. Cut the remaining dough into 12 equal pieces and shape each into a 4cm (1½in) ball. Arrange on the baking trays and flatten into 7.5cm (3in) rounds. Lightly coat with cooking spray or brush with a little olive oil.

4 Thinly slice the tomatoes. Top each pizza with 2 or 3 slices of tomato, then sprinkle each with 1 teaspoon fontina or Cheddar, a little Parmesan, a few olive slivers and oregano leaves and pepper to taste. Bake for about 10 minutes or until bubbly and the bases are golden. Serve hot. Repeat with the remaining dough to make more pizza bites.

Some more ideas

• Use reduced-fat mozzarella instead of fontina cheese.

• Try green olives instead of black ones.

Health points

• This recipe is a good example of how to use higher-fat, higher-sodium foods in small quantities. The olives provide such a flavour boost, but admittedly they do contain fat and salt. By using just a few, you get the taste you want with fewer of the things you don't.

Each serving (1 pizza) provides   **Key nutrients** 85kcals, 3g fat (of which 2g is saturated fat), 3.5g protein, 11g carbohydrate, 60mg sodium (0.15g salt), 0.6g fibre

Double-cheese pizza bites *p40*

Roast pepper pinwheels *p42*

Beef satay with ginger dipping sauce *p43*

Portobello pizzas *p46*

Roast pepper pinwheels

Wraps are a quick way to roll tasty fillings into a fun-to-eat package. Take a wrap and cut it across into pieces, and you get a bite-sized pinwheel sandwich that is equally at home in a lunchbox as it is on a buffet table.

Preparation time **15 minutes**   Cooking time **10 minutes plus chilling**   *Serves 24*

3 red peppers, cut lengthways into flat panels and deseeded

250g (9oz) canned chickpeas, rinsed and drained

3 tbsp plain low-fat yoghurt

1 tsp toasted sesame oil

1 tsp grated lemon zest

2 tbsp fresh lemon juice

2 tbsp water

3 spinach- or basil-flavoured flour tortillas (20cm/8in in diameter)

4 handfuls of mixed salad leaves

1 Preheat the grill to moderate. Grill the pepper pieces, skin-side up, for about 10 minutes or until charred. Transfer to a plate. When cool enough to handle, peel the peppers and cut into strips 1cm (½in) wide.

2 Combine the chickpeas, yoghurt, sesame oil, lemon zest, lemon juice and water in a food processor, and process until smooth.

3 Spread the mixture evenly over one side of each tortilla, leaving a 1cm (½in) border all round. Top with the salad leaves and roast peppers. Roll up each tortilla.

4 Wrap tightly in foil or cling film and refrigerate for at least 1 hour or up to 4 hours. (The rolls will become softer and easier to slice if they sit in the refrigerator for a while before serving.) Unwrap and slice each wrap across into eight pieces (each 2.5cm/1in wide) to serve.

Some more ideas

• Use yellow or orange peppers, or combine several colours of peppers for a particularly attractive pinwheel.

• Use canned cannellini beans in place of the chickpeas.

Health points

• Peppers are among the best natural sources of vitamin C. Volume for volume, peppers have 1½ times as much of this vitamin as fresh orange juice. And red, yellow and orange peppers have even more vitamin C than a green pepper.

photo, page 41

Each serving provides   **Key nutrients** 45kcals, 1g fat (of which 0g is saturated fat), 2g protein, 8g carbohydrate, 80mg sodium (0.2g salt), 1g fibre

Beef satay with ginger dipping sauce

Tempting Oriental steak bites, all dressed up for a party! Let these snacks-on-a-skewer kick off your next gathering. Prepare them ahead, so they're ready for grilling in an instant. They're lean enough to be heart-healthy!

Preparation time **25 minutes**   Cooking time **15 minutes**   *Serves 12*

350g (12oz) sirloin steak, cut 2.5cm (1in) thick, trimmed of all excess fat

3 large yellow or red peppers, each cut into 8 triangles

4 spring onions, cut into 7.5cm (3in) pieces

For the dipping sauce

125ml (4floz) rice vinegar

55g (2oz) finely chopped red pepper

2 tbsp caster sugar

1 tbsp finely chopped shallot

1½ tsp grated fresh root ginger

1–1½ tsp chilli-garlic sauce

½ tsp grated lemon zest

1 Soak twenty-four 15cm (6in) wooden or bamboo skewers in water for 30 minutes. Freeze the steak for 20 minutes.

2 To make the dipping sauce, mix together the vinegar, red pepper, sugar, shallot, ginger, chilli-garlic sauce and lemon zest in a small serving bowl.

3 Blanch the peppers in boiling water for 1 minute. Drain, rinse with cold water and pat dry with kitchen paper. Toss in a medium bowl with 2 tablespoons of the dipping sauce.

4 Preheat the grill to high. Slice the steak into 24 very thin strips, then thread a beef strip, a pepper triangle and a piece of spring onion on to each skewer, twisting the meat round the vegetables. Grill for 3–5 minutes on each side or until cooked through. Serve the satay hot, with the rest of the dipping sauce.

Some more ideas

• Make these satay sticks with chicken or turkey breast or pork fillet instead of steak.

• You can vary the vegetables too. Try mushrooms (button or larger ones cut into pieces), courgette rounds, mangetout – whatever you enjoy!

• To make the dipping sauce less hot, just omit the chilli-garlic sauce.

Health points

• Red meat can be part of a healthy eating plan as long as you consume it in healthy portion sizes. Lean beef is an important source of B vitamins and iron, and also provides outstanding protein that your body needs. Make sure, though, that your meals contain far more vegetables and whole grains than meat.

photo, page 41

Each serving provides   **Key nutrients** 55kcals, 2g fat (of which 1g is saturated fat), 7g protein, 6g carbohydrate, 33mg sodium (0.08g salt), 1g fibre

Little chicken salad rolls

There's absolutely no added fat in this Chinese-inspired appetiser. Chicken is poached in a ginger-flavoured stock, shredded and tossed with a soy-vinegar dressing and vegetables, then rolled in lettuce leaves.

Preparation time **40 minutes**   Cooking time **15 minutes**   *Serves 16*

225ml (8fl oz) low-sodium chicken stock

2 slices fresh root ginger, each 5mm (¼in) thick

450g (1lb) skinless, boneless chicken thighs or breasts

3 tbsp rice vinegar

1 tbsp low-sodium soy sauce

1 carrot, coarsely grated

1 red pepper, slivered

16 soft lettuce leaves

16 fresh mint leaves

3 tbsp finely chopped dry-roasted peanuts

For the dipping sauce

3 tbsp low-sodium soy sauce

1 tbsp rice vinegar

1 tsp caster sugar

1 To make dipping sauce, combine the soy sauce, vinegar and sugar in a small saucepan. Stir over low heat until the sugar has dissolved. Set aside to cool.

2 Bring the stock and ginger to the boil in a large frying pan over medium heat. Add the chicken. Reduce to a simmer, then cover the pan and cook for about 12 minutes or until the chicken is opaque, turning it over halfway through the cooking. Remove the chicken from the pan (discard the stock). When cool enough to handle, shred the chicken.

3 Stir together the vinegar and soy sauce in a medium bowl. Add the shredded chicken, carrot and red pepper. Toss to combine.

4 Place the lettuce leaves, hollow-side up, on the work surface. Place a mint leaf in each lettuce leaf. Dividing it evenly, spoon the chicken mixture into the lettuce leaves and sprinkle the peanuts on top. Roll up the leaves and serve with the dipping sauce.

Some more ideas

• Make these rolls with tofu instead of chicken. Sauté 225g (8oz) tofu, cut into cubes, in a little sesame oil, then mix with the vegetables.

• Use turkey breast instead of chicken.

Health points

• When you're thinking health, think colour. The more colours you have in a meal, the more likely it is that there will be a wide variety of vitamins and minerals. This dish is very colourful, with leafy greens, red peppers and carrots. It's perfect for great eating – and lowering blood pressure.

Each serving provides   Key nutrients 56kcals, 2.5g fat (of which 0.5g is saturated fat), 8g protein, 2g carbohydrate, 170mg sodium (0.425g salt), 0.5g fibre

Portobello pizzas

Portobello mushrooms have a wide, flat cap that makes an innovative base for mini pizzas. For a fabulous first course, top the mushroom with a bean purée flavoured with fresh basil and Parmesan, then layer on shredded mozzarella and tomatoes.

Preparation time **10 minutes**   Cooking time **15 minutes**   *Serves 8*

8 large portobello mushrooms, 55g (2oz) each, stalks removed

1 can (about 400g) pinto beans, rinsed and drained

125ml (4fl oz) water

25g (1oz) fresh basil, chopped

3 tbsp freshly grated Parmesan

pepper to taste

85g (3oz) reduced-fat mozzarella, coarsely grated

3 large plum tomatoes, halved, deseeded and diced or slivered

1 Preheat the oven to 200°C (400°F, gas mark 6). With a spoon, scrape out and discard the black gills from the mushrooms. Coat a baking tray with cooking spray or use a teaspoon of olive oil. Place the mushrooms rounded side up in the tray. Cover with foil and bake for about 5 minutes or until the mushrooms are tender. Remove the mushrooms from the baking tray and drain, rounded side up, on kitchen paper. Leave the oven on.

2 Meanwhile, combine the beans, water, basil, Parmesan and pepper in a medium bowl. Mash until smooth using a potato masher or large fork.

3 Return the mushrooms, rounded side down, to the baking tray. Spoon the bean mixture into the mushroom hollows and bake for 5 minutes.

4 Top with the mozzarella and tomatoes, and bake for a further 5 minutes or until the cheese has melted and the bean mixture is hot.

Some more ideas

• Use the bean filling to stuff 450g (1lb) portabellini or chestnut mushrooms, instead of the portobellos.

• Try reduced-fat Cheddar in place of the mozzarella.

• Kidney beans can be used instead of pinto beans.

Health points

• Beans are one of the highest-fibre foods you can consume. Try to buy canned beans packed without salt or sugar. If these are not available, rinse the beans well, to remove sodium, before using.

• Fresh or dried basil is teeming with powerful antioxidants. In addition, flavonoid and terpene phytochemicals in basil are under review for their potential benefit in reducing cholesterol.

photo, page 41

Each serving provides   **Key nutrients** 100kcals, 3g fat (of which 1g is saturated fat), 9g protein, 8g carbohydrate, 290mg sodium (0.72g salt), 3g fibre

Useful source of potassium (370mg)

Heavenly devilled eggs

A low-cholesterol stuffed egg? Yes, indeed! Filled with a delicious blend of egg yolks, vegetables and spices, these are lighter and creamier than traditional devilled eggs, yet have a richer flavour.

Preparation time **15 minutes**   Cooking time **25 minutes**   *Serves 10*

12 medium eggs

175g (6oz) virtually-fat-free fromage frais

2 spring onions, finely chopped

40g (1½oz) finely chopped green pepper

40g (1½oz) finely chopped red pepper

2 tsp Dijon mustard

3 tbsp finely chopped parsley

paprika to dust

1 Put the eggs in a large saucepan of cold water and bring to a full boil. Remove from the heat, cover and leave to stand for 15 minutes. Drain the eggs and rinse under cold water to cool them. Peel the eggs, then cut each lengthways in half and remove the yolk. Discard 8 yolks.

2 Arrange 20 egg white halves on a platter. Chop the remaining 4 egg white halves very finely. Mash the 4 yolks with a fork. Transfer the whites and yolks to a medium bowl. Stir in the fromage frais, spring onions, green and red peppers and mustard.

3 Pipe or spoon the yolk mixture into the egg white halves. Sprinkle with parsley and dust with paprika.

Some more ideas

• Make these eggs spicy! Add ½ tsp chilli powder or ¼ tsp cayenne pepper to the egg mixture. Or, for more heat, mix in a very finely chopped fresh green chilli.

Health points

• Eggs are not a forbidden food. Their low saturated fat content, high protein level, low price and versatility make them a useful part of your healthy eating plan.

photo, page 49

Each serving provides   **Key nutrients** 116kcals, 8g fat (of which 2g is saturated fat), 10g protein, 2g carbohydrate, 137mg sodium (0.34g salt),0.2g fibre

Sausage-stuffed chestnut mushrooms

For a delicious starter, stuff fresh mushrooms with a savoury mixture of chicken sausage, vegetables and a sprinkling of cheese. They're surprisingly low in fat and calories while being very high in taste.

Preparation time **20 minutes**   Cooking time **22 minutes**   *Serves 6*

12 large chestnut mushrooms

75g (2¾oz) plain dried breadcrumbs

2 tbsp freshly grated Parmesan cheese

55g (2oz) chicken sausages, casing removed

1 large onion, finely chopped

1 small red pepper, deseeded and finely chopped

¼ tsp pepper

1 Preheat the oven to 200°C (400°F, gas mark 6). Remove the stalks from the mushrooms; finely chop the stalks. Mix 2 tablespoons of the breadcrumbs with the Parmesan in a small bowl.

2 Lightly coat a large nonstick frying pan with cooking spray or a teaspoon of olive oil and set over a medium heat. Cook the sausages for about 5 minutes or until they begin to brown, breaking them up with the side of a spoon. Stir in the onion, red pepper and chopped mushroom stalks, and cook for about 5 minutes or until the vegetables are soft. Stir in the remaining breadcrumbs and the pepper. Remove from the heat.

3 Mound the stuffing in the mushroom caps and arrange, stuffing-side up, in a baking dish. Sprinkle with the Parmesan crumb mixture. Bake for about 9 minutes or until the mushrooms are hot and the top is golden brown.

Some more ideas

• Use the stuffing to fill 2 large portobello mushrooms, gills removed.

• Try using a low-fat spicy chicken or turkey sausage.

• For a softer filling, use fresh wholemeal breadcrumbs. Crumble the bread in a food processor or blender.

Health points

• Mushrooms may not offer many vitamins and minerals, but researchers are now discovering that they are rich in healing phytochemicals. Among the healthiest of the mushrooms are shiitakes.

Each serving provides   Key nutrients 100kcals, 3g fat (of which 1.5g is saturated fat), 5g protein, 14g carbohydrate, 230mg sodium (0.57g salt), 1.5g fibre

Sausage-stuffed chestnut
mushrooms *p48*

Heavenly devilled eggs *p47*

Chicken dumplings with sesame dipping sauce *p50*

Parmesan breadsticks *p51*

Chicken dumplings with sesame dipping sauce

Water chestnuts and chopped coriander combine with chicken, spring onions and ginger to create a Chinese-style treat. These tasty wonton-wrapped dumplings are poached, not fried, to keep them low in fat and calories.

Preparation time **30 minutes**   Cooking time **15 minutes**   *Serves 12*

225g (8oz) minced chicken

4 tbsp thinly sliced spring onions

4 tbsp finely chopped canned water chestnuts

4 tbsp chopped fresh coriander

4 tsp low-sodium soy sauce

½ tsp ground ginger

¼ tsp pepper

24 wonton wrappers, about 7.5cm (3in) square

For the dipping sauce

4 tbsp low-sodium soy sauce

1 tbsp toasted sesame oil

2 tsp rice vinegar

½ tsp caster sugar

4 tbsp thinly sliced spring onions

1 In a medium bowl, combine the chicken, spring onions, water chestnuts, coriander, soy sauce, ginger and pepper. Mix together well.

2 Working with several wonton wrappers at a time and keeping the remainder loosely covered with a damp tea towel, make the dumplings: place a heaped teaspoon of filling on the bottom half of a wrapper. With a wet finger or pastry brush, moisten two adjoining sides of the wrapper. Fold the two moistened sides over the filling to form a triangle and press to seal. Repeat with the remaining wonton wrappers and filling.

3 In a small bowl, whisk together the soy sauce, sesame oil, vinegar, sugar and spring onions for the dipping sauce.

4 Bring a large saucepan of water to the boil. Add the dumplings and cook for about 4 minutes or until they float to the surface and the filling feels firm to the touch. Drain and serve hot with the dipping sauce.

Some More Ideas

Vegetable dumplings Instead of minced chicken, mix some shredded carrots, finely diced red peppers, and 100g (3½oz) baby spinach leaves with the other filling ingredients.

Health points

• These dumplings are so low in fat because they are poached, not fried. The texture of the water chestnuts satisfies the desire for crunchy foods.

• Soy sauce usually contains a lot of sodium, so should be used sparingly and always in a low-sodium version.

photo, page 49

Each serving provides   Key nutrients 70kcals, 4g fat (of which 0.5g is saturated fat), 6g protein, 10g carbohydrate, 230mg sodium (0.57g salt), 0.2g fibre

Parmesan breadsticks

Freshly grated Parmesan, a bite of black pepper and just a hint of fresh rosemary, baked into crispy golden twists. Great to eat now or to serve to guests, and perfect to give as a gift.

Preparation time **25 minutes plus standing**   Cooking time **36 minutes**   *Makes 40*

425g (15oz) white bread flour

100g (3½oz) Parmesan cheese, freshly grated

2 tsp chopped fresh rosemary or ½ tsp dried rosemary

1 tsp pepper

1 tsp easy-blend dried yeast

300ml (10fl oz) lukewarm water

4 tbsp semolina or polenta

1 tsp olive oil

1 Mix 140g (5oz) of the flour with the Parmesan, rosemary, pepper and yeast in a large bowl. Blend in the water. Add 175g (6oz) more flour to form a soft dough. Dust a work surface with the remaining flour. Turn the dough on to the floured surface and knead for about 10 minutes or until smooth and elastic, working in the remaining flour to keep the dough from sticking. Divide the dough into two equal pieces. Cover with a damp tea towel and rest for 10 minutes.

2 Cut two 40 x 30cm (16 x 12in) sheets of greaseproof paper and sprinkle each with 1 tbsp semolina. Pat out the dough pieces on the paper into 25 x 15cm (10 x 6in) rectangles. Brush with oil and cover with tea towels. Leave to rise in a warm place for about 30 minutes or until doubled.

3 Preheat the oven to 200°C (400°F, gas mark 6). Line four baking sheets with baking parchment and sprinkle with the remaining semolina. Put one of the dough pieces into the fridge. Cut the other piece across into 20 equal strips. Holding each strip by the ends, twist and stretch until it is about 30cm (12in) long. Place the twists 2.5cm (1in) apart on the baking sheets. Leave to rise, uncovered, for 10 minutes.

4 Lightly coat the strips of dough with cooking spray or a little olive oil. Bake for 10 minutes. Remove the bread-sticks from the oven and lightly coat again with cooking spray or brush with a teaspoon of olive oil. Bake for a further 8 minutes or until golden and crisp. Transfer to a wire rack to cool. Repeat with the remaining piece of dough.

Some more ideas

• Add very finely chopped walnuts to the dough.

• Use a mixture of Parmesan and another strong grating cheese such as pecorino.

Health points

• Rosemary is believed to offer relief to ailments of the nervous system, and is rich in such anti-cancer compounds as carnosol, rosmanol and a variety of flavonoids. Additional anti-cancer substances in rosemary – cineole, geraniole and pinene – show promise in blocking tumour growth. Rosemary is highly aromatic, so be careful not to overuse it in your cooking.

photo, page 49

Each serving (2 breadsticks) provides | Key nutrients 54kcals, 1g fat (of which 0.5g is saturated fat), 2g protein, 9g carbohydrate, 28mg sodium (0.07g salt), 0.5g fibre

Guacamole with a kick

Chunks of onion, tomato and jalapeño chillies add a flavour punch to this popular dip. Low-fat yoghurt and fromage frais lighten the mix and stretch two avocados to feed a horde of hungry dunkers.

Preparation time **20 minutes plus standing**   *Serves 16*

125g (4½oz) plain low-fat yoghurt

2 small fresh jalapeño or other green chillies

2 plum tomatoes, finely chopped

1 small white onion, finely chopped

2 tbsp finely chopped fresh coriander

125g (4½oz) virtually-fat-free fromage frais

2 large avocados

2 tbsp fresh lime juice

85g (3oz) baked tortilla chips

1 Line the bottom of a sieve with muslin, a coffee filter or kitchen paper and set over a medium bowl. Spoon in the yoghurt, cover and refrigerate for 8 hours or overnight. During this time liquid will drain from the yoghurt to leave a thick and creamy yoghurt cheese.

2 Deseed the jalapeños or other chillies, then chop them finely. Mix together the jalapeños, tomatoes, onion and coriander in a large bowl. Fold in the yoghurt cheese and fromage frais.

3 Halve, stone and peel the avocados. Mash with a potato masher, sprinkling with lime juice. Quickly fold into the tomato mixture. Serve with tortilla chips.

Some more ideas

• For an even greater kick, use a hotter red chilli.

• Top the guacamole with a peeled and diced mango. The sweet mango goes well with the dip's flavours.

• Serve the guacamole with vegetable crudités instead of tortilla chips.

Health points

• Avocados are a rich source of monounsaturated fat and vitamin B_6 – a single small avocado provides over half the daily requirement for B_6. Avocados also contribute useful amounts of vitamin E and several important phyto-chemicals.

Each serving provides   Key nutrients 90kcals, 6g fat (of which 1g is saturated fat), 2g protein, 6g carbohydrate, 60mg sodium (0.15g salt), 1.5g fibre

Hot crab dip

Whether you use freshly cooked crab or crabmeat from a can, you'll enjoy the sweet seafood in this hot and creamy dip. Serve it with crispy wholemeal crackers or water biscuits.

Preparation time **10 minutes**   Cooking time **20 minutes**   *Serves 24*

350g (12oz) fresh crabmeat, or canned white crabmeat, drained

225g (8oz) reduced-fat soft cheese, at room temperature

225g (8oz) virtually-fat-free fromage frais

1 small onion, finely chopped

1 tbsp bottled horseradish

2 tsp Worcestershire sauce

¼ tsp Tabasco sauce

3 tbsp plain dried breadcrumbs

½ tsp paprika

125g (4½oz) thin, low-sodium wholemeal crackers or rice cakes

1 Preheat the oven to 180°C (350°F, gas mark 4). Coat a gratin or other baking dish with cooking spray or a teaspoon of olive oil. Pick over the crabmeat, discarding any shells and cartilage.

2 Stir the cream cheese in a medium bowl until smooth. Blend in the fromage frais, onion, horseradish, and Worcestershire and Tabasco sauces. Gently fold in the crabmeat. Spoon into the baking dish and smooth the top.

3 Combine the breadcrumbs and paprika, and sprinkle evenly over the crabmeat mixture. Bake for about 20 minutes or until bubbling. Serve piping hot with crackers.

Some more ideas

• Make this dip with canned tuna or salmon.

• Add 2 tbsp freshly grated Parmesan to the dip for extra flavour.

Health points

• Seafood such as crab is a great low-fat source of protein.

Each serving provides   Key nutrients 142kcals, 6g fat (of which 3g is saturated fat), 14g protein, 9g carbohydrate, 465mg sodium (1.16g salt), 1g fibre

Crudités with three dips

Few foods can be healthier than raw vegetable sticks, so make the most of them by serving them with tempting low-fat dips for a snack or instead of a formal first course. Or, for a light lunch, these quantities will serve 4.

Preparation time **25 minutes, plus 30 minutes soaking**   *Serves 8*

For the pesto-yoghurt dip

55g (2oz) fresh basil leaves

1 garlic clove, crushed

1 tbsp pine nuts

225g (8oz) plain low-fat yoghurt

For the fresh herb dip

175g (6oz) virtually-fat-free fromage frais

1 spring onion, finely chopped

2 tbsp finely chopped parsley

1 tbsp finely snipped fresh chives

1 tsp tarragon vinegar

For the Italian-style tomato dip

55g (2oz) sun-dried tomatoes (dry-packed)

85g (3oz) low-fat cottage cheese

85g (3oz) plain low-fat yoghurt

25g (1oz) fresh basil leaves

pepper to taste

To serve

450g (1lb) vegetable crudités, such as baby carrots, courgette sticks, green beans (blanched for 1 minute), pepper strips and broccoli florets

1 For the pesto-yoghurt dip, use a pestle and mortar to crush the basil, garlic and pine nuts to a paste. Work in the yoghurt a spoonful at a time, until thoroughly combined. Add pepper to taste. Alternatively, purée all the ingredients together in a food processor or blender. Transfer to a bowl, cover and chill.

2 For the fresh herb dip, stir all the ingredients together in a bowl until well blended. Cover tightly and chill until required.

3 For the Italian-style tomato dip, place the sun-dried tomatoes in a heatproof bowl and pour over boiling water to cover them. Leave to soak for about 30 minutes or until the tomatoes are plump and tender. Drain the tomatoes well, then pat them dry and finely chop them.

4 Purée the cottage cheese with the yoghurt in a food processor or blender. Alternatively, press the cheese through a sieve and stir in the yoghurt. Transfer to a bowl and stir in the tomatoes. Cover and chill until required.

5 Just before serving the Italian-style tomato dip, finely shred the basil and stir in with pepper to taste.

6 Serve the bowls of dips on a large platter with the crudités arranged around them.

Some more ideas

• There is a wide choice of vegetables for making crunchy, delicious crudités. For example, try celery or cucumber sticks, whole radishes, baby plum tomatoes halved lengthways, small cauliflower florets (raw or briefly cooked) and baby new potatoes cooked until tender.

• You could offer a selection of fresh fruit pieces and warm pitta bread for dipping, as well as vegetables.

Health points

• Broccoli is one of the most studied of vegetables, and for very good reason: it contains a great number of healthy nutrients such as calcium, potassium, antioxidants and other heart-friendly phyto-chemicals.

• Pine nuts are rich in a variety of minerals: magnesium, potassium, iron, zinc and copper.

Each light lunch serving provides

Key nutrients 112kcals, 6g fat (of which 1g is saturated fat), 7g protein, 8g carbohydrate, 143mg sodium (0.35g salt),1.5g fibre

Useful source of potassium (380mg)

Spiced root vegetable wedges with creamy mustard dip *p56*

Crudités with three dips *p54*

Spiced fruits, nuts and seeds *p58*

Pitta crisps with hummus *p57*

Spiced root vegetable wedges with creamy mustard dip

Lightly crushed coriander seeds and a hint of cinnamon accentuate the flavours of sweet potatoes, parsnips and carrots, baked in wedges to make dippers for a tangy mustard and yoghurt dip.

Preparation and cooking time **about 1¼ hours**   *Serves 4*

2 large carrots

2 parsnips

juice of 1 lime

2 tbsp sunflower oil

2 tbsp lightly crushed coriander seeds

½ tsp ground cinnamon

pepper to taste

675g (1½lb) sweet potatoes, peeled

For the dip

2 tsp Dijon mustard

1 tsp caster sugar

grated zest of 1 lime

200g (7oz) plain low-fat yoghurt

3 tbsp chopped fresh dill, plus extra to garnish

1 Preheat the oven to 220°C (425°F, gas mark 7). Cut the carrots and parsnips across in half. Cut the narrow halves in half lengthways and each of the larger halves into quarters lengthways. Place the prepared vegetables in a saucepan and pour in just enough water to cover them. Bring to the boil, then reduce the heat slightly and partly cover the pan. Cook for 2 minutes.

2 Meanwhile, mix together the lime juice, oil, coriander, cinnamon and pepper to taste in a large roasting tin. Cut the sweet potatoes across in half, then into thick wedges, about the same size as the pieces of carrot and parsnip. Add the sweet potato wedges to the tin and turn them in the spice mixture until they are well coated, then push them to one side of the tin.

3 Drain the carrots and parsnips and put them in the roasting tin. Use a spoon and fork to turn the hot vegetables and coat them with the spice mixture. Place the roasting tin in the oven and bake for about 40 minutes, stirring and turning the vegetables twice, until they are browned in places and tender.

4 While the vegetables are baking, make the dip. Mix together the mustard, sugar and lime zest, then stir in the yoghurt and dill. Transfer the dip to a serving bowl, cover and set aside until the vegetables are ready.

5 Remove the vegetable wedges from the oven and leave them to cool slightly. Garnish the mustard dip with a little extra dill, and serve with the vegetables.

Some more ideas

Chilli and herb dip Mix plain low-fat yoghurt with 1 small fresh green chilli, deseeded and finely chopped, 1 tbsp chopped fresh mint, 2 tbsp chopped fresh coriander and the grated zest of 1 lemon. Use the juice from the lemon in the mixture for coating the vegetables instead of lime juice.

• Coat the vegetables with a spice mixture made from lemon juice instead of lime juice, 1 tbsp caraway seeds instead of coriander seeds, and ½ tsp ground mace instead of cinnamon. Use lemon zest instead of lime zest.

Health points

• Parsnips were eaten by both the Greeks and the Romans, but the variety common today was not developed until the Middle Ages. Parsnips were an important staple food before the introduction of the potato.

photo, page 55

Each serving provides   **Key nutrients** 282kcals, 7g fat (of which 1.5g is saturated fat), 6g protein, 51g carbohydrate, 190mg sodium (0.47g salt), 7g fibre

Good source of potassium (1062mg)

Pitta crisps with hummus

This simple, easy-to-prepare snack is surprisingly rich in heart-healthy nutrients. Soft pitta breads are transformed into crisp fingers by grilling. They pair perfectly with the creamy hummus dip.

Preparation and cooking time **about 15 minutes, plus cooling**   *Serves 4*

For the hummus

1 can (about 400g) chickpeas, drained and rinsed

½ tsp ground cumin

2 garlic cloves, crushed

2 tbsp lemon juice

2 tsp olive oil

150g (5½oz) virtually-fat-free fromage frais

pepper to taste

paprika and ground cumin to garnish *(optional)*

lemon wedges to serve

For the pitta crisps

6 small pitta breads

1½ tbsp olive oil

40g (1½oz) sesame seeds

1 Put the chickpeas, cumin, garlic, lemon juice, olive oil and fromage frais in a food processor. Blend for 1–2 minutes or until very smooth, stopping and scraping down the sides of the container once or twice.

2 Alternatively, place the ingredients in a bowl, preferably with a flat bottom, and purée with a hand-held blender. For a slightly chunkier result, mash the chickpeas with a potato masher or fork until quite smooth, then stir in the other ingredients.

3 Season the hummus with pepper to taste, then spoon into a bowl. Cover and keep in the fridge until ready to serve.

4 To prepare the pitta crisps, preheat the grill to high. Spread out the pitta breads on a baking tray and lightly brush the top side with half of the olive oil. Sprinkle with half of the sesame seeds. Grill for about 1 minute or until both the bread and seeds are golden brown.

5 Turn the pittas over, brush with the remaining olive oil and sprinkle with the remaining sesame seeds. Return to the hot grill and toast for another minute or until the bread and seeds are golden brown. Using scissors, quickly cut the warm pittas across into 2cm (¾in) fingers. Leave to cool and become crisp. (The pitta crisps can be kept in an airtight tin for 1–2 days.)

6 Sprinkle the hummus with a pinch each of paprika and ground cumin, if using, then serve with the pitta crisps and lemon wedges.

Some more ideas

Aubergine dip Grill 2 medium aubergines, turning frequently, until soft and charred. Put in a plastic bag and leave until cool enough to handle. Cut into quarters and peel. Leave the flesh to drain in a colander for 15 minutes, then gently squeeze out remaining liquid. Purée the flesh in a food processor with 1 crushed garlic clove, 1 tsp ground cumin, the juice of 1 lemon, 4 tbsp tahini paste, 1 tbsp olive oil, 2 tbsp chopped fresh mint, and pepper to taste. Garnish with cayenne pepper and small fresh mint leaves.

Lebanese flat bread Slit the pitta breads round the edge and pull the halves apart. Put 2 tbsp poppy seeds, 2 tbsp toasted sesame seeds and 2 tbsp chopped fresh thyme in a mortar. Crush lightly with a pestle. Stir in 3 tbsp olive oil. Spread over the inner sides of the bread halves. Grill until golden brown. Leave to cool. Break into dipping-size pieces.

photo, page 55

Each serving provides Key nutrients 492kcals, 15g fat (of which 2g is saturated fat), 20g protein, 74g carbohydrate, 600mg sodium (1.5g salt), 6g fibre

Useful source of potassium (390mg)

Spiced fruits, nuts and seeds

This mildly spiced mix of crunchy nuts, pumpkin and sunflower seeds, tangy dried cranberries and sweet sultanas is great for nibbling as a healthy snack or with drinks. Children love it too!

Preparation and cooking time **about 1¼ hours**   *Serves 16*

1 tsp cardamom pods

2.5cm (1in) piece cinnamon stick

2 whole cloves

1 tsp black peppercorns

1 tsp cumin seeds

1 tsp coriander seeds

2 tsp finely chopped fresh root ginger

1 large egg white

25g (1oz) fine or medium oatmeal

175g (6oz) blanched almonds

175g (6oz) pecan nut halves

175g (6oz) Brazil nuts

85g (3oz) pumpkin seeds

70g (2½oz) sunflower seeds

115g (4oz) sultanas

100g (3½oz) dried cranberries

1 Preheat the oven to 120°C (250°F, gas mark ½). Lightly crush the cardamom pods with a pestle and mortar, or the side of a large knife, and discard the husks. Place the tiny seeds in a spice mill or a pestle and mortar, together with the cinnamon stick, cloves, peppercorns, and cumin and coriander seeds, and grind to a fairly fine powder.

2 Mix the ground spices with the ginger, egg white and oatmeal in a large bowl. Add the almonds, pecan halves, Brazil nuts, pumpkin seeds and sunflower seeds, and toss well to coat them all evenly with the spice mixture.

3 Spread out the nuts and seeds on a large baking sheet in a single layer. Bake, stirring occasionally, for about 1 hour or until lightly browned and crisp. Remove from the oven and leave to cool on the baking sheet.

4 Put the nuts and seeds in a bowl. Add the sultanas and cranberries, mixing well. The mixture is ready to serve, or it can be stored in an airtight container for up to 2 weeks.

Some more ideas

• If you don't have a spice mill, you can use 1 tbsp curry powder instead of the whole spices.

Hot-spiced nuts and seeds Add 1 garlic clove, crushed, and ½ tsp crushed dried chillies to the spice mixture. Use nuts and seeds only, omitting the sultanas and cranberries.

Sweet-spiced fruits, nuts and seeds Replace all spices used in the main recipe with 1 tsp ground cinnamon, ½ tsp ground ginger and ½ tsp grated nutmeg. Stir these into the egg white and oatmeal, and use to coat the nuts and seeds. Bake and cool. Mix with 55g (2oz) each chopped dried mango, dried cherries and chopped dried apple.

Health points

• Almonds are a good source of unsaturated fat. They are also rich in vitamin E and provide protein, fibre and zinc.

photo, page 55

Each serving provides   Key nutrients 318kcals, 26g fat (of which 3.5g is saturated fat), 8g protein, 14g carbohydrate, 12mg sodium (0.03g salt), 3g fibre

Useful source of potassium (440mg)

Meat

Sizzling beef fajitas

This Mexican fiesta-on-a-plate consists of strips of marinated steak, peppers and onions presented smoking-hot from the grill. It's a treat for the family, but also ideal party fare, so double or triple the recipe if you're entertaining a crowd.

Preparation time **10 minutes**   Cooking time **20 minutes**   *Serves 4*

4 tbsp fresh lime juice

1 tsp chilli powder

¾ tsp dried oregano

¾ tsp ground coriander

black pepper to taste

350g (12oz) well-trimmed sirloin steak

2 large onions, thickly sliced

2 large red peppers, cut lengthways into flat panels

4 tbsp finely chopped fresh coriander

4 flour tortillas, 18cm (7in) in diameter

250g (9oz) romaine or cos lettuce, shredded

4 tbsp plain low-fat bio yoghurt

1 Combine the lime juice, chilli powder, oregano, coriander and black pepper in a medium bowl.

2 Place the steak in a shallow bowl and spoon 2 tablespoons of the lime mixture on top; turn to coat both sides. Leave to stand while you grill the vegetables.

3 Preheat the grill to moderate. Spray the grill pan with cooking spray or wipe with a little olive oil. Place the onions and pepper pieces, skin-side up, on the pan. Grill for about 10 minutes or until the peppers are charred and the onions are golden brown. Remove from the grill. When cool enough to handle, peel the peppers and thickly slice. Add the peppers and onions to the remaining lime juice mixture together with the fresh coriander and toss.

4 Grill the steak for about 4 minutes on each side or until cooked to your taste. Leave to rest for 5 minutes before slicing thinly. Grill the tortillas for about 15 seconds on each side or until lightly browned.

5 Place the sliced steak, peppers and onions, lettuce, yoghurt and flour tortillas in serving containers. Let each person fill his or her own tortilla.

Some more ideas

• Use 2 skinless, boneless chicken breasts, 140g (5oz) each, in place of the steak. Slice the chicken into 1cm (½in) strips and, instead of grilling, sauté in 2 tsp olive oil for about 5 minutes or until cooked through.

• Use orange or yellow peppers rather than red.

• Roll up the meat mixture in large lettuce leaves instead of tortillas.

Health points

• The vegetable mixture for these fajitas provides more than twice your daily requirement for vitamin C. This important vitamin works as an antioxidant to fight off a wide range of diseases.

• Olive oil is rich in monounsaturated fats and is believed to be partly responsible for the low rates of heart disease and stroke in people in Mediterranean countries. Several studies have shown that replacing saturated fat with olive oil helps to reduce high blood cholesterol levels.

Each serving provides   Key nutrients 363kcals, 5g fat (of which 2g is saturated fat), 28g protein, 53g carbohydrate, 274mg sodium (0.68g salt), 4g fibre

Useful source of potassium (800mg)

Sizzling beef fajitas *p60*

Succulent meat loaf *p62*

Roast beef hash *p63*

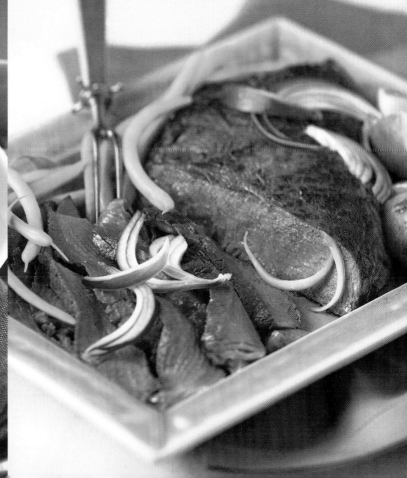

Seared sirloin with garden vegetables *p66*

Succulent meat loaf

With a few smart substitutions and techniques, you can keep all the flavour and texture of this old-fashioned favourite – but get rid of excess fat and add many more nutrients.

Preparation time **30 minutes**   Cooking time **1 hour 20 minutes**   *Serves 8*

2 large onions, chopped

2 large celery sticks, chopped

1 large green pepper, deseeded and chopped

3 garlic cloves, finely chopped

900g (2lb) lean minced beef

50g (1¾oz) fresh breadcrumbs

1 egg white

black pepper to taste

1 can (about 400g) chopped tomatoes

4 tbsp no-salt-added tomato ketchup

1 Preheat the oven to 180°C (350°F, gas mark 4). Lightly coat a 33 x 23cm (13 x 9in) baking dish and a large nonstick frying pan with cooking spray or a little olive oil. Set the pan over medium-high heat and sauté the onions, celery, green pepper and garlic for about 5 minutes or until soft. Transfer the vegetables to a large bowl.

2 Add the beef, breadcrumbs, egg white and black pepper to the vegetables and mix with your hands. Combine the tomatoes (with their juice) and ketchup in a small bowl. Add half to the meat mixture, and mix again.

3 Transfer the meat mixture to the baking dish and shape into a 25 x18cm (10 x 7in) loaf, mounding slightly in the centre. Make a lengthways groove down the centre with the side of your hand. Pour the remaining tomato mixture into the groove. Bake the meat loaf for about 1¼ hours or until an instant-read thermometer inserted in the centre reaches 74°C (165°F). Leave to stand for 10 minutes before slicing.

Some more ideas

• If you're pressed for time, make mini meat loaves in a bun tin. Bake the loaves for about 25 minutes. Freeze any leftovers in resealable plastic bags for up to 1 month; thaw before reheating. To serve, cover with foil and reheat in a 180°C (350°F, gas mark 4) oven for about 15 minutes.

• For added fibre, replace 4 tbsp of the breadcrumbs with toasted wheatgerm.

• Add a diced or grated carrot to the meat mixture.

Health points

• Garlic contains allicin, which has anti-fungal and antibiotic properties. In animal studies, other compounds in garlic have been shown to inactivitate carcinogens and suppress the growth of tumours.

photo, page 61

Each serving provides   **Key nutrients** 250kcals, 11g fat (of which 5g is saturated fat), 27g protein, 10g carbohydrate, 453mg sodium (1.13g salt), 1.5g fibre

Useful source of potassium (582mg)

Roast beef hash

The question of what to do with leftover roast beef has never been answered more deliciously or healthfully: pan-fry chunks of the Sunday roast with golden sweetcorn and nuggets of potato and carrot for a filling, family-pleasing supper.

Preparation time **10 minutes**   Cooking time **30 minutes**   *Serves 4*

450g (1lb) small new potatoes, cut into 5mm (¼in) dice

2 carrots, quartered lengthways and thinly sliced

5 tsp olive oil

1 medium onion, finely chopped

2 garlic cloves, finely chopped

200g (7oz) frozen sweetcorn kernels

pepper to taste

175g (6oz) roast beef, cut into 1cm (½in) dice

1 Cook the potatoes in a saucepan of boiling water for about 6 minutes or until almost tender. Add the carrots and cook for a further 2 minutes. Drain.

2 Coat a large nonstick frying pan with cooking spray or a teaspoon of olive oil. Add 3 teaspoons of the oil and heat over medium-low heat. Add the onion and garlic, and cook, stirring frequently, for about 7 minutes or until the onion is golden brown.

3 Increase the heat to medium-high. Add the remaining 2 teaspoons of oil. Add the potatoes and carrots, sweetcorn and pepper, and cook, stirring occasionally, for about 10 minutes or until the mixture starts to form a crust on the base.

4 Stir in the beef and press down on the mixture to make a firm cake. Cook for a further 5 minutes or until the base has a good browned crust. Serve hot.

Some more ideas

• Use sweet potatoes instead of new potatoes.

• Replace the roast beef with cooked chicken or turkey breast meat.

• Serve the hash with a salad of mixed greens and slivered red onions.

Health points

• Eating potatoes with their skin on is good for your heart. This is because the skin provides more heart-healthy nutrients, including potassium, B vitamins, and plenty of cholesterol-lowering fibre.

photo, page 61

Each serving provides   **Key nutrients** 290kcals, 11g fat (of which 3g is saturated fat), 17g protein, 34g carbohydrate, 870mg sodium (2.17g salt), 8g fibre

Stir-fried beef salad with mango

This colourful Thai-style dish is bursting with fresh flavours and deliciously contrasting textures. The dressing is completely oil-free, so despite the beef and nuts this dish is light in calories.

Preparation time **30 minutes**   Cooking time **about 10 minutes**   *Serves 4*

450g (1lb) lean sirloin steak

3 garlic cloves, finely chopped

1 tsp caster sugar

2 tsp low-sodium soy sauce

1½ tbsp sunflower oil

For the dressing

2 tsp paprika

2 tsp mild chilli powder

1½ tbsp clear honey

2.5cm (1in) piece fresh root ginger, grated

4 tbsp rice vinegar

juice of 1 lime or 1 lemon

For the salad

¼ medium red cabbage

½ cucumber

½ red pepper

1 mango, peeled, stoned and cut into strips

2 plums, sliced

55g (2oz) watercress leaves

3–4 spring onions, chopped

fresh mint and coriander leaves

2 tbsp chopped roasted unsalted peanuts

1 To make the dressing, put the paprika, chilli powder, honey, ginger and vinegar in a saucepan and slowly add 225ml (8fl oz) water, stirring. Bring to the boil, then reduce the heat and simmer for 5 minutes. Remove from the heat and stir in the lime or lemon juice. Set aside.

2 Shred the cabbage; cut the cucumber into matchsticks; and cut the pepper into thin strips. Combine all the salad ingredients, except the peanuts, in a large shallow serving dish and toss gently together until evenly mixed. Set aside.

3 Cut the steak into thin strips for stir-frying. Put the steak in a bowl with the garlic, sugar and soy sauce, and toss together so the strips of steak are seasoned. Heat a wok or nonstick frying pan over high heat, then add the oil. Add the beef and stir-fry until the strips are evenly browned and cooked to taste.

4 Spoon the stir-fried beef over the salad. Drizzle the dressing over the top and sprinkle with the peanuts. Serve immediately.

Some more ideas

• Add cubes of fresh or canned pineapple (canned in juice rather than syrup) or kiwi fruit to the salad, to increase the fruit content.

• Spice up the salad with very thin strips of fresh red chilli – particularly if you have a cold: scientists have suggested that eating chillies can help to alleviate nasal congestion.

• Replace the mango with 2 nectarines, unpeeled and sliced.

• For a vegetarian version, omit the stir-fried beef and increase the quantity of peanuts to 150g (5½oz). Peanuts are an excellent source of protein and contain much less saturated fat than meat.

Health points

• Apart from adding its delicious spiciness to the dressing, ginger also aids digestion.

Each serving provides   Key nutrients 300kcals, 13g fat (of which 3.5g is saturated fat), 30g protein, 17g carbohydrate, 200mg sodium (0.5g salt), 3g fibre

Useful source of potassium (799mg)

Seared sirloin with garden vegetables

Looking for a healthy steak? Here it is: a scrumptious sirloin, flash-cooked so it retains all its fabulous flavours and surrounded by plenty of fresh vegetables. Sirloin is among the leanest cuts of steak, yet is wonderfully succulent.

Preparation time **20 minutes**   Cooking time **35 minutes**   *Serves 8*

2 garlic cloves, finely chopped

pepper to taste

1 sirloin steak cut 4cm (1¼in) thick, about 1kg (2¼lb)

450g (1lb) medium-sized new potatoes, quartered

450g (1lb) green beans

1 large red onion, very thinly sliced

2 tbsp white wine vinegar

2 tsp extra virgin olive oil

¼ tsp caster sugar

1 Preheat the oven to 190°C (375°F, gas mark 5). Mash the garlic with the pepper using the side of a chef's knife, to form a chunky paste. Rub this on to both sides of the steak. Set aside.

2 Put the potatoes in a saucepan of water and bring to the boil. Reduce the heat and simmer for 5 minutes. Add the beans and cook for a further 3–4 minutes or until the potatoes are tender and the beans are al dente. Drain, rinse with cool water and transfer to a large bowl.

3 Put the onion in a colander and rinse with hot water. Mix together the vinegar, oil, sugar, salt and pepper in a small bowl. Set this vinaigrette aside.

4 Heat a large, heavy ovenproof frying pan over medium-high heat until very hot but not smoking. Add the steak and sear for about 3 minutes on each side or until browned. Transfer to the oven. For medium-rare steak, cook for 15–18 minutes; for medium cook for 20–23 minutes. Leave to rest for 5 minutes, then trim off any remaining fat and thinly slice the steak. To serve, arrange the potatoes, beans and onions around the steak on a platter and drizzle with the vinaigrette.

Some more ideas

• For a tasty change, roast the potatoes instead of boiling them. (This variation is shown on our cover.)

• Use 450g (1lb) cubed sweet potatoes in place of the new potatoes.

• Replace the green beans with mangetout or sugarsnap peas.

• For a mellow flavour, toss the red onion in balsamic vinegar instead of white wine vinegar.

Health points

• A 125g (4½oz) serving of beef (which is what you get in this recipe) provides a whopping supply of vitamin B_{12}. It is also an excellent source of iron and zinc.

• The red onion in this dish is particularly healthy for your cardiovascular system. In addition to being high in fibre, it offers large amounts of antioxidants, particularly quercetin, a potent flavonoid linked to a reduced risk of cancer, cardiovascular disease and cataracts.

photo, page 61

Each serving provides   Key nutrients 224kcals, 10g fat (of which 4g is saturated fat), 29g protein, 14g carbohydrate, 470mg sodium (1.17g salt), 3g fibre

Useful source of potassium (714mg)

Fusilli and meatballs

Hearty, healthy and everyone's favourite Italian dish – don't you want pasta and meatballs for supper tonight? Unlike traditional recipes, these meatballs are low in fat, yet they're full of the terrific taste you crave.

Preparation time **30 minutes**   Cooking time **1 hour 20 minutes**   *Serves 6*

1 large onion, chopped

2 garlic cloves, finely chopped

4 cans (about 400g each) no-salt-added plum tomatoes

4 tbsp chopped fresh basil

1 tbsp chopped fresh oregano or 1 tsp dried oregano

2 slices day-old firm-textured white bread

450g (1lb) lean minced beef

1 medium egg

2 tbsp semi-skimmed milk

pepper to taste

350g (12oz) long fusilli pasta

1 Coat a large saucepan with cooking spray or a teaspoon of olive oil and set over a medium-high heat. Sauté the onion and garlic for about 5 minutes or until soft. Transfer 2 tablespoons of the onion mixture to a large bowl. Set aside.

2 Whiz the tomatoes, with their juice, in a food processor until fairly smooth. Add to the saucepan. Bring to the boil over medium-high heat. Reduce the heat to medium-low. Cover and simmer, stirring often, for 30 minutes. Add the basil and oregano halfway through this time.

3 Process the bread until crumbs form. Add the crumbs, beef, egg, milk and pepper to the onion mixture in the bowl and mix just until blended. Shape into 20 meatballs about 2.5cm (1in) diameter. Coat a frying pan with cooking spray or olive oil and set over medium-high heat. Cook the meatballs, in batches, for about 8 minutes or until browned on all sides. Drain on kitchen paper. Add the meatballs to the tomato sauce. Cover and cook, stirring occasionally, for 20 minutes.

4 Meanwhile, cook the pasta according to the instructions on the packet. Drain and toss with 3 ladlefuls of the sauce in a large heated serving bowl. Spoon the meatballs and remaining sauce over the top, then serve.

Some more ideas

• Make turkey or chicken meatballs, using minced turkey or chicken breasts instead of minced beef.

• For spicy meatballs, add ½ tsp crushed dried chillies, or more to taste, to the meat mixture.

• Try other pasta shapes such as penne or rigatoni in place of the fusilli. For added fibre, choose wholemeal pasta.

• Serve the pasta with a mixed salad or a vegetable. A quickly made dish of courgettes, peppers, green beans or asparagus, sautéed in 1 tsp olive oil with some crushed garlic and black pepper, is delicious.

Health points

• Pasta with meatballs is a healthy dish, especially when you include cooked tomatoes. Studies have shown that lycopene, a phytochemical in tomatoes, is best absorbed by the body if the tomatoes are cooked, not raw.

photo, page 69

Each serving provides Key nutrients 430kcals, 10g fat (of which 4g is saturated fat), 29g protein, 60g carbohydrate, 420mg sodium (1.05g salt), 4g fibre

Good source of potassium (1079mg)

Pesto-coated pork chops

Pork chops on a menu for lower blood pressure? Yes! Pork is about 50 per cent leaner than just a few years ago, which means it's lower in saturated fat as well. To keep chops succulent, top them with a homemade pesto.

Preparation time **15 minutes**   Cooking time **8 minutes**   *Serves 4*

175g (6oz) wide noodles, made without egg

85g (3oz) fresh basil leaves

3 garlic cloves, peeled

pepper to taste

2 tbsp plain dried breadcrumbs

2 tbsp olive oil

4 pork loin chops, 1cm (½in) thick, about 115g (4oz) each

1 Preheat the grill to moderate. Cook the noodles according to the instructions on the packet.

2 Meanwhile, put the basil, garlic and pepper in a food processor. Pulse until the basil is roughly chopped. Add the breadcrumbs and process until incorporated. With the motor running, slowly add the oil through the feed tube. Set the pesto aside.

3 Coat a large, heavy ovenproof frying pan and the grill rack with cooking spray or as little olive oil. Set the frying pan over high heat. Add the chops and sauté for about 1 minute on each side or until browned. Remove from the heat. Spread both sides of the chops with the pesto and transfer to the grill rack.

4 Grill the chops for about 2 minutes on each side or until they are cooked through. Divide the noodles among four plates and top each with a pork chop.

Some more ideas

• Use skinless, boneless chicken breasts or thighs in place of the pork chops. Sauté the chicken for about 5–6 minutes on each side.

Health points

• Pork is a good source of zinc and it provides useful amounts of iron as well as vitamins from the B group, particularly B_1, B_6, B_{12} and niacin.

• Including garlic in the diet is thought to be beneficial for a healthy heart. Garlic may also be useful for clearing cold symptoms and chest infections.

Each serving provides   Key nutrients 385kcals, 12g fat (of which 1g is saturated fat), 31g protein, 39g carbohydrate, 60mg sodium (0.15g salt), 1.5g fibre

Pesto-coated pork chops *p68*

Fusilli and meatballs *p67*

Cidered pork with red cabbage *p70*

Lamb curry *p71*

Cidered pork with red cabbage

Slow cooking makes this hearty stew perfect for cool autumn days. Experiment with different types of apple – Granny Smith are tart and tangy, Golden Delicious are juicy and mild.

Preparation time **20 minutes**   Cooking time **2¼–2½ hours**   *Serves 6*

1 tbsp sunflower oil

450g (1lb) lean boneless pork shoulder, cut into bite-size chunks

2 onions, chopped

2 dessert apples, peeled, cored and diced

1 carrot, diced

2 tbsp raisins

450ml (16fl oz) cider

225ml (8fl oz) low-sodium chicken stock

2 bay leaves

¼ tsp fresh thyme leaves, or to taste

pinch of ground cinnamon

pinch of ground allspice

12 pitted prunes

½ red cabbage, cut into bite-size pieces

1 tbsp tomato purée

pepper to taste

450g (1lb) small pasta shapes, such as shells (conchiglie) or ears (orecchiette)

2 tbsp chopped parsley

1 Heat the oil in a heavy-based saucepan or flameproof casserole, add the chunks of pork and cook until they are starting to brown. Add the onions and continue to cook until the pork and onions are both lightly browned, stirring occasionally.

2 Stir in the apples, carrot, raisins, cider, stock, bay leaves, thyme, cinnamon and allspice. Bring to the boil, then reduce the heat and cover the pan. Cook over a very low heat for about 1 hour.

3 Mix in the prunes and red cabbage and cover the pan again. Continue to cook gently for about 1 hour or until the meat is very tender.

4 Stir in the tomato purée with pepper to taste. Leave to cook gently, covered, while you cook the pasta.

5 Cook the pasta in boiling water for 10–12 minutes, or according to the instructions on the packet, until al dente.

6 Drain the pasta, then divide among six bowls. Ladle the cidered pork over. Sprinkle with parsley and serve.

Some more ideas

Chunky borscht Increase the stock to 1 litre (1¾ pints). In step 3, add 3–4 grated cooked beetroot, 1 tbsp sugar and the juice of 1 lemon. Taste for sweet-sour balance, and add a little extra lemon juice or sugar, if needed. Ladle the borscht over pasta shells in deep bowls. Top each with a dollop of plain low-fat yoghurt and a sprinkling of fresh dill.

Health points

• For over 20 years, farmers have been breeding leaner pigs, and pork now contains considerably less fat than it did in the past. It also contains higher levels of the 'good' polyunsaturated fats. The average fat content of lean pork is just 3.5 per cent, much the same as skinless chicken breast.

• Prunes provide useful amounts of potassium, iron and vitamin B_6. They are also a good source of dietary fibre.

photo, page 69

Each serving provides   **Key nutrients** 468kcals, 8g fat (of which 2g is saturated fat), 27g protein, 73g carbohydrate, 134mg sodium (0.33g salt), 5g fibre

Useful source of potassium (792mg)

Lamb curry

This scrumptious curried lamb dish is prepared with everyday ingredients – most you probably have to hand right now – yet you'll be surprised by its authentic flavour. For your blood pressure's sake, we've used the leanest cut of lamb.

Preparation time **25 minutes**   Cooking time **55 minutes**   *Serves 4*

1 tsp olive oil

350g (12oz) well-trimmed lean boneless lamb, cut into 2cm (¾ in) chunks

1 medium onion, finely chopped

4 garlic cloves, finely chopped

1 tbsp grated fresh root ginger

1 tbsp curry powder

400g (14oz) cauliflower florets

300g (10½ oz) no-salt-added canned chopped tomatoes

125ml (4fl oz) water

200g (7oz) frozen peas

5 tbsp chopped fresh coriander

115g (4oz) plain low-fat yoghurt

2 tbsp plain flour

1 Heat the oil in a nonstick flameproof casserole over medium heat. Add the lamb cubes and cook for about 5 minutes or until browned all over. With a slotted spoon, transfer the lamb to a bowl or plate.

2 Add the onion, garlic and ginger to the casserole and cook, stirring frequently, for about 5 minutes or until the onion is tender. Add the curry powder and cauliflower, and stir to mix together.

3 Add the tomatoes and water and bring to the boil. Return the lamb to the casserole and reduce to a simmer. Cover and cook for about 40 minutes or until the lamb and cauliflower are tender.

4 Add peas and coriander, and cook for 3 minutes or until the peas are hot. Stir the yoghurt and flour together in a small bowl. Stir the yoghurt mixture into the sauce and cook over low heat, stirring, for about 2 minutes or until slightly thickened. Serve hot.

Some more ideas

• Use 350g (12oz) lean tender beef, cut into 2cm (¾in) chunks, in place of the lamb.

Prawn curry Substitute 450g (1lb) peeled and deveined large raw prawns for the lamb. In step 1, cook the prawns for 3 minutes, then remove to a bowl. In step 3 cook only the cauliflower for 20 minutes. Add the prawns after stirring in the yoghurt mixture in step 4.

Health points

• Turmeric, a principal component of curry powder, may help lower LDL ('bad') cholesterol and prevent blood clots.

• The combination of onion, garlic and ginger that is so common in Indian cookery is an extraordinary one-two-three punch of nutrition. All are rich in antioxidants and phyto-chemicals that may help to fight cancer, heart disease, hypertension and other chronic illnesses.

photo, page 69

Each serving provides   Key nutrients 300kcals, 12g fat (of which 5g is saturated fat), 27g protein, 22g carbohydrate, 150mg sodium (0.37g salt), 6g fibre

Fragrant lamb with spinach

This enticing curry is warmly spiced rather than fiery hot with chillies. Serve it with basmati rice, chapattis and a fresh tomato and cucumber chutney for a healthy Indian-style meal.

Preparation time **20–25 minutes**   Cooking time **1 hour 20 minutes**   *Serves 4*

2 tbsp sunflower oil

2 onions, finely chopped

4 garlic cloves, crushed

5cm (2in) piece fresh root
ginger, peeled and chopped

1 red chilli, deseeded
and sliced

2 tsp paprika

2 tsp ground cumin

2 tsp ground coriander

½ tsp ground cinnamon

seeds from 8 green cardamom
pods, crushed

2 bay leaves

pepper to taste

225g (8oz) plain low-fat yoghurt

150ml (5fl oz) water

450g (1lb) lean boneless lamb,
cubed

2 large tomatoes, chopped

225g (8oz) fresh baby spinach

4 tbsp chopped fresh coriander

sprigs of fresh coriander
to garnish

1 Heat the oil in a large saucepan or flameproof casserole. Add the onions, garlic and ginger, and sauté, stirring frequently, for about 15 minutes or until the onions are golden.

2 Stir in the chilli, paprika, cumin, coriander, cinnamon, crushed cardamom seeds, bay leaves and pepper. Stir briefly over a moderate heat, then stir in the yoghurt and water. Add the lamb, mix well and cover the pan. Simmer gently for about 1¼ hours or until the lamb is tender.

3 Add the tomatoes, spinach and chopped fresh coriander. Cook, stirring, for 2–3 minutes or until the tomatoes have softened slightly and the spinach has wilted. Remove the bay leaf. Serve garnished with coriander sprigs.

Some more ideas

• The basic curry sauce in this recipe can be used to cook other meats or vegetables. Cubes of skinless, boneless chicken or turkey breast are delicious, as are lean boneless pork chops. All of these need only 40 minutes simmering in the sauce. A mixed vegetable curry – halved new potatoes, cauliflower florets, sliced carrots, and chunks of parsnip – is good too. Use 675g (1½lb) total weight and simmer for 30 minutes.

Tomato chutney Serve this with the curry. Finely chop and mix together 4 plum tomatoes, ½ cucumber, 1 small onion, 1 deseeded fresh green chilli and 4 tbsp chopped fresh coriander.

Health points

• Cardamom is believed to help relieve digestive problems such as indigestion, flatulence and stomach cramps, and it can help prevent acid regurgitation and belching.

Each serving provides   Key nutrients 325kcals, 19g fat (of which 7g is saturated fat), 28g protein, 11g carbohydrate, 219mg sodium (0.54g salt), 2.5g fibre

Good source of potassium (1000mg)

Fragrant lamb with spinach *p72*

Veal Marsala *p75*

Veal escalopes with lemon garlic sauce *p76*

Leg of lamb with double mint sauce *p74*

Leg of lamb with double mint sauce

Whether it's spring or not, treat yourself to lamb! A small leg serves 6 and is surprisingly low in fat. The crowning jewel of a fresh mint sauce simmers up in seconds, yet tastes as if it took much more time.

Preparation time **20 minutes**   Cooking time **55 minutes plus standing**   *Serves 6*

For the sauce

200g (7oz) mint jelly

2 tbsp fresh lemon juice

4 tbsp chopped fresh mint

For the lamb

1 boneless leg of lamb, well trimmed, about 1kg (2¼lb)

2 garlic cloves, chopped

1 tbsp chopped fresh rosemary

pepper to taste

1 large lemon, halved

150ml (5fl oz) dry white wine or low-sodium chicken stock

1 Preheat the oven to 200°C (400°F, gas mark 6). Lightly coat a roasting tin with cooking spray or a teaspoon of olive oil. Combine the mint jelly, lemon juice and fresh mint in a small saucepan. Stir over medium heat for about 5 minutes or until the jelly melts. Remove from the heat and set aside.

2 Meanwhile, slash the lamb in half horizontally, cutting three-quarters of the way through. Open and spread flat like a book. Put the meat between two pieces of cling film and pound with a meat mallet or rolling pin to about 2.5cm (1in) thickness.

3 Brush about 2 tablespoons of the mint sauce over the lamb, then sprinkle with the garlic, rosemary and pepper. Squeeze the juice from one lemon half over the lamb. Roll up the lamb from one wide side and tie with kitchen string, in both directions. Transfer to the roasting tin, seam-side down. Squeeze the remaining lemon half over the lamb and pour on the wine.

4 Roast for about 50 minutes or until cooked to your taste. Leave to rest for 10 minutes. Meanwhile, reheat the remaining mint sauce. Remove the strings from the lamb and cut into 1cm (½in) slices. Serve with the mint sauce.

Some more ideas

• Although lamb and mint sauce is a traditional pairing, you can prepare a 1kg (2¼lb) joint of lean boneless beef or pork in the same way.

• Serve this dish with steamed asparagus and roast new potatoes.

Health points

• Lamb is a rich-tasting meat. Over the years it has become much leaner due to consumer demand for less fatty meats. While still not as lean as pork or poultry are, lamb is very flavourful and so can often be served in smaller portions.

photo, page 73

Each serving provides   Key nutrients 361kcals, 18g fat (of which 9g is saturated fat), 33g protein, 11g carbohydrate, 148mg sodium (0.37g salt), 0.2g fibre

Useful source of potassium (563mg)

Veal Marsala

Elegant enough for guests, easy enough for every day! Lean veal escalopes cook in a jiffy, and the Marsala sauce with mushrooms adds plenty of class.

Preparation time **15 minutes**   Cooking time **12 minutes**   *Serves 4*

450g (1lb) veal escalopes

pepper to taste

35g (1¼oz) plain flour

15g (½oz) butter, cut into
4 pieces

280g (10oz) large button
mushrooms, thinly sliced

175ml (6fl oz) dry Marsala wine

3 tbsp chopped flat-leaf parsley

1 Preheat the oven to 120°C (250°F, gas mark ½). Put a baking tray on the middle shelf of the oven to heat.

2 Place the veal escalopes between pieces of greaseproof paper and pound with a meat mallet, from the centre out, to 3mm (⅛in) thickness. Sprinkle with pepper. Put the flour in a plastic bag. Add the veal, a few slices at a time, and shake to coat them.

3 Coat a large nonstick frying pan with cooking spray or a little olive oil and set over high heat. Melt one piece of butter in the pan, tilting to coat. Sauté a few pieces of veal at a time for about 1 minute on each side or until browned; do not crowd the pan. Transfer the escalopes to the hot baking tray in the oven. Repeat with the remaining ecalopes, adding more butter to the pan as needed.

4 Add the mushrooms to the frying pan and sauté for about 3 minutes or until golden. Pour in the Marsala and scrape up all the browned bits from the bottom. Cook for about 2 minutes or until the juices are reduced to 125ml (4fl oz). Return the escalopes to the pan, stacking them on top of each other if necessary. Turn to coat with the hot pan juices. Sprinkle with parsley and serve.

Some more ideas

• For a more economical dish, substitute skinless, boneless chicken or turkey breasts for the escalopes.

• Instead of button mushrooms use 2 large portobello mushrooms – their rich taste and meaty texture will elevate the delicate flavour of veal from sublime to divine! Or consider using shiitake mushrooms, which also have an earthy, full flavour and feature heart-healthy phytochemicals not found in other mushrooms.

Health points

• Compared with many beef and lamb cuts, veal is lower in both fat and saturated fat. It's also a good source of vitamin B_2 and niacin, which aid in metabolising fat.

• Mushrooms are a good source of copper, a mineral that is important for healthy bones. Copper also helps the body to absorb iron from food.

photo, page 73

Each serving provides   Key nutrients 230kcals, 7g fat (of which 2g is saturated fat), 26g protein, 8g carbohydrate, 160mg sodium (0.4g salt), 1.5g fibre

Useful source of potassium (755mg)

Veal escalopes with lemon garlic sauce

There's a whole head of garlic in this recipe, but after slow roasting, it comes out of the oven tasting mild and sweet. The mashed roast garlic adds a sublime but subtle perfume to the sauce.

Preparation time **5 minutes**   Cooking time **50 minutes**   *Serves 4*

For the sauce

1 head garlic

150ml (5fl oz) low-sodium chicken stock

4 tbsp fresh lemon juice

2 tsp cornflour

For the veal

4 veal escalopes, 115g (4oz) each

1 tbsp Dijon mustard

1 lemon, very thinly sliced

1 Preheat the oven to 190°C (375°F, gas mark 5). Wrap the garlic in foil and bake for about 45 minutes or until tender (the packet will feel soft when pressed). When cool enough to handle, cut off the top of the bulb, squeeze out the garlic pulp into a small bowl and mash until smooth.

2 Preheat the grill to moderate. Brush the escalopes with the mustard. Top each escalope with 3 lemon slices. Grill the escalopes for about 2 minutes or until cooked through. Transfer the escalopes to a platter and cover loosely with foil to keep warm.

3 In a small saucepan, whisk the stock and lemon juice into the cornflour. Whisk in the roasted garlic. Bring to the boil over medium heat and boil for 1 minute or until the sauce is lightly thickened. Spoon the sauce over the veal and serve immediately.

Some more ideas

Garlic bread Use roasted garlic as it is prepared in step 1 to spread over slices of whole-grain bread instead of butter.

• You can substitute turkey or pork escalopes for the veal.

Health points

• The sulphur compounds in garlic may protect blood vessels against the accumulation of fatty plaque that can lead to heart disease and stroke.

photo, page 73

Each serving provides   Key nutrients 150kcals, 4g fat (of which 1g is saturated fat), 25g protein, 5g carbohydrate, 460mg sodium (1.15g salt), 0.5g fibre

Useful source of potassium (519mg)

Poultry

Citrus-grilled chicken breasts with melon salsa

Capture the spirit of summer with this refreshing mix of sweet melon, salad greens, chicken and citrus, spiked with green chilli. It's healthy, carefree eating at its best.

Preparation time **20 minutes**   Cooking time **10 minutes**   *Serves 4*

4 skinless, boneless chicken breasts, about 115g (4oz) each

pepper to taste

1 fresh jalapeño or other green chilli

6 tbsp fresh lime juice

1 garlic clove, finely chopped

2 tsp low-sodium soy sauce

For the salsa

1 large cucumber

1 small orange-fleshed melon, cut into 2.5cm (1in) cubes

175g (6oz) cherry tomatoes, halved

2 tbsp very thinly sliced fresh basil

To serve

85g (3oz) mixed salad leaves

1 Preheat the grill to moderate. Sprinkle the chicken on both sides with pepper. Deseed the chilli, then finely chop it. Stir together 2 tablespoons lime juice, the garlic, soy sauce and 1 teaspoon of the chopped chilli in a shallow dish. Add the chicken and turn to coat. Cover and leave to marinate at room temperature, turning once, while preparing the salsa.

2 Halve the cucumber lengthways. Remove the seeds with the tip of a teaspoon. Place the cucumber cut-side down on a board and cut into thin slices. Combine the cucumber, melon, tomatoes, basil, and remaining chilli and lime juice in a medium bowl. Toss together, then set aside.

3 Discard the marinade. Lightly coat the chicken breasts all over with cooking spray or a little olive oil. Grill the chicken for about 5 minutes on each side or until the juices run clear.

4 Transfer the chicken to a cutting board and cut diagonally into strips about 1cm (½in) wide. Toss with the cucumber mixture. Divide the salad leaves among four plates and spoon the chicken and melon mixture on top.

Some more ideas

• Other lean meat – turkey breast, pork fillet or beef steak – can replace the chicken.

• For a dish with less heat, omit the chilli and use 1 tsp mild chilli powder. Use half in the marinade for the chicken and half in the salsa.

• Add 150g (5½oz) pineapple chunks (fresh or canned in its own juice) to the salsa.

• Serve over torn romaine or cos lettuce leaves instead of mixed salad leaves.

Health points

• Orange-fleshed melons, such as cantaloupe or Charentais, are an excellent source of betacarotene, a powerful antioxidant that has anti-carcinogenic properties.

• Chillies have ample amounts of vitamin C – more than sweet peppers do. Capsaicin, the chemical that causes the heat, is also very healthy.

Each serving provides   Key nutrients 180kcals, 4g fat (of which 1g is saturated fat), 28g protein, 10g carbohydrate, 210mg sodium (0.52g salt), 2g fibre

Good source of potassium (909mg)

Chicken with apples *p80*

Citrus-grilled chicken breasts with melon salsa *p78*

Chicken and cashew pancakes *p86*

Greek chicken pitta pockets *p83*

Chicken with apples

Looking for a meal that can be on the table in 30 minutes yet is elegant enough for a dinner party? This dish looks and tastes like it comes from a fine French bistro, but with far healthier ingredients.

Preparation time **10 minutes**   Cooking time **20 minutes**   *Serves 4*

For the apples

2 medium shallots, finely chopped

2 dessert apples, peeled and cut into 5mm (¼in) slices

225ml (8fl oz) apple juice

175ml (6fl oz) low-sodium chicken stock

1 tbsp Calvados or apple juice

For the chicken

35g (1¼oz) plain flour

pepper to taste

4 skinless, boneless chicken breasts, 140g (5oz) each

2 tbsp whipping cream

1 Lightly coat a large heavy nonstick frying pan with cooking spray or a little olive oil and set over a medium-high heat. Sauté the shallots for about 2 minutes or until soft. Add the apples and sauté for 3 minutes or until lightly browned. Add the apple juice, stock and Calvados. Cook, stirring, for about 5 minutes or until the apples are tender. Transfer to a medium bowl. Wipe the pan clean.

2 Mix together the flour and pepper on a sheet of grease-proof paper. Coat the chicken breasts with the seasoned flour, pressing with your hands so the flour adheres and the chicken is flattened evenly.

3 Lightly coat the frying pan again with spray or oil and set over medium-high heat. Cook the chicken for about 3 minutes on each side or until browned and almost cooked through. Return the apple mixture and any juices to the pan and bring to the boil, stirring. Reduce the heat and simmer for 2 minutes. Stir in the cream and serve.

Some more ideas

• Serve this dish with wild rice and green beans, with diced mango for dessert.

• Substitute turkey fillets for the chicken breasts.

• Stirring in cream at the end gives the sauce a satiny smoothness. Only a small amount is needed to give a satisfying richness, and this won't ruin your healthy eating goals.

Health points

• Apples contain ellagic acid, an antioxidant substance that protects against heart disease and cancer. They also contain rutin, a chemical that teams up with vitamin C to maintain blood-vessel health.

photo, page 79

Each serving provides   Key nutrients 265kcals, 5g fat (of which 2g is saturated fat), 35g protein, 19g carbohydrate, 140mg sodium (0.35g salt), 1.5g fibre

Useful source of potassium (680mg)

Basmati chicken pilaf

This colourful one-pot dish is very simple to make and ideal for a tasty and nutritious midweek meal. Coconut milk, gentle spices and fresh coriander add an exotically fragrant note. Serve with a mixed green salad.

Preparation time **10 minutes**   Cooking time **20–25 minutes**   *Serves 4*

2 tbsp olive oil

1 onion, chopped

1 garlic clove, crushed

1 red pepper, deseeded and diced

450g (1lb) skinless, boneless chicken breasts, cut into thin strips

175g (6oz) button mushrooms, halved

2 small courgettes, sliced

300g (10½oz) basmati rice, rinsed

1 tsp ground coriander

1 tsp ground cumin

1 tsp ground cinnamon

150ml (5fl oz) reduced-fat coconut milk

400ml (14fl oz) hot low-sodium chicken stock

pepper to taste

2 tbsp chopped fresh coriander

sprigs of fresh coriander to garnish

1 Heat the oil in a saucepan and add the onion, garlic, red pepper and chicken. Cook over a fairly high heat, stirring, for 4–5 minutes or until the chicken has lost its pinkness.

2 Add the mushrooms, courgettes, rice, ground coriander, cumin and cinnamon. Cook, stirring, for 1 minute.

3 Pour in the coconut milk and hot stock, and season with pepper to taste. Bring to the boil, then cover, reduce the heat and simmer for 10–15 minutes or until the rice is tender and has absorbed the liquid.

4 Remove from the heat. Stir in the chopped coriander, then cover again and leave to stand for 5 minutes. Serve hot, garnished with coriander sprigs.

Some more ideas

Gingery turkey pilaf Use strips of turkey breast instead of chicken. Sauté them in the oil with 2 sliced leeks, a 2.5cm (1in) piece of fresh root ginger, finely chopped, 1 crushed garlic clove and 1 deseeded and finely diced fresh red chilli. Add the rice with 250g (9oz) sliced baby corn and 175g (6oz) frozen peas. In step 3, replace the coconut milk with dry white wine or additional stock, then cook as in the main recipe. In step 4, stir in chopped fresh flat-leaf parsley instead of fresh coriander.

• Use shiitake or chestnut mushrooms instead of button mushrooms.

Health points

• Coconut milk can provide a rich, creamy taste in many South-east Asian-inspired dishes. By using a light coconut milk rather than the regular, you'll save 2–3 grams of fat.

Each serving provides   Key nutrients 515kcals, 11g fat (of which 5g is saturated fat), 35g protein, 66g carbohydrate, 152mg sodium (0.38g salt), 2g fibre

Useful source of potassium (842mg)

Poached chicken breasts in vegetable and herb sauce

A tender chicken breast absorbs the essence of a seasoned poaching liquid, which keeps the meat succulent. Here, the chicken picks up the gentle onion flavour of leeks and the fresh taste of tarragon.

Preparation time **15 minutes**   Cooking time **36 minutes**   *Serves 4*

450ml (16fl oz) dry white wine or 225ml (8fl oz) each apple juice and water

3 medium celery sticks, chopped

1 large leek, thoroughly washed and chopped

1 medium carrot, chopped

225ml (8fl oz) low-sodium chicken stock

1 tbsp chopped parsley

1 tbsp chopped fresh tarragon

4 skinless, boneless chicken breasts

1 tbsp plain flour

15g (½oz) butter

pepper to taste

1 In a large frying pan over moderately high heat, bring the wine (or apple juice), celery, leek, carrot, stock, parsley and tarragon to the boil. Add the chicken breasts, reduce the heat to low and simmer, covered, for 25 minutes. Remove the chicken from the pan, cover with foil and keep warm.

2 Increase the heat under the pan to moderate and boil the poaching liquid, uncovered, for 5 minutes.

3 Remove 4 tablespoons of the mixture to a small bowl. Add the flour and whisk until smooth. Stir this into the rest of the mixture in the pan and cook, stirring, for about 3 minutes or until the sauce boils and thickens slightly.

4 Remove from the heat and swirl in the butter. Add pepper to taste. Transfer the chicken to warmed serving plates and spoon over the sauce.

Some more ideas

Poached fish in vegetable and herb sauce Substitute 450g (1lb) plaice fillets for the chicken. Add to the poaching liquid in step 1 and simmer, covered, for 5–6 minutes or until just cooked, then remove from the pan and finish the sauce as in the recipe.

• Change the herbs, using chopped fresh basil or thyme rather than tarragon.

• Use skinless, boneless turkey breast (fillets) instead of the chicken.

Health points

• While celery is relatively high in sodium for a vegetable (35mg per stick), it also contains unique compounds called phthalides that some people believe may lower blood pressure. How phthalides work is under review – preliminary studies indicate that the compounds may reduce the level of some hormones that constrict blood vessels.

Each serving provides   **Key nutrients** 280kcals, 5g fat (of which 3g is saturated fat), 34g protein, 7g carbohydrate, 170mg sodium (0.42g salt), 1.5g fibre

Useful source of potassium (762mg)

Greek chicken pitta pockets

These chicken pitas are packed with tasty salad leaves and a sauce made from cucumbers and yoghurt. They are incredibly easy to prepare, so when you are short of time, skip the fast food and try these instead.

Preparation time **15 minutes**   Cooking time **about 8 minutes**   *Serves 4*

675g (1½lb) skinless, boneless chicken breasts

4 tbsp instant polenta

½ tsp onion powder

1 tsp paprika

1 tsp cumin seeds

pepper to taste

2 tbsp olive oil

4 pitta breads, wholemeal or white

115g (4oz) mixed herb salad leaves

For the sauce

7.5cm (3in) piece cucumber, grated

225g (8oz) plain low-fat yoghurt

1 large garlic clove, crushed

1 tsp mint sauce

1 tbsp chopped fresh mint

1 Cut the chicken breasts into thin strips. Mix together the polenta, onion powder, paprika, cumin seeds and pepper in a plastic bag. Add the chicken strips, a few at a time, and toss well to coat all over. Remove, shaking off the excess, and set aside on a plate while making the sauce.

2 To make the sauce, squeeze the grated cucumber, in handfuls, to remove excess moisture, then put into a bowl. Add the remaining ingredients and stir to mix. Set aside.

3 Preheat the grill to high. Heat a ridged griddle or heavy frying pan and add half the oil, swirling it around the pan until lightly coated. Add half the chicken strips and cook over high heat for 2–3 minutes or until golden brown all over and cooked through, turning once. Keep hot while cooking the remaining chicken strips, using the rest of the oil.

4 Meanwhile, warm the pitta breads under the grill for 1 minute on each side. Split down the side of each pitta to make a pocket.

5 Fill the pitta pockets with the salad leaves. Pile in the chicken strips, spoon over the sauce and serve.

Some more ideas

Middle Eastern chicken sandwich Put the chicken breasts between sheets of cling film and pound with a rolling pin to a thickness of about 1cm (½in) all over. Lightly beat 1 egg and pour on to a plate. Put 100g (3½oz) fine fresh white breadcrumbs on another plate. Season each chicken breast with pepper, then dip into the egg and coat both sides in breadcrumbs, patting them on lightly. Heat half the oil in a ridged griddle or frying pan and cook the chicken breasts, two at a time, for 6 minutes or until golden, turning once. Finely shred ½ small head each of white and red cabbage, and thinly slice 1 sweet white onion. Toss with 2 tbsp chopped parsley and 2 tbsp lemon juice. Spoon 1 tbsp hummus into each warmed pitta pocket, add some cabbage salad and fill with the hot chicken breasts.

photo, page 79

Each serving provides   Key nutrients 530kcals, 13g fat (of which 3g is saturated fat), 48g protein, 58g carbohydrate, 490mg sodium (1.2g salt), 3g fibre

Good source of potassium (953mg)

Sautéed chicken with caramelised onions

Here, savoury sautéed chicken breasts are paired with sweetly cooked onions and a fresh rosemary and thyme sauce. Spinach tagliatelle makes a good accompaniment.

Preparation time **7 minutes**   Cooking time **22 minutes**   *Serves 4*

675g (1½lb) medium onions

4 skinless, boneless chicken breasts, about 115g (4oz) each

pepper to taste

4 tsp butter

2 tbsp caster sugar

5 tbsp low-sodium chicken stock

1 tsp chopped fresh rosemary

1 tsp chopped fresh thyme

1 tbsp red wine vinegar

1 Cut each onion into 6 wedges. Sprinkle the chicken with pepper.

2 Coat a large nonstick frying pan with cooking spray or a little olive oil. Add 2 teaspoons butter and melt over a medium-high heat. Sauté the chicken for about 3 minutes on each side or until browned. Transfer to a plate.

3 Reduce the heat to medium, and melt the remaining butter in the pan. Sauté the onions with 1 tablespoon of the sugar for about 8 minutes or until they are golden brown and caramelised. Stir frequently, breaking the onions apart as they cook. Add the stock and boil for about 2 minutes or until it has evaporated.

4 Stir in the rosemary, thyme and remaining sugar. Return the chicken to the pan and sprinkle with the vinegar. Cook for a further 4 minutes or until the juices from the chicken run clear.

Some more ideas

• Use caramelised onions to top a homemade pizza, or stuff into pitta pockets along with fresh vegetables for a vegetarian sandwich. Or just serve as a side dish.

• Replace the chicken breasts with boneless pork loin chops or turkey breast fillets.

• Does chopping onions make you cry? Blame it on the sulphuric compounds in the vegetable. One remedy is to leave the root end intact; this is where the compounds are concentrated. Or freeze the onion for 20 minutes before cutting, to inhibit the chemical release.

Health points

• Caramelising the onions produces a rich flavour, and makes them much more palatable. The same cooking process can bring out the best flavour in other vegetables, such as peppers and carrots.

Each serving provides   Key nutrients 249kcals, 6g fat (of which 3g is saturated fat), 29g protein, 21g carbohydrate, 140mg sodium (0.35g salt), 2.5g fibre

Useful source of potassium (697mg)

Chicken and cashew pancakes

Chicken stir-fried with carrots, celery and cabbage, then lightly flavoured with orange and sesame, makes a delicious filling for pancakes. This dish is sure to meet with your family's approval.

Preparation time **15–20 minutes**   Cooking time **about 30 minutes**   *Serves 4*

For the pancakes

115g (4oz) plain flour

pepper to taste

1 egg, beaten

300ml (10fl oz) skimmed milk

1 tsp sunflower oil

For the filling

55g (2oz) unsalted cashews

1 tbsp sunflower oil

300g (11oz) skinless, boneless chicken breasts, cut into strips

1 garlic clove, crushed

1 tsp finely chopped fresh root ginger

1 fresh red chilli, deseeded and finely chopped *(optional)*

2 carrots, cut into matchstick strips

2 celery sticks, cut into matchstick strips

grated zest of ½ orange

200g (7oz) Savoy cabbage, shredded

1 tbsp low-sodium soy sauce

1 tbsp toasted sesame oil

1 To make the pancakes, sift the flour into a bowl and add the pepper to taste. Make a well in the centre. Mix the egg with the milk, then pour into the well. Gradually whisk the flour into the egg and milk to form a smooth batter.

2 Use a little of the oil to lightly grease a flat griddle or large frying pan and place it over medium heat. Pour in a little of the batter and swirl it evenly across the surface, then cook for 2 minutes to form a pancake. Toss the pancake or flip it over with a spatula and cook on the other side for about 30 seconds. Slide out on to a warm heatproof plate and cover with a sheet of greaseproof paper.

3 Cook the remaining batter in the same way, making 8 pancakes in all and stacking them up, interleaved with greaseproof paper. Add a little more oil to the pan between pancakes, as necessary. When all the pancakes have been made, cover the pancake stack with foil, sealing it well. Set aside and keep warm.

4 To make the filling, heat a wok or large frying pan. Add the cashews and stir-fry them over medium heat for a few minutes or until golden. Remove to a plate and set aside.

5 Add the oil to the pan, then add the chicken, garlic, ginger and chilli, if using. Stir-fry for 3 minutes. Add the carrots and celery, and stir-fry for a further 2 minutes. Add the orange zest and cabbage, and stir-fry for 1 minute. Sprinkle over the soy sauce and sesame oil, and stir-fry for another minute. Return the cashews to the pan and toss to mix with the other ingredients.

6 Divide the stir-fry filling among the warm pancakes and fold them over or roll up. Serve immediately, with a little extra soy sauce to sprinkle.

Some more ideas

Sesame duck pancakes Stir-fry 300g (11oz) skinless, boneless, sliced duck breast with 1 crushed garlic clove and 2 tsp finely chopped fresh root ginger in 1 tbsp sunflower oil for 3–4 minutes. Add 1 tbsp dry sherry, 1 tbsp low-sodium soy sauce and 1 tsp honey, then add 150g (5½oz) bean sprouts and toss to mix. While the duck is cooking, parboil 85g (3oz) fine Chinese egg noodles in boiling water for 2–3 minutes; drain and add to the stir-fry with 1 tsp toasted sesame oil and 6 chopped spring onions. Toss together until hot, then divide the stir-fry among the pancakes and roll up or fold over.

Health points

• Cashews are a rich source of protein, fibre and minerals such as iron, magnesium and selenium. Although cashews are high in fat, the majority of it is the 'healthy' monounsaturated type.

photo, page 79

Each serving provides   Key nutrients 367kcals, 16g fat (of which 3g is saturated fat), 26g protein, 31g carbohydrate, 260mg sodium (0.65g salt), 4g fibre

Useful source of potassium (600mg)

Chicken en papillote with carrots and courgettes

This colourful dish shows how easy it can be to make a healthy chicken dish without sacrificing any flavour – or slaving over a hot stove.

Preparation time **15 minutes**   Cooking time **30 minutes**   *Serves 4*

4 skinless, boneless chicken breasts, 675g (1½ lb) in total

115g (4oz) mushrooms, sliced

2 carrots, cut into 4cm (1½in) matchsticks

2 courgettes, cut into 4cm (1½in) matchsticks

2 tbsp olive oil

1 tbsp chopped basil

2 tbsp lemon juice

pepper to taste

1 Preheat the oven to 190°C (375°F, gas mark 5). Cut out 4 sheets of foil about 30cm (12in) square. Place a chicken breast in the centre of each sheet and arrange one-quarter of the vegetables on top.

2 In a small bowl, whisk together the oil, basil, lemon juice and pepper to taste. Spoon this seasoning mixture evenly over the chicken and vegetables.

3 Fold two opposite sides of the foil sheet over the chicken and vegetables, then fold the other sides over and tuck the ends under.

4 Place the parcels on a baking tray and bake for about 30 minutes. Unwrap and transfer the chicken and vegetables to plates, with all the juices in the parcels.

Some more ideas

• Substitute skinless, boneless turkey breast for the chicken.

• Cut matchstick pieces of fennel and use in place of either the carrots or courgettes.

• Use yellow courgettes rather than green ones.

Health points

• The vegetables add heart-healthy betacarotene and vitamins A and C; and the mushrooms provide glutamic acid, which is believed to boost the immune system.

• When you bake poultry with herbs and vegetables in a sealed foil or paper parcel (en papillote), it cooks in its own juices, thus creating exquisite flavours with little fat or sodium needed.

Each serving provides   **Key nutrients** 260kcals, 9g fat (of which 1.5g is saturated fat), 42g protein, 5g carbohydrate, 120mg sodium (0.3g salt), 2g fibre

Good source of potassium (990mg)

Country Captain chicken

This traditional American dish was created in the nineteenth century, when India was considered to be the most exotic place on earth. The flavourings offered a welcome change from plain old chicken stew.

Preparation time **10 minutes**   Cooking time **35 minutes**   *Serves 4*

2 tsp olive oil

4 skinless, boneless chicken breasts, 140g (5oz) each

1 small onion, thinly sliced

3 garlic cloves, finely chopped

1 tbsp curry powder

300ml (10fl oz) no-salt-added canned chopped tomatoes

25g (1oz) dried apricots, thinly sliced

pepper to taste

½ tsp dried thyme

25g (1oz) flaked almonds

1 Heat the oil in a large nonstick flameproof casserole over medium heat. Add the chicken and sauté for 3 minutes on each side or until golden brown. With tongs or a slotted spoon, transfer the chicken to a plate.

2 Add the onion and garlic to the casserole and cook for about 5 minutes or until the onion is tender.

3 Stir in the curry powder and cook for 1 minute. Add the tomatoes with their juice, the apricots, thyme and pepper, and bring to the boil.

4 Return the chicken (and any accumulated juices) to the casserole. Reduce to a simmer, cover and cook for about 20 minutes or until the chicken is cooked through. The dish can now be cooled and refrigerated, then reheated in the oven preheated to 160°C (325°F, gas mark 3). Serve sprinkled with the flaked almonds.

Some more ideas

• Substitute boneless turkey breast for the chicken.

• Add 75g (2½oz) sultanas to the sauce.

• When in peak season, use fresh tomatoes instead of canned ones. Coarsely chop 3 peeled, cored and deseeded medium tomatoes.

Health points

• Tomatoes are an excellent source of the phytochemical lycopene, which may help fight heart disease. Lycopene is most available when tomatoes are cooked with a little fat, as they are in this recipe.

• Dried apricots are a good source of vitamin A and fibre. As they are portable, they can be a handy snack.

• Orange and red fruits and vegetables, such as mangoes, red cabbage and red peppers, are excellent sources of beta-carotene and vitamin C – both antioxidants that help to protect against heart disease and cancer.

Each serving provides   Key nutrients 240kcals, 7g fat (of which 1g is saturated fat), 36g protein, 7g carbohydrate, 127mg sodium (0.31g salt), 2g fibre

Good source of potassium (926mg)

Moroccan chicken with couscous

Aromatic cumin, coriander and cinnamon give these chicken breasts a Middle Eastern flavour, and including chickpeas further enhances the ethnic theme. Courgettes and sugarsnap peas add colour and all the benefits of fresh vegetables.

Preparation and cooking time **30 minutes**   *Serves 4*

450g (1lb) skinless, boneless chicken breasts

1 tbsp olive oil

1 large onion, finely chopped

2 garlic cloves, finely chopped

1 tsp ground cumin

1 tsp ground coriander

1 cinnamon stick

2 large courgettes, halved lengthways and sliced

1 can (about 400g) no-salt-added chopped tomatoes

200ml (7fl oz) low-sodium vegetable stock

225g (8oz) sugarsnap peas

1 can (about 410g) chickpeas, drained and rinsed

For the couscous

250g (9oz) couscous

400ml (14fl oz) boiling water

1 tbsp olive oil

10g (¼oz) butter

pepper to taste

chopped fresh coriander to garnish

1 Cut the chicken on the diagonal into strips about 1cm (½in) thick. Heat the oil in a wok or heavy frying pan. Add the chicken, onion and garlic, and cook over medium-high heat, stirring constantly, for about 2 minutes or until the chicken turns white with golden brown flecks.

2 Reduce the heat to low and add the ground cumin and coriander and cinnamon stick. Cook, stirring constantly, for 1 minute. Add the courgettes and stir well, then add the tomatoes with their juice and the stock. Cook for 5 minutes, stirring occasionally.

3 Meanwhile, put the couscous in a saucepan (off the heat) and pour over the boiling water. Add the oil. Stir well, then cover and leave to soak for 5 minutes.

4 Add the sugarsnap peas and chickpeas to the chicken mixture. Cook for a further 5 minutes, stirring frequently.

5 Stir the butter into the couscous and cook over a moderate heat for 3 minutes, fluffing up with a fork to separate the grains. Season with pepper. Pile the couscous on to a serving platter. Spoon the chicken on top and garnish with chopped coriander. Serve hot.

Some more ideas

Prawn and bean couscous Replace the chicken with 450g (1lb) cooked, peeled prawns (thawed if frozen) and the chickpeas with canned black-eyed beans. Instead of courgettes and sugarsnap peas, use 225g (8oz) each frozen peas, thawed, and green beans. In step 1, cook the onion and garlic in the oil for 2 minutes.

Health points

• Believing chickpeas to be powerful aphrodisiacs, the Romans fed them to their stallions to improve their performance. Although this reputation seems to have been forgotten now, chickpeas do contribute good amounts of soluble fibre as well as useful amounts of iron, folate, vitamin E and manganese to the diet.

Each serving provides   Key nutrients 460kcals, 11g fat (of which 3g is saturated fat), 40g protein, 52g carbohydrate, 180mg sodium (0.45g salt), 5g fibre

Good source of potassium (1100mg)

Chicken with rosemary and orange sauce *p92*

Moroccan chicken with couscous *p90*

Chicken jamboree *p94*

Orange-glazed poussins *p93*

Chicken with rosemary and orange sauce

There's no denying that skinless chicken breast is the most versatile and healthy of meats. Try this herb and citrus pan sauce for a chicken dish with minimal fat and maximum flavour.

Preparation time **10 minutes**   Cooking time **15 minutes**   *Serves 4*

2 tsp olive oil

4 skinless, boneless chicken breasts, 140g (5oz) each

2 shallots, finely chopped

1½ tsp grated orange zest

½ tsp finely chopped fresh rosemary

150ml (5fl oz) orange juice

1 tbsp orange marmalade

pepper to taste

1 tbsp fresh lemon juice

1 tsp cornflour blended with 1 tbsp water

1 Heat the oil in a large nonstick frying pan over medium heat. Add the chicken breasts and cook for about 5 minutes on each side or until golden brown and cooked through. Transfer the chicken to a plate and cover loosely with foil to keep warm.

2 Add the shallots to the frying pan and cook, stirring, for 3 minutes or until light golden. Stir in the orange zest, rosemary, orange juice, marmalade and pepper, and bring to the boil. Stir in the lemon juice.

3 Stir in the cornflour mixture and cook, stirring, for about 1 minute or until the sauce is slightly thickened. Slice the chicken and serve with the sauce spooned on top.

Some more ideas

• Use skinless, boneless turkey fillets or boneless pork chops instead of chicken.

• Substitute apricot jam for the orange marmalade.

• Serve this dish with steamed brown rice and grilled vegetables.

Health points

• The potassium in the orange juice will help to lower your risk of stroke, while the pectin found in the marmalade is a cholesterol-lowering type of soluble fibre.

• Shallots, whose taste falls somewhere between onion and garlic, are a good source of vitamin B_6, which helps manufacture amino acids in the body.

photo, page 91

Each serving provides   **Key nutrients** 200kcals, 4g fat (of which 0.5g is saturated fat), 34g protein, 8g carbohydrate, 327mg sodium (0.82g salt), 0.2g fibre

Useful source of potassium (600mg)

Orange-glazed poussins

Poussins are small immature chickens, and typically weigh 400–450g (14–16oz) each. With this recipe, the poussins are basted during roasting with a delicious orange and Earl Grey tea mixture.

Preparation time **20 minutes**   Cooking time **1 hour plus standing**   *Serves 4*

1 Earl Grey tea bag

4 tbsp boiling water

2 medium oranges

150g (5½oz) orange marmalade

4 poussins, about 450g (1lb) each

2 medium onions, sliced

8 sprigs of fresh rosemary

8 sprigs of fresh thyme

1 Preheat the oven to 190°C (375°F, gas mark 5). Steep the tea bag in the boiling water in a small saucepan for 5 minutes. Discard the tea bag. Squeeze the juice from 1 of the oranges into the tea, then stir in the marmalade until melted. Keep warm. Cut the second orange into quarters (do not peel).

2 Wash and dry the poussins. Loosen the breast skin slightly. Stuff the large cavity of each bird with 1 orange quarter, one-quarter of the onion slices, 1 rosemary sprig and 1 thyme sprig. Tie the legs together with kitchen string. Place the poussins, breast-side up, on a rack in a roasting tin. Brush all over and under the skin with about one-quarter of the tea glaze. Pour enough water into the tin to cover the bottom (the water should not reach the rack).

3 Roast for about 1 hour, basting over and under the skin every 20 minutes with the remaining glaze, until browned and the juices run clear. Leave the poussins to rest for 10 minutes. Discard the rosemary, thyme, onions and orange quarters from the cavities. Garnish with the remaining herb sprigs, and serve. Remove and discard the skin before eating.

Some more ideas

Orange-roasted chicken
Instead of poussins, use a 1.5kg (3½lb) chicken. Stuff all the onion, orange quarters and herb sprigs into the cavity. Roast at 200°C (400°F, gas mark 6) for at least 1½ hours or until the juices run clear, brushing with the glaze.

• Use sugar-free apricot jam instead of orange marmalade.

Health points

• Removing the skin from poultry – either before cooking or before eating – keeps the fat content very low.

• Two of the compounds that garlic contain – allicin and sulphoraphane – are believed to help reduce the risk of cancer. Some studies suggest that they may also help reduce the risk of blood clots forming, thus helping to prevent heart disease.

photo, page 91

Each serving provides   Key nutrients 390kcals, 44g fat (of which 1g is saturated fat), 56g protein, 35g carbohydrate, 166mg sodium (0.41g salt), 2g fibre

Good source of potassium (1016mg)

Chicken jamboree

This healthy chicken and vegetable casserole makes an easy midweek meal. To make it even quicker, you could use supermarket washed-and-cut carrots and broccoli, ready to go from packet to pan.

Preparation time **10 minutes**   Cooking time **about 20 minutes**   *Serves 4*

2 tbsp sunflower oil

450g (1lb) skinless, boneless chicken breasts, cut into small cubes

1 small onion, chopped

225g (8oz) button mushrooms

1 bay leaf

2 large sprigs of fresh thyme or ½ tsp dried thyme

3 large sprigs of fresh tarragon or ½ tsp dried tarragon (optional)

grated zest of 1 small lemon or ½ large lemon

125ml (4fl oz) dry sherry

300ml (10fl oz) boiling water

225g (8oz) baby carrots

pepper to taste

225g (8oz) broccoli florets

1 tbsp cornflour

2 tbsp cold water

3 tbsp chopped parsley

1 Heat the oil in a large sauté pan. Add the chicken and brown the pieces over a high heat for 3 minutes, stirring constantly. Reduce the heat to medium. Stir in the onion, mushrooms, bay leaf, thyme, tarragon, if used, and lemon zest. Cook for 4 minutes or until the onion and mushrooms are beginning to soften.

2 Pour in the sherry and boiling water. Add the carrots and seasoning to taste, and stir to mix all the ingredients. Bring to the boil, then reduce the heat and cover the pan. Simmer for 5 minutes.

3 Stir in the broccoli florets. Increase the heat to bring the liquid back to a steady simmer. Cover the pan and cook for about 5 minutes or until the pieces of chicken are tender and the vegetables are just cooked. Remove and discard the bay leaf and the herb sprigs.

4 Blend the cornflour to a smooth paste with the cold water. Stir the paste into the casserole and simmer, stirring constantly, for about 2 minutes or until thickened and smooth. Stir in the parsley and serve.

Some more ideas

Creamy chicken mushroom casserole Increase the quantity of button mushrooms to 350g (12oz) and omit the broccoli. Simmer for 5 minutes longer in step 2. Stir in 4 tbsp single cream after thickening with the cornflour, then heat for a few more seconds.

• Small patty pan squash are good in this casserole. Trim off and discard the stalk ends from 225g (8oz) squash and slice them horizontally in half. Add them to the pan with the broccoli. When cooked, the patty pan should be tender but still slightly crunchy.

• Use fine oatmeal to thicken rather than cornflour.

Health points

• This recipe uses vegetables to extend a modest amount of chicken. Served with whole grains such as brown rice, it makes a well-balanced meal, especially if followed by fresh fruit for a vitamin boost.

photo, page 91

Each serving provides   **Key nutrients** 273kcals, 8g fat (of which 1.5g is saturated fat), 31g protein, 13g carbohydrate, 100mg sodium (0.25g salt), 4g fibre

Good source of potassium (900mg)

Chicken and apricot casserole

Chicken thighs are excellent in a casserole, being very tender and full of flavour. Fresh apricots and a bulb of fennel make good partners, especially when spiced up with cumin.

Preparation time **15 minutes**   Cooking time **50 minutes**   *Serves 4*

2 tbsp sunflower oil

8 boneless chicken thighs, about 450g (1lb) in total

1 onion, sliced

2 garlic cloves, chopped

2 tsp ground cumin

2 tsp ground coriander

300ml (10fl oz) low-sodium chicken stock

3 carrots, halved crossways, then each half cut into 6–8 thick fingers

1 bulb of fennel, halved lengthways, then cut crossways into slices

5 apricots, stoned and quartered

pepper to taste

chopped fennel leaves from the bulb to garnish

1 Heat the oil in a large frying pan and sauté the chicken thighs, turning occasionally, for 5–10 minutes or until golden brown all over. Remove from the pan. Add the onion and garlic to the pan and sauté for 5 minutes or until soft.

2 Stir in the cumin and coriander, and fry for 1 minute, then add the stock. Return the chicken to the pan and add the carrots and fennel. Bring to the boil. Stir well, then cover and simmer gently for about 30 minutes or until the chicken is tender. Remove the lid. If there is too much liquid, boil to reduce it slightly.

3 Add the apricots to the casserole and stir gently to mix. Simmer over a low heat for a further 5 minutes.

4 Season to taste with pepper. Sprinkle with the fennel leaves and serve.

Some more ideas

• Replace the apricots with 1 fresh mango, cut into slices or chunks. Sprinkle with fresh coriander instead of fennel leaves.

• Use 1 can (about 400g) apricot halves in natural juice, drained and cut in half, instead of fresh apricots.

• Plain boiled rice, or saffron rice, is a good accompaniment to this dish, as are boiled new potatoes or baked potatoes.

Health points

• Both apricots and carrots provide some vitamin A in the form of beta-carotene, which gives them their distinctive colour, but carrots are by far the better source, providing about 20 times more of this nutrient per 100g (3½oz) than apricots do. Vitamin A is essential for proper vision and increasingly valued for its role as an antioxidant, helping to prevent cancer and coronary heart disease.

Each serving provides   Key nutrients 230kcals, 9g fat (of which 2g is saturated fat), 25g protein, 13g carbohydrate, 250mg sodium (0.625g salt), 4g fibre

Good source of potassium (867mg)

Turkey piccata

Friends coming to supper on a week night? Versatile turkey breast to the rescue! In this case, the turkey is cooked like veal escalopes, in a classic garlic and lemon sauce with capers. You'll have dinner ready in the time it takes to set the table.

Preparation time **10 minutes**   Cooking time **10 minutes**   *Serves 4*

1 tbsp olive oil

4 turkey escalopes, 115g (4oz) each

2 tbsp plain flour

For the sauce

2 garlic cloves, finely chopped

1 tsp grated lemon zest

4 tbsp lemon juice

225ml (8fl oz) low-sodium chicken stock

1 tsp cornflour blended with 1 tbsp water

2 tsp capers, rinsed and drained

2 tbsp chopped parsley

1 Heat the oil in a large nonstick frying pan over medium heat. Dredge the turkey in flour, shaking off the excess. Sauté the turkey for about 2 minutes on each side or until golden brown and cooked through. With tongs or a slotted spoon, transfer the turkey to a plate; cover loosely with foil to keep warm.

2 Add the garlic to the pan and cook, stirring, for 1 minute. Add the lemon zest, lemon juice and chicken stock to the pan and bring to the boil. Boil for 1 minute.

3 Stir in the cornflour mixture and capers, and simmer for 1 minute or until slightly thickened. Stir in the parsley. Serve the turkey with the sauce spooned on top.

Some more ideas

• One way to increase the flavour of lean meat is to coat it lightly with flour before sautéing. The turkey finishes up tender and juicy, with a tempting golden crust.

• Chicken and veal escalopes are also delicious prepared piccata style.

• Serve this dish with brown rice tossed with slivered almonds and with steamed broccoli. Poached plums would be perfect for dessert.

Health points

• Not only does lemon zest enhance flavour, but its high vitamin C content is a potent antioxidant.

Each serving provides   Key nutrients 108kcals, 4g fat (of which 1g is saturated fat), 29g protein, 8g carbohydrate, 160mg sodium (0.4g salt), 0.5g fibre

Useful source of potassium (495mg)

Turkey piccata *p96*

Turkey escalopes with fruity sauce *p98*

Turkey Stroganoff *p99*

Spicy turkey chilli with spaghetti *p100*

Turkey escalopes with fruity sauce

Summer berries have to compete with one another for attention, but come late autumn, the cranberry stands alone. Its jewel-like colour makes it not just an attractive addition to any dish but a healthful one as well.

Preparation time **10 minutes**   Cooking time **15 minutes**   *Serves 4*

1 tbsp olive oil

4 turkey escalopes, 115g (4oz) each, halved crossways

1 tbsp cornflour

125ml (4fl oz) low-sodium chicken stock

For the sauce

100g (3½oz) fresh or frozen cranberries

4 tbsp apple juice concentrate

2 tsp soft dark brown sugar

2 tsp grated lime zest

¼ tsp crushed dried chillies

115g (4oz) canned pineapple chunks in natural juice

1 To make the sauce, combine the cranberries, apple juice concentrate, brown sugar, lime zest and chilli flakes in a small saucepan. Bring to the boil over medium heat and cook, stirring occasionally, for about 10 minutes or until the cranberries have popped and are glossy. Stir in the pineapple. (The fruit mixture can be made up to 3 days ahead and refrigerated. Return to room temperature before proceeding.)

2 Heat the oil in a large nonstick frying pan over medium heat. Dust the turkey with the cornflour and cook for 1 minute on each side or until golden brown and cooked through. Transfer the turkey to a platter and cover loosely with foil to keep warm.

3 Add the stock to the pan and bring to the boil, stirring. Remove from the heat, stir in the fruit mixture and spoon over the turkey.

Some more ideas

• Use pork or chicken escalopes in place of turkey.

• For an orangey flavour, try substituting orange juice concentrate for the apple juice concentrate and orange zest for the lime zest.

Health points

• Adding fruit to main meals helps you to reach your 5-a-day goal, while adding personality and sweetness to otherwise routine flavours.

• Cranberries, while not often thought of as a fruit to eat every day, are brimming with vitamin C and antioxidant properties, as well as heart-healthy fibre.

photo, page 97

Each serving provides   Key nutrients 220kcals, 5g fat (of which 1g is saturated fat), 28g protein, 19g carbohydrate, 100mg sodium (0.25g salt), 1g fibre

Useful source of potassium (527mg)

Turkey Stroganoff

Here's a creamy dish you can enjoy without guilt! Substitute turkey for the customary beef and boost the flavour with portobello mushrooms. It's just as tasty as the original but so much better for your blood pressure.

Preparation time **10 minutes**   Cooking time **18 minutes**   *Serves 4*

350g (12oz) roast turkey breast, cut into 5 x 1cm (2 x ½in) strips

pepper to taste

2 portobello mushrooms, 115g (4oz) each

225g (8oz) tagliatelle, made without egg

2 tsp poppy seeds

1 small red onion, thinly sliced

15g (½oz) butter

1½ tbsp plain flour

350ml (12fl oz) low-sodium beef stock

115g (4oz) fromage frais

1½ tsp Dijon mustard

1 Sprinkle the turkey strips with pepper. Remove and discard the stalks from the mushrooms, cut the caps into quarters and thinly slice. Cook the tagliatelle in a pot of boiling water according to the packet instructions. Drain, then toss with the poppy seeds in the empty cooking pot. Keep warm.

2 While the tagliatelle is cooking, coat a large nonstick frying pan with cooking spray or a little olive oil and set over medium-high heat. Sauté the onion for 2 minutes. Add the mushrooms and sauté for a further 5–6 minutes or until the mushrooms are tender. Transfer to a large bowl.

3 Melt the butter in the pan over medium heat. Add the flour and cook, stirring, for 1 minute. Gradually whisk in the stock. Cook, stirring, for about 4 minutes or until the sauce thickens and boils.

4 Reduce the heat to low. Blend in the fromage frais and mustard. Add the turkey and the reserved vegetables with accumulated juices to the pan. Cook until heated through (do not boil). Divide the tagliatelle among four plates and spoon the Stroganoff on top.

Some more ideas

• Prepare this dish using roast chicken breast instead of turkey.

• Rather than portobellos, use shiitake, chestnut or white button mushrooms.

Health points

• The leanest of poultry is skinless turkey breast – 100g (3½oz) of cooked meat has only about 1g of fat.

• Fromage frais makes this dish creamy with much less fat than the original recipe. To prevent the sauce from curdling, be sure to cook over low heat and never let the sauce boil.

• Onions contain a type of dietary fibre called fructo-oligosaccharides (FOS), which is also found in chicory, leeks, garlic, Jerusalem artichokes, asparagus, barley and bananas. It is believed to stimulate the growth of friendly bacteria in the gut while inhibiting bad bacteria.

photo, page 97

Each serving provides   Key nutrients 425kcals, 10g fat (of which 4g is saturated fat), 40g protein, 52g carbohydrate, 200mg sodium (0.5g salt), 3g fibre

Useful source of potassium (821mg)

Spicy turkey chilli with spaghetti

Sweet peppers and warm spices flavour this family-style chilli, made with minced turkey rather than the traditional beef for a lower fat content, and served on spaghetti to boost the carbohydrate value.

Preparation time **10 minutes**   Cooking time **about 25 minutes**   *Serves 4*

1 tbsp sunflower oil

1 large garlic clove, crushed

1 onion, finely chopped

2 red or green peppers, deseeded and finely chopped

1½ tsp cayenne pepper, or to taste

2 tsp ground cumin

1 tsp dried oregano

450g (1lb) minced turkey

2 cans (about 400g each) no-salt-added chopped tomatoes

1 can (about 400g) red kidney beans, drained and rinsed

pepper to taste

450g (1lb) spaghetti

For the topping

150g (5½oz) plain low-fat yoghurt

1 spring onion, finely chopped

4 tbsp finely chopped mixed fresh herbs, such as parsley, coriander and chives

1 First make the topping. Mix the yoghurt with the spring onion and herbs. Cover and chill until needed.

2 Heat the oil in a large frying pan. Add the garlic and sauté for 30 seconds. Add the onion and red or green peppers, and sauté, stirring occasionally, for 5 minutes or until softened.

3 Stir in the cayenne pepper, ground cumin and oregano, and continue to cook, stirring occasionally, for about 2 minutes. Add the turkey and cook, stirring occasionally, until it is browned and crumbly.

4 Stir in the tomatoes with their juice and the kidney beans, and add seasoning to taste. Bring to the boil, then reduce the heat and simmer for 15 minutes.

5 Meanwhile, cook the spaghetti in boiling water according to the packet instructions. Drain well.

6 Divide the spaghetti among four plates and spoon an equal amount of turkey chilli over each serving. Top with the herb-flavoured yoghurt and serve.

Some more ideas

• Use black or pinto beans instead of kidney beans.

• For a vegetarian chilli, omit the minced turkey and use 2 cans of kidney beans.

• To increase the fibre content of this dish, use wholemeal spaghetti or noodles.

Health points

• Turkey is a good source of zinc and many B vitamins, particularly B_1, B_{12} and niacin. It also provides iron.

• Red kidney beans are low in fat. They provide good amounts of vitamins B_1, niacin and B_6, and useful amounts of iron. They are also a good source of soluble fibre, which can help to reduce high levels of cholesterol in the blood.

photo, page 97

Each serving provides   Key nutrients 675kcals, 7g fat (of which 1g is saturated fat), 51g protein, 108g carbohydrate, 168mg sodium (0.42g salt), 10g fibre

Good source of potassium (1260mg)

Seafood

Poached salmon with cucumber and dill sauce

You've hooked a prizewinning catch with this one! Supper for four in just 20 minutes – fresh salmon fillets topped with creamy cucumber and fresh dill sauce. And it's oh-so-good for you.

Preparation time **10 minutes**   Cooking time **10 minutes**   *Serves 4*

For the salmon

225ml (8fl oz) dry white wine or low-sodium chicken stock

350ml (12fl oz) water

2 spring onions, sliced

8 black peppercorns

4 salmon fillets, 115g (4oz) each

For the sauce

175ml (6fl oz) virtually-fat-free fromage frais

50g (1¾oz) diced peeled cucumber

2 tbsp snipped fresh dill

1 tbsp fresh lemon juice

pepper to taste

sprigs of fresh dill to garnish

1 Combine the wine and water in a large nonstick frying pan and stir in the spring onions and peppercorns. Place the salmon in the pan in a single layer. Bring just to the boil over high heat. Reduce the heat to medium-low, cover and simmer for 6 minutes or until the fish flakes when tested with a fork.

2 Meanwhile, stir together the fromage frais, cucumber, dill, lemon juice and pepper in a medium bowl to make a sauce. Refrigerate if not serving immediately.

3 Carefully transfer the salmon fillets with a fish slice to a large platter. Garnish with fresh dill sprigs. Serve hot or chilled, with the sauce.

Some more ideas

• Do you like your salmon hot or cold? This recipe works either way. To serve cold, squeeze lemon juice over the poached fillets, cover with cling film and chill for at least 2 hours or overnight. Make the cucumber and dill sauce just before it's time to serve.

• Serve the salmon hot with steamed jasmine rice tossed with toasted almonds, or cold on a bed of salad greens. Accompany with French or green beans tossed with a little vinaigrette and slices of Galia or Charentais melon.

Health points

• Although the fat in salmon is of the heart-friendly type, the fish is still high in calories. By poaching it instead of sautéing, you bypass the fat calories from the oil.

• Despite being very light, virtually-fat-free fromage frais makes a rich and creamy sauce for the salmon.

Each serving provides Key nutrients 300kcals, 16g fat (of which 6g is saturated fat), 26g protein, 3g carbohydrate, 71mg sodium (0.18g salt), 0.2g fibre

Useful source of potassium (522mg)

Lemon-glazed plaice fillets

Wondering what to make for supper? Here's a smart solution – grill fish fillets on top of fresh lemon slices. Then top them with a light citrus sauce. It's all ready in less than 25 minutes.

Preparation time **15 minutes**   Cooking time **8 minutes**   *Serves 4*

5 large lemons

1 tbsp olive oil

1 garlic clove, finely chopped

4 plaice fillets, 115g (4oz) each

pepper to taste

6 large fresh basil leaves, finely shredded

For the sauce

125ml (4fl oz) low-sodium chicken stock

1½ tsp cornflour

2 tsp caster sugar

1 Grate the zest from one of the lemons and squeeze out the juice. Cut another lemon into 8 wedges. Cut the remaining 3 lemons into 12 slices of 5mm (¼in) thickness. Heat the oil in a small saucepan over medium heat. Add the garlic and cook until golden. Whisk in the lemon juice, then remove from the heat.

2 Coat the grill rack with cooking spray. Preheat the grill to medium. Lightly brush both sides of the fish fillets with the garlic mixture and sprinkle with salt and pepper. Place 3 lemon slices on the grill rack and put a fish fillet on top. Repeat with the remaining lemon slices and fish. Arrange the lemon wedges alongside the fish on the rack. Grill the fish, without turning, for about 6 minutes or until just opaque throughout. Grill the lemon wedges for about 2 minutes on each side or until browned.

3 Meanwhile, blend the stock and cornflour in a cup until smooth. Whisk this mixture into the remaining garlic mixture together with the sugar and ¼ teaspoon lemon zest. Bring to the boil over medium-high heat and cook for about 1 minute or until the sauce thickens.

4 Transfer the fish to plates, lemon slices underneath. Spoon the sauce over the fish and sprinkle with the basil and remaining lemon zest. Garnish with the grilled lemon wedges.

Some more ideas

• If plaice is not available, you can use fillets of other flat fish. Halibut and lemon sole are both good choices.

Health points

• Citrus fruits such as lemon are particularly good for hypertension. They are rich in vitamin C, potassium and pectin as well as providing phytochemicals that may benefit numerous other conditions as well, including allergies, asthma, cancer, cataracts, stroke, heart disease and even the common cold.

• Most nutrition experts recommend eating at least 175g (6oz) of fish per week. Fish has more protein, fewer calories and less fat than most meats.

photo, page 105

Each serving provides | **Key nutrients** 150kcals, 5g fat (of which 0.5g is saturated fat), 20g protein, 8g carbohydrate, 360mg sodium (0.9g salt), 0g fibre

Useful source of potassium (360mg)

Sole en papillote

A packet, a parcel, a papillote – an elegant envelope with supper inside! If you've never cooked fish this way, give it a try. Cooking en papillote seals in the food's natural flavour and juices, and the presentation is bound to impress!

Preparation time **15 minutes**   Cooking time **15 minutes**   *Serves 4*

140g (5oz) fresh spinach, washed and trimmed

1 medium onion, chopped

4 lemon sole or plaice fillets, 115–175g (4–6oz) each

pepper to taste

2 medium tomatoes, chopped

4 medium carrots, cut into matchstick strips

4 spring onions, sliced

125ml (4fl oz) dry white wine or low-sodium chicken stock

2 tsp olive oil

8 thin lemon slices

4 sprigs of fresh thyme

1 Preheat the oven to 200°C (400°F, gas mark 6). Cut out four 38cm (15in) squares of baking parchment and fold each in half diagonally, forming triangles. Open and coat with cooking spray or a little olive oil.

2 Divide the spinach and onion among the parchment squares. Cut the fish fillets in half crossways. Top each portion of spinach with 2 fillet halves, overlapping them slightly. Sprinkle each with pepper. Top evenly with tomatoes, carrots and spring onions. Drizzle each with 2 tablespoons wine or stock and ½ teaspoon of oil, then add 2 lemon slices and 1 thyme sprig.

3 Fold the parchment over the filling. Fold the two open sides of each triangle over to seal. Fold over the points at the ends of the creased side, making a five-sided packet. Lightly coat the packets with cooking spray or olive oil and place them on a baking tray.

4 Bake for about 15 minutes or until the packets puff. Transfer to plates and cut open the tops of the packets (be careful of steam). Serve immediately.

Some more ideas

• Cooking in a packet is so versatile. You can use any kind of fish. Lean, white fish turn out very moist even though they have little natural fat. Oil-rich fish such as salmon are also delicious cooked this way.

• Just cook the vegetables en papillote, without the fish, to serve as an accompaniment.

Health points

• By cooking fish in a sealed parcel, more of the natural juices are retained. When you cook small pieces of lean fish in the oven, they tend to turn out dry and tasteless.

• Spinach has a tremendous wealth of disease-fighting carotenoids and phytochemicals that team up with vitamins to help protect against cancer, high cholesterol and vision problems.

Each serving provides   Key nutrients 200kcals, 4g fat (of which 0.5g is saturated fat), 22g protein, 13g carbohydrate, 200mg sodium (0.5g salt), 4g fibre

Useful source of potassium (817mg)

Sole en papillote *p104*

Lemon-glazed plaice fillets *p103*

Scallop and cherry tomato sauté *p106*

Crispy tuna steaks in citrus sauce *p107*

Scallop and cherry tomato sauté

Scallops are infinitely adaptable, pairing well with many vegetables and herbs, spices and sauces. Here, these succulent shellfish are sautéed with cherry tomatoes, seasoned with garlic and basil, and enlivened with a vermouth-based sauce.

Preparation time **5 minutes**   Cooking time **10 minutes**   *Serves 4*

450g (1lb) scallops

4 tsp cornflour

2 tsp olive oil

3 garlic cloves, finely chopped

350g (12oz) cherry tomatoes

150ml (5fl oz) dry vermouth, white wine or low-sodium chicken stock

15g (½oz) fresh basil, chopped

1 tbsp cold water

1 Dredge the scallops in 3 teaspoons of the cornflour, shaking off the excess. Heat the oil in a large nonstick frying pan over medium heat. Add the scallops and sauté for about 3 minutes or until golden brown and cooked through. With a slotted spoon, transfer the scallops to a bowl.

2 Add the garlic to the pan and cook for 1 minute. Add the tomatoes and cook for a further 4 minutes or until they begin to collapse. Add the vermouth or stock and basil to the pan. Bring to the boil and cook for 1 minute.

3 Meanwhile, stir together the remaining 1 teaspoon cornflour and cold water in a small bowl. Add this mixture to the pan and cook, stirring, for about 1 minute or until the sauce is slightly thickened.

4 Return the scallops to the pan, reduce to a simmer and cook for 1 minute or just until heated through.

Some more ideas

Prawn and cherry tomato sauté Substitute 450g (1lb) large, peeled and deveined, raw prawns for the scallops and cook as in step 1. Then return the prawns to the pan as in step 4.

• Omit the scallops and just make the tomato and basil mixture as a vegetable side dish. Start with step 2, but add the olive oil to sauté the garlic. Skip step 4.

Health points

• When a dish is very low in calories (like this one), the percentage of calories from fat can seem high, even though there is just a small amount of fat in the recipe. However, the fat that is used here is heart-friendly olive oil, which is a healthy monounsaturated fat. Moreover, the mineral-rich scallops are naturally low in both saturated and total fat.

photo, page 105

Each serving provides   Key nutrients 213kcals, 4g fat (of which 1g is saturated fat), 26g protein, 10g carbohydrate, 216mg sodium (0.54g salt), 1g fibre

Useful source of potassium (517mg)

Crispy tuna steaks in citrus sauce

Their meaty texture makes tuna steaks a favourite with those who say they don't like fish. Here, a crisp crust keeps the tuna juicy and provides a delicious contrast. Who could resist?

Preparation time **15 minutes**   Cooking time **9 minutes**   *Serves 4*

For the sauce

2 large oranges

350ml (12fl oz) orange juice

2 tbsp dry white wine *(optional)*

2 tbsp cornflour

For the tuna steaks

2 tbsp chopped fresh coriander

2 tbsp cornmeal (maize meal) or polenta

pepper to taste

4 tuna steaks, 1cm (½in) thick, 175g (6oz) each

4 tsp olive oil

1 Peel and segment the oranges. Whisk together the orange juice, wine (if using) and cornflour in a small saucepan until smooth. Bring to the boil over medium-high heat and cook, stirring, for about 2 minutes or until the sauce thickens. Remove from the heat and stir in the orange segments. Keep warm.

2 Mix the coriander, cornmeal and pepper in a shallow dish. Coat both sides of the tuna steaks with the cornmeal mixture, pressing firmly so it adheres.

3 Heat 2 teaspoons of the oil in a large, heavy frying pan over medium-high heat until hot but not smoking. Sear the tuna for about 2–3 minutes on each side for medium-rare, or longer according to your taste. Add the remaining oil just before turning the fish. Serve with the sauce.

Some more ideas

• Meaty fish such as tuna hold their shape well when cooked like this. You can prepare salmon, swordfish and shark steaks in the same way.

Health points

• Tuna is a member of the mackerel family, all of which are high in omega-3 fatty acids. Like most fish, tuna is also rich in B vitamins, including niacin and vitamins B_1 and B_6.

photo, page 105

Each serving provides | **Key nutrients** 370kcals, 12g fat (of which 3g is saturated fat), 43g protein, 23g carbohydrate, 100mg sodium (0.25g salt), 0.5g fibre

Good source of potassium (931mg)

Spaghettini with seafood

Cooked in a delicious wine-enriched tomato sauce, a nutritious mix of seafood makes an elegant partner for the long, thin pasta called spaghettini. Prepare a leafy mixed side salad to go with this dinner party main course.

Preparation time **25 minutes**   Cooking time **about 45 minutes**   *Serves 4*

2 tbsp olive oil

1 onion, chopped

2–3 garlic cloves, chopped

2 tbsp chopped parsley

225ml (8fl oz) dry white wine

1 can (about 400g) chopped tomatoes

pinch of crushed dried chillies

¼ tsp caster sugar

pinch of saffron threads

pepper to taste

8–12 mussels, scrubbed and beards removed

2 squid, cleaned, then tentacles cut into bite-size pieces and bodies cut into rings

450g (1lb) raw king or tiger prawns, peeled and deveined

450g (1lb) spaghettini

sprigs of fresh oregano or marjoram to garnish

1 Heat the oil in a large saucepan, add the onion and sauté for 5–7 minutes or until softened but not browned. Add the garlic and parsley, and cook for 1 minute.

2 Pour in the wine and bring to the boil. Regulate the heat so that the wine boils steadily, and cook for 15 minutes or until the wine has almost all evaporated.

3 Stir in the tomatoes with their juice, the crushed chillies, sugar and saffron. Reduce the heat and cook gently for 15 minutes. Season with pepper.

4 Add the mussels. Cover and cook over medium heat for about 5 minutes or until the mussels start to open. Add the squid and prawns, and cook for a further 3–4 minutes or until the prawns turn from blue-grey to pink. Remove from the heat. Discard any mussels that have not opened, then cover the pan to retain the heat.

5 Meanwhile, cook the spaghettini in a large pot of boiling water according to the packet instructions. Drain and return to the empty pot. Add some of the tomato sauce and toss the pasta until coated.

6 Serve the pasta with the remaining tomato sauce and seafood piled on top, garnished with small sprigs of fresh oregano or marjoram.

Some more ideas

• In summer, you can use 1kg (2¼lb) ripe plum tomatoes, peeled and diced, instead of the canned tomatoes. The cooking time for the sauce will be about 5 minutes longer. (You may need a little more sugar to balance the tangy flavour of fresh tomatoes.)

• Replace the squid with 200g (7oz) cooked or canned, drained cannellini beans.

Health points

• Shellfish contain useful amounts of B vitamins, in particular B_{12}, and they are a good source of the antioxidant selenium.

• Wine and tomatoes make a sauce that is far lower in fat than one that is cream-based.

• Onions and garlic contain allicin, which has anti-fungal and antibiotic properties.

Each serving provides   Key nutrients 650kcals, 10g fat (of which 1.5g is saturated fat), 48g protein, 90g carbohydrate, 450mg sodium (1.12g salt), 4.5g fibre

Good source of potassium (1050mg)

Classic grilled Dover sole *p110*

Spaghettini with seafood *p108*

Salmon with pepper and sweetcorn relish *p114*

Steamed fish with ginger and sesame *p111*

Classic grilled Dover sole

Dover sole is a real treat and its superb taste can be fully appreciated when it is simply grilled. New potatoes with fresh mint and baby leaf spinach complement this most elegant of fish dishes.

Preparation and cooking time **30 minutes**   *Serves 4*

4 small Dover sole, about 225g (8oz) each, cleaned and skinned

900g (2lb) baby new potatoes, scrubbed

1 large sprig of fresh mint

40g (1¼oz) unsalted butter

finely grated zest and juice of 1 large lemon

pepper to taste

450g (1lb) baby leaf spinach

freshly grated nutmeg *(optional)*

To garnish

sprigs of fresh mint

lemon wedges

1 Preheat the grill to high. Cut a piece of foil to fit the grill pan and lay the fish on top.

2 Put the potatoes in a saucepan, cover with boiling water and add the sprig of mint. Cook for about 15 minutes or until the potatoes are just tender.

3 Meanwhile, melt the butter in a small saucepan and mix in the lemon zest and juice. Season with pepper. Brush this lemon butter over the fish and grill for 5–6 minutes on each side, turning the fish carefully, until the flesh close to the bone flakes easily when tested with a knife.

4 While the sole fillets are cooking, steam the spinach for 2–3 minutes or until just wilted. Season with pepper and nutmeg, if used, to taste.

5 Drain the potatoes and put into a warmed serving dish. Add plenty of black pepper, toss gently and garnish with mint sprigs. Transfer the sole to warmed dinner plates and spoon over any cooking juices from the grill pan. Add lemon wedges and serve, with the potatoes and spinach.

Some more ideas

• Other, less expensive flat fish such as halibut or lemon sole are also delicious when grilled with lemon butter. Allow 4–5 minutes cooking on each side. Instead of spinach, serve with broccoli florets steamed until just tender.

• Smooth, creamy mashed potatoes flavoured with herbs also go well with grilled sole. Peel and cut up 900g (2lb) potatoes and cook in boiling water for 15–20 minutes or until tender. Drain thoroughly, then mash until smooth. Beat in 2 tsp butter and 100ml (3½fl oz) semi-skimmed milk. Season to taste, then mix in 3 tbsp chopped fresh herbs – a combination of parsley and chives is particularly good.

Health points

• Sole is a useful source of vitamin B_{12}, which plays a critical role in the production of DNA and RNA, the genetic material in cells.

photo, page 109

Each serving provides   Key nutrients 440kcals, 13g fat (of which 6g is saturated fat), 43g protein, 38g carbohydrate, 443mg sodium (1.11g salt), 5g fibre

Excellent source of potassium (1911mg)

Steamed fish with ginger and sesame

Steaming is unbeatable when it comes to heart-healthy cuisine. Since no fat is used for cooking, these ginger and coriander-scented fillets have the luxury of a splash of aromatic sesame oil.

Preparation time **10 minutes**   Cooking time **10 minutes**   *Serves 4*

2 tbsp grated fresh root ginger

3 garlic cloves, finely chopped

½ tsp grated lime zest

4 tbsp chopped fresh coriander

4 tilapia fillets, 140g (5oz) each

2½ tsp toasted sesame oil

For the sauce

2 tbsp fresh lime juice

125ml (4fl oz) water

1 tsp cornflour blended with
1 tbsp water

4 tbsp chopped fresh coriander

1 Combine the ginger, garlic, lime zest and coriander in a small bowl. Lay the fillets skinned-side up on the work surface and sprinkle with the coriander mixture. Fold the fillets in half. Drizzle the sesame oil over the folded fish and place on a heatproof plate.

2 Place a rack in a wok or frying pan large enough to hold the plate of fish, and add water to come up almost to the rack. Cover and bring to a simmer.

3 Carefully place the plate of fish on the rack over the simmering water. Cover and steam for about 5 minutes or until cooked through. With a fish slice, transfer the fish to a platter and cover loosely to keep warm.

4 To make the sauce, pour the cooking liquid from the plate into a small saucepan. Add the lime juice and water, and bring to the boil. Stir in the cornflour mixture and cook, stirring, for about 1 minute or until the sauce is lightly thickened. Stir in the coriander. Serve the sauce with the fish.

Some more ideas

• Fillets of lemon sole or plaice work equally well in this dish.

Steamed fish Italian style In place of the ginger, garlic, lime zest and coriander, make a mixture of chopped garlic, finely diced onion, chopped fresh basil, and diced deseeded tomato. Fill the tilapia with this mixture. For the sauce in step 4, add lemon juice instead of lime and replace the coriander with chopped fresh thyme, oregano or basil.

Health points

• A 115g (4oz) serving of tilapia has 20g of protein and less than 1g of fat, all of it heart-healthy omega-3 oil. Tilapia is becoming increasingly popular, not only due to its mild taste and sumptuous texture, but also thanks to improved fish-farming techniques.

• Flavourful dishes like this improve the chances you'll meet the recommendation of eating seafood at least twice a week.

photo, page 109

Each serving provides   Key nutrients 140kcals, 3g fat (of which 0.5g is saturated fat), 26g protein, 2g carbohydrate, 86mg sodium (0.21g salt), 0g fibre

Useful source of potassium (511mg)

Sauté of king prawns

If you've ever wondered how some people can give great dinner parties on short notice, here's the secret: fast dishes that impress. With steamed rice and asparagus, this is simplicity itself.

Preparation time **20 minutes**   Cooking time **10 minutes**   *Serves 6*

675g (1½lb) raw king or tiger prawns

3 tsp olive oil

3 garlic cloves, finely chopped

150ml (5fl oz) low-sodium fish stock

3 tbsp fresh lemon juice

good pinch of crushed dried chillies

1 tsp cornflour blended with 1 tbsp water

4 tbsp chopped parsley

1 Peel the prawns. To devein them, make a shallow cut along the back of each prawn and remove the black vein.

2 Pour the olive oil into a large non-stick frying pan and heat over a medium heat. Add the garlic and cook briefly until tender.

3 Add the prawns and cook, stirring frequently, for about 3 minutes. Add the stock, lemon juice and crushed chillies, and bring to the boil. Cook for about 1 minute or until the prawns are opaque throughout.

4 With a slotted spoon, transfer the prawns to serving plates. Bring the liquid in the pan to the boil, stir in the cornflour mixture and cook, stirring, for about 1 minute or until the sauce is lightly thickened. Stir in the parsley and spoon the sauce over the prawns.

Some more ideas

Sauté of scallops Instead of prawns, use large scallops. Cook the scallops for only 1 minute before adding the stock and lemon juice. Then cook for another minute or so until the scallops are opaque.

• Add more garlic if you are a garlic lover!

• Serve with plain steamed rice and asparagus, with fresh pineapple for dessert.

Health points

• Despite a reputation for being high in cholesterol, prawns are actually good for your heart. They are rich in omega-3 fatty acids, vitamin B_{12}, selenium and zinc, and their cholesterol levels, weight for weight, are not much different from those in lean beef or poultry.

Each serving provides   Key nutrients 164kcals, 4g fat (of which 0.5g is saturated fat), 30g protein, 4g carbohydrate, 350mg sodium (0.87g salt), 0g fibre

Useful source of potassium (425mg)

Salmon with pepper and sweetcorn relish

The rich flavour of salmon is a clue to its bountiful supply of heart-healthy omega-3 fatty acids – and just about everybody loves the taste. Here, the spice-rubbed fish is served with a colourful confetti of diced vegetables.

Preparation time **10 minutes**   Cooking time **10 minutes**   *Serves 4*

¼ tsp plus 2 tbsp caster sugar

1 tsp ground coriander

½ tsp ground cinnamon

¼ tsp ground cardamom

pepper to taste

4 salmon steaks, 175g (6oz) each

½ tsp yellow mustard seeds

5 tbsp white wine vinegar

1 courgette, cut into 5mm (¼in) dice

1 orange or red pepper, cut into 5mm (¼in) dice

150g (5½oz) sweetcorn kernels, fresh or frozen and thawed

1 Spray the grill rack with cooking spray or coat it with a little olive oil. Preheat the grill to medium. Combine the ¼ teaspoon sugar, coriander, cinnamon, cardamom and pepper in a small saucepan. Measure out 1¼ teaspoons of the spice mixture and rub into one side of each salmon steak.

2 For the relish, add the remaining 2 tablespoons sugar to the spice mixture in the saucepan together with the mustard seeds and vinegar. Bring to the boil over medium heat. Add the courgette, pepper and sweetcorn kernels, and cook for about 4 minutes or until the pepper is just tender.

3 Place the salmon, spice-side down, on the grill rack and grill, without turning, for about 5 minutes. Serve the salmon topped with the relish.

Some more ideas

• Use swordfish or tuna steaks in place of the salmon.

• Serve the pepper and sweetcorn relish with grilled chicken, steak or pork.

• New potatoes and a rocket salad go well with the salmon, with fresh berries for dessert.

Health points

• Whether you use fresh or frozen sweetcorn, you will still get the same nutrients: fibre, folate, potassium and vitamin C. Sweetcorn also provides the added nutritional benefits of carotenoids, which are important disease-fighting phytochemicals.

• Salmon is a rich source of omega-3 fatty acids, a type of polyunsaturated fat thought to help protect against coronary heart disease and strokes by making blood less 'sticky' and therefore less likely to clot. A diet rich in omega-3 fatty acids may also be helpful in the prevention and treatment of arthritis.

photo, page 109

Each serving provides   Key nutrients 400kcals, 20g fat (of which 4g is saturated fat), 37g protein, 18g carbohydrate, 81mg sodium (0.2g salt), 1g fibre

Useful source of potassium (700mg)

Fish baked on a bed of broccoli, sweetcorn and red pepper

Baking fish fillets on top of cut fresh vegetables creates an easy and nutritious meal. You can change the vegetables, depending on what is in season or to suit your personal tastes.

Preparation time **15 minutes**   Cooking time **50 minutes**   *Serves 4*

4 firm white fish fillets, 115–175g (4–6oz) each, fresh or frozen and thawed

2 tbsp oil-free French or Italian dressing

1 tbsp fine dried breadcrumbs

1 tbsp freshly grated Parmesan cheese

¼ tsp paprika

1 tbsp olive oil

225g (8oz) broccoli florets

150g (5½oz) fresh or frozen and thawed sweetcorn kernels

1 red pepper, deseeded and cut into thin strips

1 small red onion, thinly sliced

2 tbsp chopped parsley

1 tbsp chopped fresh basil

pepper to taste

1 Place the fish in a shallow baking dish and brush lightly with the dressing. Cover and refrigerate. In a small bowl, stir the breadcrumbs with the Parmesan cheese and paprika.

2 Preheat the oven to 220°C (425°F, gas mark 7). Brush four individual ovenproof dishes (or one large dish) with the oil. In a large bowl, combine the broccoli, sweetcorn, red pepper, onion, parsley, basil and pepper.

3 Divide the vegetable mixture evenly among the dishes. Cover with foil and bake for 35–40 minutes or until the vegetables are just tender.

4 Uncover the dishes and top the vegetables with the fish fillets. Cover again and bake for 8–10 minutes or until the fish is just cooked and still moist in the thickest part. Uncover the dishes, sprinkle with the breadcrumb mixture and bake, uncovered, for a further 2–3 minutes or until the topping is golden brown.

Some more ideas

• Use the crumb mixture to top any cooked vegetable.

• Substitute 450g (1lb) peeled and deveined raw king prawns for the fish fillets. In step 4, bake for only 4 minutes. Then uncover the dishes, sprinkle with the crumb mixture and bake for 1–2 minutes.

Health points

• This recipe is a good example of how to plan for portion sizes. When it is served in individual dishes, just the right amounts of protein and vegetables are supplied.

• Broccoli is one of the most important, nutrient-rich vegetables. It is a member of the cruciferous family and contains ample amounts of fibre, vitamin C and phyto-chemicals for all kinds of disease prevention.

Each serving provides

Key nutrients 226kcals, 6g fat (of which 1.5g is saturated fat), 27g protein, 16g carbohydrate, 248mg sodium (0.62g salt), 3g fibre

Useful source of potassium (600mg)

Summer salmon and asparagus

Fresh young vegetables and succulent salmon make this an excellent speedy casserole to prepare for special occasions. The leek, tender asparagus and sugarsnap peas all cook quickly and look superb.

Preparation time **10 minutes**   Cooking time **about 20 minutes**   *Serves 4*

4 salmon fillets, about 140g (5oz) each

200g (7oz) baby leeks

225g (8oz) tender asparagus spears

150g (5½oz) sugarsnap peas

4 tbsp dry white wine

200ml (7fl oz) low-sodium fish or vegetable stock

15g (½oz) unsalted butter, cut into small pieces

pepper to taste

1 tbsp snipped fresh chives to garnish

1 Run your fingertips over each salmon fillet to check for any stray bones, pulling out any that remain between the flakes of fish. Arrange the baby leeks in a single layer in the bottom of a large, shallow flameproof casserole. Lay the pieces of salmon on top. Surround the fish with the asparagus spears and sugarsnap peas. Pour in the wine and stock, and dot the butter over the fish. Season with pepper.

2 Bring to the boil, then cover the casserole tightly and reduce the heat so the liquid simmers gently. Cook the fish and vegetables for 12–14 minutes or until the salmon is pale pink all the way through and the vegetables are tender. Sprinkle the chives over the salmon and serve.

Some more ideas

Mackerel and carrots Season mackerel fillets and fold them loosely in half, with the skin outside. Use baby carrots, or large carrots cut into short, thick sticks, instead of the asparagus, and medium-dry cider instead of the wine. Add 2 sprigs of fresh rosemary to the vegetables before putting the mackerel on top, then pour in the cider and stock.

Asian-style fish casserole Use cod or halibut fillet instead of salmon, 4 spring onions instead of the leeks, and 225g (8oz) whole button mushrooms instead of the asparagus. Arrange the vegetables and fish as in the main recipe, adding 4 tbsp Chinese rice wine or dry sherry with the stock instead of white wine. Omit the butter and sprinkle 1 tbsp low-sodium soy sauce, 1 tbsp grated fresh root ginger and 1 tbsp toasted sesame oil over the fish. Garnish with chopped fresh coriander instead of chives, and serve with plain boiled rice.

Each serving provides   Key nutrients 330kcals, 19g fat (of which 5g is saturated fat), 32g protein, 5g carbohydrate, 200mg sodium (0.5g salt), 2g fibre

Useful source of potassium (848mg)

Vegetarian

Baked rice with wild mushrooms and cheese

Brown rice, with its nutty taste, takes well to robust additions like wild mushrooms and sun-dried tomatoes. Add some well-flavoured vegetarian cheese too, and a little will go a long way.

Preparation time **20 minutes**   Cooking time **50 minutes**   *Serves 6*

20g (¾oz) dried porcini mushrooms

600ml (1 pint) hot water

25g (1oz) dry-pack sun-dried tomatoes

1 tsp olive oil

1 large onion, finely chopped

3 garlic cloves, finely chopped

185g (6½oz) long-grain brown rice

pepper to taste

½ tsp dried sage

60g (2¼oz) reduced-fat mature Cheddar cheese, grated

2 tbsp freshly grated Parmesan cheese

1 Place the porcini in a small bowl and pour 350ml (12fl oz) of the hot water over them. Put the sun-dried tomatoes in a separate small bowl and pour the remaining hot water over them. Allow to soak for about 20 minutes or until softened.

2 Scoop the mushrooms out of their soaking liquid and finely chop them. Strain the soaking liquid through a fine-mesh sieve into a bowl. Strain the sun-dried tomato soaking liquid into the same bowl and set aside. Coarsely chop the tomatoes.

3 Preheat the oven to 180°C (350°F, gas mark 4). Heat the olive oil and 3 tablespoons of the mushroom and tomato soaking liquid in a medium saucepan over medium heat. Add the onion and garlic to the pan and cook for about 7 minutes or until the onion is golden.

4 Add the rice, stirring to coat. Add the mushrooms and tomatoes, the remaining soaking liquid, sage and pepper, and bring to the boil. Transfer the rice mixture to a 20cm (8in) square baking dish. Cover with foil, transfer to the oven and bake for about 40 minutes or until the rice is tender and all the liquid has been absorbed. Sprinkle the hot rice with the Cheddar and Parmesan cheeses before serving.

Some more ideas

• You can make this dish with other dried mushrooms, such as Chinese black mushrooms. Or use sliced fresh chestnut mushrooms and replace the mushroom soaking water with low-sodium vegetable stock in step 4.

• To vary the flavour, try other reduced-fat firm or hard cheeses suitable for grating.

Health points

• The concentrated flavour of dried porcini and sun-dried tomatoes enriches this dish without adding any fat, sugar or salt. These wonderful taste enhancers can be kept in your storecupboard for a long time.

• Brown rice is a particularly good grain for blood pressure. It is rich in magnesium, folate and other nutrients, as well as insoluble fibre. Many of these nutrients get stripped out in the milling process that is used to produce white rice.

photo, page 123

Each serving provides   Key nutrients 180kcals, 5g fat (of which 2g is saturated fat), 8g protein, 32g carbohydrate, 110mg sodium (0.27g salt), 1.5g fibre

Spanish rice

Traditional versions of this Mediterranean red rice dish begin with fatty sausage. This vegetarian version makes a very colourful and satisfying dish.

Preparation time **20 minutes**   Cooking time **33 minutes**   *Serves 6*

1 medium onion, finely chopped

1 large green pepper, deseeded and finely chopped

1 celery stick, finely chopped

2 garlic cloves, finely chopped

115g (4oz) button mushrooms, sliced

175g (6oz) long-grain white rice

350ml (12fl oz) low-sodium tomato juice

225ml (8fl oz) low-sodium vegetable stock

pepper to taste

1 bay leaf

6 plum tomatoes, halved, deseeded and diced

1 Lightly coat a deep nonstick frying pan with cooking spray or a teaspoon of olive oil. Heat, then sauté the onion, green pepper, celery and garlic for about 3 minutes or until the onion is almost soft. Stir in the mushrooms and rice, and sauté for a further 2 minutes or until the rice turns golden.

2 Stir in the tomato juice, stock, pepper and bay leaf. Bring to the boil over medium-high heat. Cover and reduce the heat, then simmer, stirring occasionally, for about 15 minutes. Stir in the tomatoes.

3 Cover again and continue cooking for about 10 minutes or until the rice is tender and all liquid is absorbed. Fluff the rice with a fork to check that it is cooked and to keep the rice from sticking together. Discard the bay leaf before serving.

Some more ideas

• Add 250g (9oz) frozen peas in step 3 during the last 8 minutes of cooking.

• Although not traditional, you could make Spanish rice with brown rice instead of the white, and greatly boost both the nuttiness of the dish and its nutritional value. In step 3, cover and cook brown rice for 40–50 minutes or until tender.

Health points

• Tomato juice is an excellent liquid to cook with. It adds flavour and colour to your dishes, as well as helping to minimise fattier additions like butter or oil. Best of all, it is rich in nutrients that are great for blood pressure and the heart, such as beta carotene, lycopene and vitamin C.

Each serving provides   Key nutrients 150kcals, 1.5g fat (of which 0.5g is saturated fat), 4g protein, 32g carbohydrate, 60mg sodium (0.15g salt), 2g fibre

Useful source of potassium (430mg)

Rice pilaf with dried fruits and almonds

Pilaf always begins with a grain – often rice. But the ingredients can vary: you can add dried fruits and sweet spice or vegetables and herbs. This version is bursting with flavour.

Preparation time **15 minutes**   Cooking time **40 minutes, plus standing**   *Serves 6*

12 dried apricot halves

15g (½oz) butter

1 medium onion, chopped

175g (6oz) jasmine or long-grain white rice

¼ tsp ground cardamom

pepper to taste

600ml (1 pint) low-sodium vegetable stock

75g (2¾oz) sultanas

40g (1½oz) slivered almonds, toasted

sprigs of fresh rosemary to garnish

1 Snip the apricots with kitchen scissors into small slivers. Melt the butter in a large nonstick saucepan over medium heat. Add the onion, rice, cardamom and pepper, and sauté for about 8 minutes or until the rice is toasted.

2 Stir in the stock, sultanas, almonds and apricots, and bring to the boil. Reduce the heat to medium-low. Cover and simmer for about 25 minutes or until the stock is all absorbed. Remove from the heat and leave to stand for 5 minutes. Fluff with a fork, then serve garnished with rosemary sprigs.

Some more ideas

Herbed rice pilaf Use 185g (6½oz) long-grain brown rice instead of jasmine rice. Sauté 1 chopped green pepper along with the rice and onion, and use 2 tsp chopped fresh thyme and 1 tsp chopped fresh rosemary instead of the cardamom. Replace the sultanas, almonds and apricots with 40g (1½oz) chopped toasted pecan nuts.

Health points

• Dried apricots are fat-free and full of nutrients that are good both for blood pressure and lowering cholesterol levels, such as potassium, lycopene, beta-carotene and pectin. In addition, apricots are a rich source of iron. While the drying process removes apricots' store of vitamin C, many other nutrients are enhanced.

Each serving provides   Key nutrients 240kcals, 7g fat (of which 2g is saturated fat), 5g protein, 44g carbohydrate, 75mg sodium (0.19g salt), 2g fibre

Useful source of potassium (400mg)

Bulghur wheat with spring vegetables

The tartness of lemon juice plus the refreshing fragrance of mint make this a dish that will brighten any meal. Bulghur is a form of cracked wheat that cooks fast and easily.

Preparation time **45 minutes**   Cooking time **10 minutes**   *Serves 6*

225g (8oz) bulghur wheat

800ml (1 pint 9fl oz) boiling water

2 tbsp olive oil

3 tbsp fresh lemon juice

pepper to taste

2 leeks, halved lengthways and cut crossways into 2.5cm (1in) pieces

2 garlic cloves, finely chopped

12 asparagus spears, cut into 5cm (2in) lengths

140g (5oz) frozen peas, thawed

4 tbsp chopped fresh mint

1 Combine the bulghur wheat and boiling water in a large heatproof bowl. Leave to soak for about 30 minutes or until the bulghur is tender; stir after 15 minutes. Drain the bulghur in a large fine-mesh sieve.

2 Whisk together 1 tablespoon of the oil, the lemon juice and pepper in a large bowl. Add the drained bulghur wheat and fluff with a fork to separate the grains and mix them with the dressing.

3 Heat the remaining 1 tablespoon oil in a medium frying pan over low heat. Add the leeks and garlic, and cook for about .005 minutes or until the leeks are tender. Transfer to the bowl with the bulghur wheat.

4 Steam the asparagus for about 4 minutes or until tender. Add the peas during the final 30 seconds of steaming. Add the vegetables to the bulghur wheat together with the mint and toss to combine. Serve at room temperature or chilled.

Some more ideas

• Use couscous instead of bulghur wheat. Just cover the couscous with boiling water and soak for 5 minutes.

• Serve this hearty dish with roast red peppers. Offer fresh figs for dessert.

Health points

• Bulghur wheat provides a number of nutrients: protein, niacin, insoluble fibre, phytoestrogens and vitamin E, all of which work to keep your heart healthy. Plus, it is a great source of potassium which is very helpful for controlling high blood pressure.

• Bulghur wheat is a good, low-fat complex carbohydrate. It contains useful amounts of some of the B vitamins, particularly B_1, as well as copper and iron.

Each serving provides   Key nutrients 200kcals, 5g fat (of which 0.5g is saturated fat), 6g protein, 33g carbohydrate, 130mg sodium (0.3g salt), 3g fibre

Baked rice with wild mushrooms and cheese *p118*

Bulghur wheat with spring vegetables *p122*

Quinoa pilaf with cherries and walnuts *p126*

Barley pilaf with herbs *p125*

Sunny risotto with carrots

The moment you take a bite of this rich-tasting, aromatic risotto you'll forget how healthy it is. The secret to its incredibly appealing texture is the liquid-absorbing rice starch.

Preparation time **15 minutes**   Cooking time **35 minutes**   *Serves 4*

2 tsp olive oil

1 small onion, finely chopped

2 large carrots, cut into 5mm (¼in) dice

225g (8oz) arborio rice

125ml (4fl oz) dry white wine

400ml (14fl oz) low-sodium vegetable stock

225ml (8fl oz) carrot juice

125ml (4fl oz) water

pepper to taste

4 tbsp freshly grated Parmesan cheese

1 Heat the oil in a medium nonstick saucepan over moderate heat. Add the onion and sauté for about 5 minutes or until tender. Add the carrots and sauté for a further 4 minutes or until just tender. Add the rice, stirring to coat.

2 Add the wine and cook, stirring occasionally, for 2 minutes or until it has evaporated by half.

3 Mix together the stock, carrot juice and water. Add the stock mixture, a ladleful at a time, to the rice and cook, stirring. Wait until each addition of liquid has been absorbed before adding the next. Total cooking time will be about 20 minutes. Remove from heat, then stir in the Parmesan cheese and pepper.

Some more ideas

• For a deeper colour and a more Spanish flavour, add a pinch of saffron threads to the stock mixture in step 3.

• This is a good dish to make when you have friends or family in the kitchen with you. You can have one of them do the stirring for you!

Health points

• The beta-carotene in carrots that is so good for vision is equally important for healthy skin and hair. 140g (5oz) of cooked carrots provides three times the recommended daily intake of beta-carotene.

• Carrots were known to the Greeks and Romans, although they were not widely used in Europe until the Middle Ages. Early varieties were red, purple or black; the familiar orange variety was developed in Holland in the 17th century.

Each serving provides

Key nutrients 354kcals, 8g fat (of which 4g is saturated fat), 11g protein, 58g carbohydrate, 200mg sodium (0.5g salt), 2g fibre

Useful source of potassium (400mg)

Barley pilaf with herbs

Like rice, barley can be cooked as fluffy, separate kernels, or made risotto-style, as in this delicious dish – gently and steadily stirred with liquid to produce a smooth, creamy texture.

Preparation time **10 minutes**   Cooking time **55 minutes**   *Serves 6*

2 tsp olive oil

1 medium onion, finely chopped

3 garlic cloves, finely chopped

2 carrots, thinly sliced

150g (5½oz) pearl barley

¾ tsp dried sage

¾ tsp dried thyme

750ml (1¼ pints) water

1 tsp slivered lemon zest

pepper to taste

4 tbsp freshly grated Parmesan cheese

1 Heat the oil in a medium saucepan over medium heat. Add the onion and garlic, and cook for about 5 minutes or until the onion is tender and golden brown.

2 Add the carrots to the pan and cook for about 5 minutes or until tender. Add the barley, stirring to combine.

3 Add the sage, thyme and water, and bring to the boil. Reduce to a simmer and cook, stirring frequently, for about 45 minutes or until the barley is tender.

4 Stir in the lemon zest, pepper and Parmesan until evenly combined. Serve hot.

Some more ideas

• This recipe is also great made with long-grain brown rice instead of barley.

• Flavour the pilaf with other dried herbs such as basil and oregano. Substitute ¾ tsp of each of these for the sage and the thyme.

Health points

• Barley is abundant with lignans, which are phytochemicals that help lower cholesterol. The plant sterols found in barley may also assist in reducing total and LDL cholesterol. Barley is also rich in selenium and vitamin E.

photo, page 123

Each serving provides   Key nutrients 160kcals, 5g fat (of which 2g is saturated fat), 6g protein, 25g carbohydrate, 85mg sodium (0.21g salt), 1g fibre

Quinoa pilaf with cherries and walnuts

Grain-like quinoa (pronounced KEEN-wah) is not a grain at all, but the seed of a plant related to Swiss chard. Here, it is cooked with a creative mixture of tastes — thyme, cherries and walnuts — to make a great side dish.

Preparation time **10 minutes**   Cooking time **30 minutes**   *Serves 12*

2 tsp olive oil

1 large onion, finely chopped

350g (12oz) quinoa

450ml (16floz) boiling water

pepper to taste

½ tsp dried thyme

140g (5oz) dried cherries

70g (2½oz) toasted and coarsely chopped walnuts

1 Heat the oil in a nonstick flameproof casserole over medium heat. Add the onion and cook, stirring frequently, for about 7 minutes or until golden brown.

2 Meanwhile, place the quinoa in a large dry frying pan over medium heat and cook, stirring often, for about 5 minutes or until lightly toasted.

3 Add the quinoa to the casserole. Stir in the boiling water, pepper and thyme. Return to the boil, then cover and simmer for 10 minutes. Uncover and continue cooking, stirring occasionally, for 10–12 minutes or until the liquid has been absorbed and the quinoa is tender.

4 Remove from the heat and stir in the cherries and walnuts. Serve hot, at room temperature or chilled.

Some more ideas

• Use dried cranberries in place of dried cherries.

• Make this pilaf with long-grain brown rice instead of quinoa. Use 185g (6½oz) rice and 450ml (16fl oz) boiling water. Follow the directions for steps 2 and 3, cooking the brown rice for 40–50 minutes.

Health points

• Quinoa is suddenly popular, but it is an ancient grain, dating back about 4000 years and consumed by the Aztecs. It is particularly high in lysine, an amino acid necessary for the synthesis of protein, making it one of the best sources of plant protein. Plus, it provides lots of magnesium, potassium, zinc, vitamin E, iron and fibre.

• Walnuts provide useful amounts of vitamin E, many of the B vitamins and potassium.

photo, page 123

Each serving provides   **Key nutrients** 180kcals, 6g fat (of which 0.5g is saturated fat), 5g protein, 25g carbohydrate, 25mg sodium (0.06g salt), 0.5g fibre

Useful source of potassium (386mg)

Millet with spinach and pine nuts

Bright green spinach and golden apricots add rich colour and flavour to this easy grain-and-vegetable dish.
Serve it with stews and casseroles that have plenty of sauce.

Preparation time **10 minutes**   Cooking time **20–25 minutes**   *Serves 4*

200g (7oz) millet

55g (2oz) dried apricots, roughly chopped

900ml (1½ pints) low-sodium vegetable stock

35g (1¼oz) pine nuts

225g (8oz) baby spinach leaves

juice of ½ lemon

pepper to taste

1 Put the millet and dried apricots into a large saucepan and stir in the stock. Bring to the boil, then lower the heat. Simmer for 15–20 minutes or until all the stock has been absorbed and the millet is tender.

2 Meanwhile, toast the pine nuts in a small frying pan until they are golden brown and fragrant. Set aside.

3 Add the spinach and lemon juice to the millet, with pepper to taste. Cover the pan and leave over a very low heat for 4–5 minutes, to wilt the spinach.

4 Stir the millet and spinach mixture gently, then spoon into a serving bowl. Scatter the toasted pine nuts on top and serve immediately.

Some more ideas

Aubergine with millet and sesame seeds Cut 2 medium aubergines into dice. Heat 2 tbsp olive oil in a large frying pan, add the aubergines and cook over a high heat until browned. Remove from the heat and stir in 200g (7oz) millet and 900ml (1½ pints) vegetable stock. Return to the heat and bring to the boil. Stir, then reduce the heat and simmer for 15–20 minutes or until all the stock has been absorbed and the millet is tender. Season with pepper to taste. Transfer to a serving bowl and scatter over 1 tbsp thinly sliced spring onions, 2 tbsp chopped fresh coriander and 2 tbsp toasted sesame seeds.

Health points

• Millet provides useful amounts of iron and B vitamins, and as it is not highly milled, it retains all its nutritional value.

• Pine nuts are a good source of vitamin E and potassium. They also contribute useful amounts of magnesium, zinc and iron.

Each serving provides   Key nutrients 290kcals, 7g fat (of which 0.5g is saturated fat), 10g protein, 48g carbohydrate, 250mg sodium (0.62g salt) 3g fibre

Useful source of potassium (682mg)

Kasha with onions and mushrooms

Imagine a meal you'd relish in the depth of a Russian winter and you'll understand the warming, sustaining qualities of kasha, which in Britain is what we call roasted buckwheat grains.

Preparation time **10 minutes**   Cooking time **35 minutes**   *Serves 4*

1 tbsp olive oil

2 large onions, halved and thinly sliced

2 tsp caster sugar

350g (12oz) shiitake mushrooms, stalks discarded and caps thickly sliced

½ tsp dried sage

pepper to taste

175g (6oz) kasha (roasted buckwheat grains)

225ml (8fl oz) water

175ml (6fl oz) carrot juice

1 Heat the oil in a large frying pan over medium-high heat. Add the onions, sprinkle them with the sugar and cook, stirring frequently, for about 15 minutes or until golden brown and tender.

2 Add the mushrooms, sage and pepper, and cook, stirring frequently, for a further 5 minutes or until the mushrooms are tender.

3 Meanwhile, place the kasha in a medium frying pan over medium heat and cook, stirring frequently, for about 5 minutes or until lightly toasted.

4 Combine the water and carrot juice in a medium saucepan over a medium heat and bring to the boil. Add the kasha, cover and cook for about 10 minutes or until tender. Fluff with a fork, then transfer to the frying pan with the onion mixture and toss together to combine.

Some more ideas

• This recipe works well with other grains too. For example, use 185g (6½oz) couscous or long-grain brown rice. Skip step 3, and in step 4 cook couscous for 5 minutes or brown rice for 40 minutes.

• Use chestnut mushrooms in place of shiitake.

Health points

• Although buckwheat has the word 'wheat' in its name, it is not wheat at all, but the grain-like fruit of a leafy plant related to rhubarb. Robust in flavour and texture, buckwheat cooks up like a wheat grain. And it contains plenty of cholesterol-lowering soluble fibre, along with protein, magnesium and B vitamins.

• Carrot juice and shiitake mushrooms add antioxidant power and helpful minerals to this delicious dish.

Each serving provides   Key nutrients 232kcals, 4g fat (of which 0.5g is saturated fat), 7g protein, 46g carbohydrate, 30mg sodium (0.07g salt), 3g fibre

Useful source of potassium (561mg)

Lentil risotto *p130*

Kasha with onions and mushrooms *p128*

Wild rice with walnuts *p131*

Nutty lemon barley *p132*

Lentil risotto

Lentils add extra flavour and texture to this Italian-style mushroom risotto. Serve with roast or grilled vegetables, such as peppers and courgettes, or a mixed salad, for a satisfying lunch.

Preparation time **30 minutes**   Cooking time **45 minutes**   *Serves 4*

175g (6oz) green lentils

500ml (18fl oz) low-sodium vegetable stock

1 tbsp olive oil

1 onion, finely chopped

1 garlic clove, crushed

3 celery sticks, chopped

1 red pepper, deseeded and diced

1 tsp ground coriander

1 tsp ground cumin

225g (8oz) mushrooms, sliced

175g (6oz) arborio rice

200ml (7fl oz) dry white wine

3 tbsp coarsely chopped fresh coriander, plus extra to garnish

pepper to taste

4 tbsp freshly grated Parmesan cheese

1 Cook the lentils in a saucepan of boiling water for 20 minutes. Drain and set aside. Place the stock in the saucepan and bring to simmering point over medium heat. Lower the heat so the stock is simmering gently.

2 Heat the oil in another large saucepan and add the onion, garlic and celery. Cook, stirring occasionally, for about 5 minutes or until softened. Add the red pepper and the ground coriander and cumin. Cook for a further 1 minute, stirring.

3 Add the mushrooms, rice and lentils, and stir to mix. Pour in the wine and add a ladleful of the hot stock. Bring to a gentle boil and bubble until most of the liquid has been absorbed, stirring frequently.

4 Add another ladleful of stock and cook until it is absorbed, stirring frequently. Repeat this gradual addition of the hot stock until it has all been added. The rice should be creamy and tender but still with some 'bite', and the lentils cooked.

5 Stir in the chopped coriander and season with pepper to taste. Serve hot, sprinkled with the Parmesan and extra chopped coriander.

Some more ideas

• Instead of green lentils, try the tiny Puy lentils.

Pearl barley risotto Soften 2 sliced leeks and 1 crushed garlic clove in 1 tbsp olive oil. Add 1 deseeded and diced red or yellow pepper, 250g (9oz) pearl barley, 2 tsp dried herbes de Provence, 200ml (7fl oz) dry white wine and 100ml (3½fl oz) hot vegetable stock. Simmer for 45 minutes, gradually adding a further 400–500ml (14–17fl oz) hot stock and stirring frequently, until the pearl barley is cooked and tender. Meanwhile, steam 225g (8oz) broccoli florets and cook 175g (6oz) frozen peas. Stir these into the risotto and season with salt and pepper to taste. Serve hot, topped with the Parmesan.

Health points

• Lentils are the small seeds of a variety of leguminous plants. They are a good source of protein, complex carbohydrate, dietary fibre and B vitamins.

photo, page 129

Each serving provides   Key nutrients 360kcals, 8g fat (of which 3g is saturated fat), 15g protein, 48g carbohydrate, 360mg sodium (0.9g salt), 3.5g fibre

Useful source of potassium (572mg)

Wild rice with walnuts

Usher in autumn with this wholesome blend of wild rice, nuts and dried fruit. Wild rice is often said to have a nut-like flavour, so teaming it with toasty walnuts makes perfect sense.

Preparation time **15 minutes**   Cooking time **1 hour 20 minutes**   *Serves 4*

2 tsp olive oil

1 small onion, finely chopped

2 garlic cloves, finely chopped

2 celery sticks, cut into 1cm (½in) dice

1 carrot, quartered lengthways and thinly sliced crossways

160g (5¾oz) wild rice

350ml (12fl oz) carrot juice

350ml (12fl oz) water

pepper to taste

¼ tsp dried thyme

4 tbsp coarsely chopped walnuts

4 tbsp dried cranberries or raisins

1 Heat the oil in a medium nonstick saucepan over low heat. Add the onion and garlic and cook, stirring frequently, for about 7 minutes or until the onion is tender.

2 Add the celery and carrot, and cook, stirring frequently, for a further 5 minutes or until the carrot is tender.

3 Stir in the wild rice. Add the carrot juice, water, pepper and thyme, and bring to the boil. Reduce to a simmer, then cover and cook for about 1 hour or until the wild rice is tender (check after 45 minutes).

4 Meanwhile, toast the walnuts in a small frying pan over low heat, stirring frequently, for about 5 minutes or until they are crisp and fragrant. Stir the walnuts and cranberries or raisins into the wild rice just before serving.

Some more ideas

• Wild rice is expensive. To stretch your supply, use half long-grain brown rice and half wild rice; they take the same length of time to cook and their flavours and textures are complementary.

• Use almonds and raisins or sultanas in place of the walnuts and cranberries.

Health points

• Cooking the rice in carrot juice rather than stock or water adds a touch of sweetness and colour to the dish and boosts its beta-carotene content.

• Wild rice isn't a true rice, but the seed of an aquatic grass from a different botanical family. It has more protein than other rices, and is a good source of potassium, zinc and B vitamins.

photo, page 129

Each serving provides   **Key nutrients** 350kcals, 13g fat (of which 1.5g is saturated fat), 6.5g protein, 54g carbohydrate, 72mg sodium (0.18g salt), 2.5g fibre

Useful source of potassium (630mg)

Nutty lemon barley

Barley is a slightly chewy grain with a sweet flavour that is too often consigned to just soup. Cooked in a spicy broth, barley makes a welcome change from potatoes or rice as the starchy component of a meal.

Preparation time **10 minutes**   Cooking time **55–60 minutes**   *Serves 8*

2 tbsp olive oil

2 onions, finely chopped

3 celery sticks, finely chopped

200g (7oz) pearl barley, rinsed

600ml (1 pint) low-sodium vegetable stock

1 tsp finely grated lemon zest

½ tsp dried oregano

pepper to taste

2 tbsp sunflower seeds

1 tbsp fresh lemon juice

4 tbsp sultanas

2 tbsp chopped parsley

1 Heat the oil in a wide heavy saucepan over moderate heat. Add the onions and celery, and sauté, stirring, for about 7 minutes or until softened and lightly browned. Stir in the barley until coated with oil. Pour in the stock and add the lemon zest, oregano and pepper to taste.

2 Bring to the boil, then reduce the heat and cover the pan. Simmer, stirring occasionally, for about 40 minutes or until the barley is nearly cooked through and almost all the liquid is absorbed.

3 Meanwhile, toast the sunflower seeds in a dry nonstick frying pan over moderate heat, stirring frequently or shaking the pan, until golden brown. Remove from the heat and transfer to a plate.

4 Stir the lemon juice and sultanas into the barley mixture and cover the saucepan again. Remove from the heat and allow the mixture to stand for about 5 minutes. Gently stir the toasted sunflower seeds and chopped parsley into the barley until just mixed, then serve.

Some more ideas

• Substitute orange zest and orange juice for the lemon zest and juice.

• Replace the sunflower seeds with pumpkin seeds.

• Use snipped dates or dried apricots in place of the sultanas.

Health points

• Barley is one of the first crops cultivated by man and has been a staple of healthy diets since biblical times. 200g (7oz) pearl barley provides 6g of fibre, making it one of the more fibre-rich grains available. It is also a great source of iron, potassium and B vitamins.

• Toasted sunflower seeds contain a wide variety of useful minerals, including copper, phosphorus and magnesium, as well as fibre and protein.

photo, page 129

Each serving provides   **Key nutrients** 170kcals, 5g fat (of which 0.5g is saturated fat), 4g protein, 29g carbohydrate, 63mg sodium (0.16g salt), 1g fibre

Bulghur wheat pilaf with tomato, onions and basil

The next time you're looking for a simple, healthy dish to serve, try this nutty-tasting grain as a delicious switch from rice.

Preparation time **15 minutes**   Cooking time **45 minutes**   *Serves 8*

200g (7oz) bulghur wheat

2 tbsp olive or sunflower oil

3 onions, thinly sliced

1 garlic clove, finely chopped

350ml (12fl oz) low-sodium vegetable stock

350ml (12fl oz) low-sodium tomato juice

1 tomato, coarsely chopped

2 tbsp chopped fresh basil or 1 tbsp dried basil

pepper to taste

1 Place the bulghur wheat in a fine sieve and rinse under cold running water. Stir so that all the grains are well rinsed, then drain.

2 Heat the oil in a large nonstick frying pan. Add the onions and garlic, and sauté, stirring often, until softened and dark golden brown. Stir in the stock and tomato juice. Bring to the boil. Add the drained wheat.

3 Cover and simmer for 15 minutes, stirring occasionally. Stir in the tomato, basil and pepper. Simmer for a few minutes longer or until the liquid is absorbed. Serve warm.

Some more ideas

• Serve the pilaf for lunch, with a mixed salad and some fresh fruit to follow.

• Make this dish spicy by adding 1 jalapeño chilli or other fresh green chilli, finely chopped, to the onions and garlic in step 2.

Health points

• Bulghur wheat, sometimes called cracked wheat, is made from whole-wheat berries, so it's high in fibre and B vitamins.

• The combination of olive oil, garlic, basil and tomatoes is not only a classic Mediterranean flavouring, but is a one-two-three punch against bad health. Each ingredient contains unique nutrients that help the heart and fight disease.

Each serving provides   Key nutrients 150kcals, 3.5g fat (of which 0.5g is saturated fat), 4g protein, 25g carbohydrate, 52mg sodium (0.13g salt), 1g fibre

Refried bean burritos

The creamy texture of pinto beans makes them the perfect partner for strong flavours and spices. The beans aren't actually refried, but are simmered first, then cooked gently in a little oil.

Preparation and cooking time **1¾ hours, plus 8 hours soaking**   *Serves 6*

250g (9oz) dried pinto beans, soaked for at least 8 hours

2 onions (1 quartered and 1 finely chopped)

3 garlic cloves (2 whole and 1 finely chopped)

2 bay leaves

1½ tbsp sunflower oil

pepper to taste

For the salsa

450g (1lb) firm, ripe tomatoes, diced

1 fresh green chilli, deseeded and finely chopped

finely grated zest and juice of 1 lime

pinch of caster sugar

3 tbsp chopped fresh coriander

To serve

6 large flour tortillas

115g (4oz) reduced-fat Cheddar cheese, grated

1 cos lettuce, shredded

115g (4oz) plain low-fat bio yoghurt

1 Drain the soaked beans and rinse under cold running water. Put them in a large pan, cover with plenty of fresh water and add the quartered onion, 2 peeled garlic cloves and the bay leaves. Bring to the boil and boil rapidly for 10 minutes, then reduce the heat, partly cover and simmer gently for 45–60 minutes or until tender.

2 Meanwhile, make the salsa by mixing together the tomatoes, chilli, lime zest and juice, sugar and coriander in a bowl. Cover and leave at room temperature until ready to serve.

3 When the beans have finished cooking, spoon out 150ml (5fl oz) of the cooking liquid and reserve. Drain the beans, discarding the onion and bay leaves but reserving the garlic.

4 Heat the oil in a large frying pan, add the finely chopped onion and garlic, and cook gently for about 10 minutes or until soft. Add the reserved whole garlic cloves, a ladleful of the beans and a few spoonfuls of the reserved cooking liquid. Mash with a fork to break up the beans and garlic cloves.

5 Continue adding the beans, a ladleful at a time, together with a little of the liquid, cooking over a low heat and mashing, to make a dryish, slightly textured purée. Season with pepper to taste.

6 Meanwhile, heat the tortillas in the oven or in a microwave according to the packet instructions.

7 Spoon the refried beans into the middle of the tortillas. Sprinkle with the cheese and the shredded lettuce, then add the yoghurt. Roll up the tortillas to enclose the filling and serve immediately, with the tomato and chilli salsa.

Some more ideas

Refried bean quesadillas Use 200g (7oz) grated reduced-fat Cheddar cheese. Heat a large frying pan over medium-low heat. Take one of the tortillas, place it in the pan and spoon 2–3 tbsp of the refried beans in the middle. Sprinkle one-eighth of the cheese over the beans and around the edge of the tortilla. Fold the tortilla over the filling to make a half-moon shape and press the edges together gently, so that the melting cheese seals them. Cook for 1 minute, then turn over and cook the other side for 1 minute. Keep warm in the oven while you fill and cook the remaining tortillas. Serve with a mango salsa made by mixing 1 finely chopped ripe mango with 2 deseeded and sliced fresh chillies (1 green and 1 red) and the juice of ½ lime.

Health points

• Flour tortillas, also called wraps, provide complex carbohydrate, and make a great alternative to bread.

Each serving provides   Key nutrients 411kcals, 8g fat (of which 3g is saturated fat), 23g protein, 67g carbohydrate, 352mg sodium (0.88g salt), 9g fibre

Good source of potassium (1000mg)

Tuscan-style baked polenta *p136*

Refried bean burritos *p134*

Three beans and rice *p138*

Chickpea and vegetable eggah *p137*

Tuscan-style baked polenta

Polenta is the much loved 'mashed potatoes' of northern Italy. In this recipe, Parmesan-flavoured 'soft' polenta provides the topping for beans and a creamy mushroom sauce.

Preparation time **45 minutes**   Cooking time **20 minutes**   *Serves 4*

25g (1oz) dried porcini mushrooms

450ml (16fl oz) skimmed milk

1½ tbsp olive oil

15g (½oz) butter

2 celery sticks, thinly sliced

225g (8oz) chestnut mushrooms, sliced

3 tbsp plain flour

2 tsp lemon juice

pepper to taste

1 can (about 410g) borlotti beans, drained and rinsed

175g (6oz) instant polenta

2 eggs, lightly beaten

4 tbsp freshly grated Parmesan cheese

1 Place the dried mushrooms and 250ml (9fl oz) of the milk in a small saucepan. Bring just to the boil, then remove from the heat and set aside to soak.

2 Heat the oil and butter in a wide saucepan over moderate heat. Add the celery and cook gently, stirring occasionally, for 3–4 minutes or until softened. Raise the heat, add the chestnut mushrooms and cook, stirring, for about 3 minutes.

3 Add the flour and cook, stirring, for 2 minutes. Gradually mix in the remaining milk and cook, stirring well, until the mixture just comes to the boil and thickens.

4 Strain the milk from the porcini mushrooms and add it to the mushroom and celery sauce. Bring back to the boil, stirring. Coarsely chop the porcini and add to the pan. Simmer for 2 minutes, then add the lemon juice and season with pepper to taste.

5 Pour the mushroom sauce into a shallow ovenproof dish and spread out in an even layer. Scatter the beans on top. Set aside.

6 Preheat the oven to 200°C (400°F, gas mark 6). In a heavy saucepan, cook the polenta in 750ml (1¼ pints) boiling water, or according to the packet instructions, until it is thick. Remove from the heat and briskly stir in the eggs and about half of the grated Parmesan. Season with pepper to taste.

7 Pour the polenta mixture over the mushrooms and beans. Sprinkle the remaining Parmesan cheese over the top. Bake for about 20 minutes or until the filling is bubbling and the top is lightly browned. Serve hot.

Some more ideas

• Replace the borlotti beans with cannellini beans.

• Spread 450g (1lb) spinach, steamed, well drained and coarsely chopped, over the mushroom sauce before adding the beans.

Health points

• Polenta is very versatile – it can be served soft with fish, meat and vegetable dishes as an alternative to pasta or rice, or it can be left to set, then cut up and grilled or sautéed. It is particularly useful for those who need to follow a wheat or gluten-free diet.

photo, page 135

Each serving provides   **Key nutrients** 500kcals, 18g fat (of which 7g is saturated fat), 27g protein, 59g carbohydrate, 249mg sodium (0.62g salt), 8g fibre

Useful source of potassium (1123mg)

Chickpea and vegetable eggah

This thick and chunky Arab-style omelette is served flat, not rolled or folded, and is more like a cake. It is packed with vegetables and chickpeas, and is equally delicious hot or cold.

Preparation and cooking time **30 minutes**   *Serves 4*

2 tbsp olive oil

1 small onion, chopped

1 garlic clove, crushed

1 tsp ground cumin

1 tsp ground coriander

pinch of cayenne pepper

225g (8oz) new potatoes, scrubbed and cut into 1cm (½in) dice

1 small red pepper, deseeded and diced

1 small aubergine, cut into 1cm (½in) dice

5 tbsp water

1 can (about 410g) chickpeas, drained and rinsed

6 eggs

2 tbsp chopped fresh coriander

pepper to taste

1 Heat 1 tablespoon of the oil in a 25cm (10in) nonstick frying pan with a flameproof handle. Add the onion and cook for 2–3 minutes or until starting to soften. Stir in the garlic, cumin, ground coriander and cayenne pepper, and continue cooking for 1 minute, stirring constantly.

2 Add the remaining 1 tablespoon of oil to the pan, then add the potatoes, red pepper and aubergine. Continue sautéing for 5 minutes, stirring frequently, until the vegetables are lightly browned.

3 Add the water, cover and steam for 5 minutes. Then remove the lid and continue cooking until all excess liquid has evaporated. Stir in the chickpeas.

4 Lightly beat the eggs in a large mixing bowl. Add the chopped coriander and season with pepper to taste. Add the vegetable and chickpea mixture from the pan and stir to mix.

5 Preheat the grill to high. Coat the frying pan with cooking spray or a teaspoon of olive oil and heat over a medium heat. Pour in the egg mixture, spreading out the vegetables evenly. Cook the omelette, shaking the pan from time to time, for 3–4 minutes or until almost set; there will still be some uncooked egg mixture on the top.

6 Place the pan under the grill and cook the omelette for 2 minutes or until the top looks set. Remove from the heat and allow the omelette to rest in the pan for 2 minutes, then slide it on to a serving plate or board. Serve hot, cut into wedges.

Some more ideas

Butter bean eggah Omit the ground cumin and coriander and the aubergine, and add 2 diced courgettes with the water in step 3. Replace the chickpeas with butter beans. In step 4, add the finely grated zest of 1 lemon to the beaten eggs with the vegetables and butter beans.

Health points

• New potatoes cooked in their skins have a higher fibre content than peeled potatoes. The nutrients just under the skin are also preserved when potatoes are only scrubbed and not peeled.

• Eggs are still an inexpensive source of protein. A whole egg only has a total of 5g of fat, making it well worth including in a healthy food plan.

photo, page 135

Each serving provides   **Key nutrients** 310kcals, 16g fat (of which 3.5g is saturated fat), 18g protein, 24g carbohydrate, 137mg sodium (0.34g salt), 6g fibre

Useful source of potassium (436mg)

Three beans and rice

Colourful three-bean salad is as easy to make as it is delicious. When you add rice and lots of vegetables, it becomes a substantial, nutritious one-dish meal.

Preparation time **about 50 minutes**   *Serves 4*

250g (9oz) long-grain rice

2 carrots, thinly sliced

115g (4oz) green beans, cut into 2.5cm (1in) lengths

1 can (about 400g) red kidney beans, drained and rinsed

1 can (about 400g) black-eyed beans, drained and rinsed

1 can (about 400g) chickpeas, drained and rinsed

1 large ripe tomato, coarsely chopped

1 small red pepper, deseeded and chopped

1 small red onion, chopped

1 tbsp sunflower oil

1 tbsp coarse mustard

2 tsp caster sugar

3 tbsp red wine vinegar, or to taste

1 tbsp chopped fresh thyme

1 garlic clove, chopped

pepper to taste

1 Put the rice in a saucepan, cover with water and bring to the boil. Reduce the heat and simmer for about 15 minutes, or according to the packet instructions, until tender. Drain and leave to cool.

2 Meanwhile, drop the carrots into another pan of boiling water and cook for 3 minutes. Add the green beans and cook for a further 4 minutes or until the vegetables are tender. Drain and refresh under cold running water.

3 Place the carrots and green beans in a mixing bowl and add the kidney beans, black-eyed beans, chickpeas, tomato, red pepper and red onion.

4 Whisk together the oil, mustard, sugar, vinegar, thyme, garlic and pepper to taste in a small bowl. Drizzle this dressing over the bean salad and toss well to combine everything. Serve the bean salad over the rice, or gently fold the rice into the bean salad.

Some more ideas

• Replace the green beans with 225g (8oz) broccoli, broken into small florets.

Mexican-style bean and sweetcorn salad
Combine 400g (14oz) frozen sweetcorn kernels, cooked and drained, with 1 can (about 400g) borlotti beans, drained and rinsed. Add 3 spring onions, sliced; 1 chopped large ripe tomato; 2 small peppers (1 red and 1 green), deseeded and chopped; and 3 tbsp chopped fresh coriander. Make the dressing with 2 tbsp olive oil, the juice of 1 large lime, 2 chopped garlic cloves, ½ tsp mild chilli powder, ½ tsp ground cumin, and seasoning to taste. Add to the salad and toss well. Toast 3 small corn tortillas under a hot grill for 1 minute or until crisp, then crumble them over the salad.

Health points

• This salad provides excellent amounts of fibre, both the soluble and insoluble types.

photo, page 135

Each serving provides   Key nutrients 530kcals, 5g fat (of which 0.5g is saturated fat), 25g protein, 100g carbohydrate, 84mg sodium (0.21gsalt), 18g fibre

Useful source of potassium (1189mg)

Spicy lentil dhal

Potato and cauliflower are a favourite combination for curry and they are delicious cooked with lentils in a mildly spiced sauce. Serve with a fresh carrot chutney, sliced banana mixed with plain low-fat yoghurt, and basmati rice or naan bread.

Preparation time **25 minutes**   Cooking time **about 55 minutes**   *Serves 4*

2 tbsp sunflower oil

1 large onion, chopped

1– 2 garlic cloves, crushed

2 tbsp finely chopped fresh root ginger

2 tbsp mild curry paste

175g (6oz) red lentils

1 tsp ground cumin

1 tsp turmeric

450g (1lb) small new potatoes, halved

1 small cauliflower, broken into florets

1 red pepper, deseeded and coarsely chopped

4 tomatoes, skinned and quartered

225g (8oz) baby spinach leaves

handful of fresh coriander leaves

For the chutney

3 carrots, coarsely grated

1 green chilli, deseeded and finely chopped

juice of 1 lime

2 tbsp chopped fresh coriander

1 Heat the oil in a large saucepan over medium-low heat. Add the onion, garlic and ginger, and cook for 5 minutes. Stir in the curry paste and cook for a further 2 minutes.

2 Stir in the lentils, cumin, turmeric and 1 litre (1¾ pints) water. Bring to the boil, then cover the pan and simmer gently for 10 minutes. Stir in the potatoes and cook for 10 minutes, then add the cauliflower and cook for another 10 minutes. Add the pepper and tomatoes, and simmer for 5 minutes.

3 Meanwhile, prepare the chutney. Mix together the grated carrots, chilli, lime juice and chopped coriander. Transfer to a serving dish.

4 Stir the spinach into the curry and cook for 2 minutes or until just wilted. Stir in the coriander leaves and serve with the fresh carrot chutney.

Some more ideas

• The vegetables can be varied according to what is available. Try chunks of courgette and aubergine with, or instead of, the cauliflower, or small whole okra or cut green beans with the tomatoes.

• Additional beans can be added. Black-eyed beans and chickpeas are particularly good. If using dried beans, soak them overnight, then cook them in boiling water for 45–60 minutes or until almost tender. Canned beans need only be drained and rinsed, then added towards the end of the cooking time.

Health points

• This curry is full of vegetables. Together with the lentils, they provide valuable dietary fibre, vitamins and minerals.

• Raw accompaniments, like the carrot chutney here, boost the vitamin content of a meal and provide complementary textures and flavours.

Each serving provides   **Key nutrients** 400kcals, 10g fat (of which 1.5g is saturated fat), 19g protein, 60g carbohydrate, 260mg sodium (0.65g salt), 10g fibre

Excellent source of potassium (1789mg)

Falafel pittas

Falafel, the traditional Middle Eastern bean patties, are usually deep-fried. This version, delicately spiced and crunchy with grated carrot, is baked for a lower-fat result, but is just as delicious.

Preparation time **15 minutes**   Cooking time **15–20 minutes**   *Serves 4*

1 can (about 400g) chickpeas, drained and rinsed

1 tsp olive oil

½ tsp ground cumin

good pinch of cayenne pepper

good pinch of turmeric

1 garlic clove, crushed

1 tbsp lemon juice

1 medium carrot, finely grated

1 tbsp chopped fresh coriander

black pepper to taste

4 large pitta breads

1 cos lettuce or romaine heart, shredded

2 plum tomatoes, thinly sliced

8 tbsp plain low-fat yoghurt

2 tbsp chopped fresh mint

1 Preheat the oven to 200°C (400°F, gas mark 6). Line a baking tray with baking parchment. Put the chickpeas in a bowl with the oil and use a potato masher to mash them until smooth. Mix in the cumin, cayenne pepper, turmeric, garlic, lemon juice, carrot, coriander, and black pepper to taste. Alternatively, mix all the ingredients, except the carrot and coriander, in a food processor; transfer the mixture to a bowl and stir in the carrot and coriander.

2 Shape the mixture into 16 flat, round patties, each about 3cm (1¼in) across. Place them on the parchment-lined baking sheet. Bake for 15–20 minutes or until crisp and lightly browned, turning them over halfway through the cooking time.

3 About 3 minutes before the falafel have finished cooking, put the pitta breads in the oven to warm. Then split the breads in half widthwise and gently open out each half to make a pocket.

4 Half-fill the pitta bread pockets with the shredded lettuce and sliced tomatoes, then divide the falafel among them. Mix together the yoghurt and mint, season with black pepper to taste, and drizzle over the falafel. Serve hot.

Some more ideas

• The falafel are also delicious cold, with the minted yoghurt, salad, and warm pitta bread.

• Choose wholemeal pitta breads for more fibre.

• Serve the falafel as a party appetizer without the bread. Spear each one with a cocktail stick and serve the yoghurt mint sauce for dipping.

Health points

• Chickpeas are used all over the world, although they are best known for their use in Middle Eastern and Indian dishes. They are close to being a perfect food – high in protein, complex carbohydrates and fibre; low in fat, cholesterol and salt; and loaded with important nutrients, including potassium, folate and iron.

photo, page 143

Each serving provides   Key nutrients 330kcals, 4g fat (of which 1g is saturated fat), 15g protein, 61g carbohydrate, 365mg sodium (0.91g salt), 10g fibre

Useful source of potassium (456mg)

Lentils with macaroni

This highly spiced dish from Egypt is perfect for vegetarians because it is so rich with protein, due to the combination of lentils and pasta. You'll love the interesting texture and mix of flavours.

Preparation time **10–15 minutes**   Cooking time **about 1 hour**   *Serves 4*

250g (9oz) Puy lentils, rinsed

3 tsp sunflower oil

1 large onion, very thinly sliced

1 tsp sugar

2 tsp ground cumin

2 tsp ground coriander

¼ tsp cayenne pepper

225g (8oz) macaroni

2 tbsp finely chopped fresh coriander or parsley

pepper to taste

For the tomato sauce

1 tbsp sunflower oil

1 large garlic clove, crushed

½ tsp turmeric

2 cans (about 400g each) no-salt-added chopped tomatoes

pinch of sugar

1 Put the lentils in a heavy saucepan and pour in enough water to cover them by 7.5cm (3in). Bring to the boil, then reduce the heat and simmer for 20–30 minutes or until tender. Drain well and keep warm.

2 While the lentils are cooking, heat 1½ teaspoons of the oil in a large nonstick frying pan over high heat. Add the onion and stir to coat with the oil, then reduce the heat and cook, stirring frequently, for about 20 minutes or until soft. Stir in the sugar, raise the heat and continue cooking, stirring, until the onion is dark brown and crisp. Immediately pour on to kitchen paper to drain.

3 To make tomato sauce, heat the oil in the saucepan you used to cook the lentils. Add the garlic and sauté for 30 seconds, stirring. Stir in the turmeric and sauté for a further 30 seconds. Pour in the tomatoes with their juice and add the sugar. Bring to the boil, stirring. Reduce the heat and simmer, stirring occasionally, for 10–15 minutes or until the sauce thickens a little. Season to taste.

4 Heat the remaining 1½ teaspoons oil in the frying pan, add the cumin, coriander and cayenne pepper, and fry, stirring, for 30 seconds. Add the lentils and stir in seasoning to taste. Keep warm over a very low heat.

5 Cook the macaroni in boiling water according to the packet instructions. Drain well. Spoon the macaroni on to a serving platter and top with the spiced lentils and the tomato sauce. Sprinkle with the chopped coriander and top with the crisp onions. Serve at once.

Some more ideas

• Add 1 deseeded and thinly sliced red pepper in step 4, cooking it in the oil until slightly softened before adding the spices and cooked lentils.

Health points

• Lentils are an excellent source of iron and of dietary fibre, particularly the soluble type. They also provide useful amounts of many B vitamins.

• An onion topping like this is traditionally deep-fried, but here it is cooked in a small amount of oil in a nonstick pan, to reduce the fat content.

photo, page 143

Each serving provides Key nutrients 480kcals, 8g fat (of which 1g is saturated fat), 24g protein, 83g carbohydrate, 93mg sodium (o.23g salt), 9g fibre

Good source of potassium (1265mg)

Saffron couscous with peppers

Serve this salad warm or cool as a main dish for four, or as a main course accompaniment for six.
Either way, it is a flavoursome vegetarian dish that has real meal appeal.

Preparation time **about 1 hour, plus optional cooling**   *Serves 4*

1 large garlic clove, crushed

3 tbsp olive oil

4 large sprigs of fresh rosemary

1 large yellow pepper,
deseeded and cut into strips

1 large red pepper, deseeded
and cut into strips

2 courgettes, cut into 2.5cm
(1in) chunks

2 tomatoes, skinned, deseeded
and diced

4½ tsp lemon juice

harissa or other chilli sauce,
to taste

pepper to taste

large handful of chopped fresh
coriander

For the couscous

600ml (1 pint) low-sodium
vegetable stock

10–12 saffron threads

350g (12oz) couscous

1 bay leaf, torn in half

50g (1¾oz) sultanas or raisins

2 tsp butter

2 spring onions, finely chopped

1 Preheat the oven to 200°C (400°F, gas mark 6). Place the garlic and oil in a small bowl and set aside to infuse. Lay the rosemary sprigs in a roasting tin.

2 Meanwhile, for the couscous, put the stock and saffron in a saucepan. Bring to the boil, then cover, remove from the heat and leave to infuse.

3 Using your hands, rub the pepper and courgette pieces with a little of the garlic-flavoured oil so they are well coated. Place the peppers in the roasting tin on top of the rosemary and roast for 10 minutes. Then add the courgettes and continue roasting, turning the vegetables over once or twice, for 20–25 minutes or until tender and slightly charred.

4 Pour the remaining garlic-infused oil into a large bowl. Whisk in the lemon juice, and harissa and seasoning to taste, to make the dressing.

5 As soon as the vegetables are cooked, transfer them to the bowl containing the dressing and add the tomatoes. Stir to coat with the dressing, then set aside to cool.

6 Bring the saffron-infused stock to the boil. Add the couscous, bay leaf and sultanas. Stir well, then cover and remove from the heat. Leave to stand for 5 minutes.

7 Add the butter to the couscous and place over a medium heat. Cook for 1–2 minutes, fluffing with a fork to separate the grains. Remove the bay leaf. Stir in the spring onions and season to taste. Leave the couscous to cool until just warm or allow it to cool completely, as preferred.

8 Place the couscous on a serving platter. Top with the vegetables and any dressing remaining in the bowl, scatter over the chopped herbs and serve. .

Some more ideas

• For a heartier dish, add
1 can (about 400g) chickpeas,
drained and rinsed, to the hot
vegetables.

Health points

• Mixing couscous with
delicious roast vegetables
makes a main dish that offers
a low-fat vegetarian alternative
to a lamb stew with couscous.

Each serving provides   **Key nutrients** 370kcals, 12g fat (of which 3g is saturated fat), 8g protein, 61g carbohydrate, 240mg sodium (0.6g salt), 2.5g fibre

Useful source of potassium (586mg)

Falafel pittas *p140*

Saffron couscous with peppers *p142*

Braised vegetables with falafel and yoghurt sauce *p144*

Lentils with macaroni *p141*

Braised vegetables with falafel and yoghurt sauce

Try these bite-size falafel with a simple vegetable casserole. Made with canned chickpeas and then baked, the falafel are quick and easy to prepare. They're good cold as well as hot.

Preparation time **30 minutes**   Cooking time **about 1 hour**   *Serves 4*

2 tbsp olive oil

1 garlic clove, crushed

2 large onions, sliced

2 large yellow or red peppers, deseeded and sliced

2 medium courgettes

300ml (10fl oz) low-sodium vegetable stock

350g (12oz) cherry tomatoes, halved

pepper to taste

For the falafel

2 cans (400g each) chickpeas, drained and rinsed

8 spring onions, chopped

6 tbsp chopped parsley

2 tbsp chopped fresh coriander

2 tbsp ground coriander

For the sauce

½ cucumber, grated

85g (3oz) watercress leaves, shredded

85g (3oz) rocket, shredded

3 tbsp chopped fresh mint

grated zest of 1 lime

200g (7oz) plain low-fat yoghurt

1 First make the falafel. Brush a shallow baking dish with a little oil. Put the chickpeas in a bowl and mash with a potato masher, then mix in the spring onions, parsley, fresh and ground coriander, and seasoning to taste. Alternatively, mix the ingredients in a food processor. With your hands, shape the mixture into 24 balls, slightly larger than walnuts, placing them in the prepared dish. Set aside.

2 Preheat the oven to 200°C (400°F, gas mark 6). Heat the oil in a flameproof casserole. Add the garlic, onions and peppers. Stir well, then cover and cook, stirring frequently, for about 15 minutes or until the vegetables are soft.

3 Stir in the courgettes and stock. Bring to the boil, then cover the casserole and transfer it to the oven. Place the falafel in the oven at the same time. Cook for 20 minutes.

4 Add the tomatoes to the casserole and stir. Cover and return it to the oven. Use a spoon and fork to turn the falafel, taking care not to break them. Cook the casserole and falafel for a further 20 minutes or until the vegetables are tender and the falafel are crisp and lightly browned.

5 Meanwhile, to make the yoghurt sauce, squeeze the cucumber in handfuls to remove excess moisture. Put it into a bowl. Stir in the watercress, rocket, mint, lime zest and yoghurt. Add seasoning to taste and transfer to a serving dish. Cover and chill until ready to serve.

6 Transfer the falafel to a serving dish. Serve with the casserole and yoghurt sauce.

Some more ideas

Ratatouille Use 1 large onion, and add 1 diced aubergine with the courgettes. Replace the cherry tomatoes with 450g (1lb) skinned and quartered plum tomatoes.

• For a punchy flavour, add 2 crushed garlic cloves and the grated zest of 1 lemon to the falafel mixture.

• Basil is good in the yoghurt sauce: shred a handful of fresh leaves and add them with or instead of the rocket.

Health points

• Watercress has been considered something of a superfood for many centuries. Hippocrates wrote about its medicinal values in 460 BC and built the world's first hospital next to a stream so he could grow fresh watercress. Watercress provides vitamins C and E, and carotenoid compounds. It also contributes substantial amounts of folate, niacin and vitamin B$_6$.

photo, page 143

Each serving provides   **Key nutrients** 351kcals, 11g fat (of which 2g is saturated fat), 20g protein, 47g carbohydrate, 200mg sodium (0.5g salt), 11g fibre

Good source of potassium (1404mg potassium)

Green pasta with white beans

Here's proof that pasta sauce doesn't need meat to be hearty. Rosemary and garlic-flavoured tomato juice thickened with mashed beans makes a light sauce that nicely coats this elegant but easy spinach penne.

Preparation time **10 minutes**   Cooking time **15 minutes**   *Serves 4*

1 tbsp olive oil

1 carrot, thinly sliced on the diagonal

5 garlic cloves, finely chopped

½ tsp dried rosemary

225ml (8fl oz) low-sodium tomato juice

1 can (about 400g) cannellini beans, rinsed and drained

350g (12oz) spinach penne

½ tsp cracked black pepper

1 Heat the oil in a large frying pan over low heat. Add the carrot, garlic and rosemary. Cook, stirring occasionally, for about 5 minutes or until the carrot is tender.

2 Stir in the tomato juice and bring to the boil. Add the beans and, with a potato masher, mash about one-quarter of them.

3 Meanwhile, cook the pasta in large pot of boiling water according to the packet instructions. Drain, reserving 125ml (4fl oz) of the pasta cooking liquid.

4 Transfer the hot pasta to a large bowl. Add the reserved pasta cooking liquid, the bean mixture and the pepper, and toss to combine. Serve hot.

Some more ideas

• Serve roast red peppers with wholemeal French bread as an antipasto, and then offer fresh fruit salad for dessert.

• Use red kidney beans instead of cannellini beans.

Health points

• This recipe contains plenty of garlic, which contains potent phytochemicals including allicin, which has anti-fungal and antibiotic properties. For best benefit, always eat fresh garlic, not garlic powder or garlic salt. Garlic in capsule form does not give you the same effect as the fresh.

• 100g (3½oz) of cooked beans provides nearly 6g of fibre, making beans one of the best sources of heart-healthy fibre.

photo, page 147

Each serving provides   **Key nutrients** 440kcals, 5g fat (of which 1g is saturated fat), 18g protein, 94g carbohydrate, 65mg sodium (0.16g salt), 8.5g fibre

Useful source of potassium (717mg)

Persian-style squash couscous

Wonderfully exotic and colourful, this vegetarian salad captures the flavours of ancient Persian cooking: date and sultana couscous makes a bed for butternut and patty pan squashes with peppers and orange.

Preparation time **about 1 hour**   *Serves 4*

1 butternut squash, about 750g (1lb 10oz)

2 peppers (1 red and 1 yellow), halved and deseeded

225g (8oz) baby patty pan squashes, halved if large

1 orange, cut into large chunks

4 bay leaves

1 cinnamon stick, halved

2 garlic cloves, chopped

1 tbsp olive oil

For the couscous

1 tbsp olive oil

1 onion, finely chopped

2 garlic cloves, chopped

75g (2½oz) stoned dates, chopped

75g (2½oz) sultanas

1 cinnamon stick

2 tsp grated fresh ginger

150ml (5fl oz) dry white wine

250g (9oz) couscous

1 can (about 400g) chickpeas, drained and rinsed

2 tbsp each chopped fresh mint and parsley

juice of 1 orange

1 Preheat the oven to 200°C (400°F, gas mark 6). Peel the butternut squash and cut in half lengthways. Remove the seeds, and cut across into thick slices. Cut each pepper half into 12 pieces. Put the squash and peppers in a roasting tin with the patty pans, orange, bay leaves, cinnamon stick and garlic. Drizzle over the olive oil. Roast, turning once, for about 25 minutes or until browned and tender.

2 Meanwhile, prepare the couscous. Heat the oil in a saucepan, add the onion and garlic, and sauté for 5 minutes. Add the dates, sultanas, cinnamon, ginger and wine. Cover and cook gently for 5 minutes. Remove from the heat. Stir in the couscous and chickpeas, then add 300ml (10fl oz) boiling water. Cover and leave to stand for 5 minutes.

3 Add the parsley, mint and orange juice to the couscous. Mix in and fluff up with a fork. Spoon the couscous on to four plates and top with the roast vegetables. Serve warm or at room temperature.

Some more ideas

Aubergine and pearl barley salad Replace the butternut squash with 2 aubergines, cut into thick slices. Instead of the couscous, put 225g (8oz) pearl barley in a saucepan with 1 chopped onion, 1 halved cinnamon stick, and 900ml (1½ pints) vegetable stock. Bring to the boil, then cover and simmer for 1 hour or until the barley is just tender. Drain if necessary and cool, then toss with 85g (3oz) toasted walnut pieces, 1 tbsp chopped fresh mint, 1 tbsp chopped parsley, the grated zest and juice of 1 lemon and 1 tbsp olive oil. Serve topped with the roast vegetables.

Health points

• Dried dates are rich in potassium, niacin, copper, iron and magnesium. Both dates and sultanas are a valuable source of soluble fibre.

Each serving provides   Key nutrients 540kcals, 9g fat (of which 1g is saturated fat), 17g protein, 96g carbohydrate, 27mg sodium (0.07g salt), 10g fibre

Good source of potassium (1651mg)

Green pasta with white beans *p145*

Persian-style squash couscous *p146*

Noodles with roast vegetables *p149*

Penne primavera *p148*

Penne primavera

This classic Italian pasta dish is traditionally made with young spring vegetables from the garden. Today vegetables are available year-round, so this dish can be made any time.

Preparation time **15 minutes**   Cooking time **15 minutes**   *Serves 4*

350g (12oz) penne or other pasta shapes

225g (8oz) asparagus

225g (8oz) green beans, cut into 5mm (¼in) lengths

225g (8oz) shelled fresh peas

175g (6oz) shelled young broad beans

1 tbsp olive oil

1 onion, chopped

1 garlic clove, chopped

115g (4oz) button mushrooms, chopped

1 tbsp plain flour

225ml (8fl oz) dry white wine

2 tbsp single cream

2 tbsp chopped mixed fresh parsley and thyme

pepper to taste

4 fresh sage leaves, shredded

1 Cook the pasta in boiling water for 10–12 minutes or until al dente. Drain well.

2 While the pasta is cooking, cut the asparagus into 4cm (1½in) lengths, keeping the tips separate. Drop the pieces of asparagus stalk, the green beans, peas and broad beans into a saucepan of boiling water. Bring back to the boil and cook for 5 minutes. Add the asparagus tips and cook for a further 2 minutes. Drain thoroughly. (Slip the skins off the broad beans if you think they might be tough.)

3 Heat the oil in a saucepan. Add the onion and cook for 3–4 minutes or until softened. Add the garlic and mushrooms, and continue to cook, stirring occasionally, for 2 minutes.

4 Stir in the flour, then gradually pour in the wine and bring to the boil, stirring. Simmer until the sauce is thickened. Stir in the cream and herbs with pepper to taste. Add the vegetables to the sauce and heat through gently for 1–2 minutes, without boiling.

5 Divide the pasta among four serving bowls and spoon the sauce over the top. Serve immediately.

Some more ideas

• Other young, tender green vegetables can be used in place of or in addition to those suggested here. For example, try courgettes and broccoli.

• Use frozen peas instead of fresh, adding them with the asparagus tips.

Health points

• Peas provide good amounts of the B vitamins B_1, niacin and B_6. They also provide dietary fibre, particularly the soluble variety, some folate and vitamin C.

photo, page 147

Each serving provides Key nutrients 510kcals, 8g fat (of which 2g is saturated fat), 21g protein, 84g carbohydrate, 218mg sodium (0.11g salt), 11g fibre

Good source of potassium (983mg)

Noodles with roast vegetables

Oven-roasted vegetables, tender and scented with garlic, make a chunky dressing that is great with wide noodles. A sprinkling of crunchy sunflower seeds adds texture.

Preparation time about **20 minutes**   Cooking time **about 45 minutes**   *Serves 4*

1 aubergine, cut into large chunks

2 courgettes, cut into large chunks

2 red peppers, quartered and deseeded

1 green pepper, quartered and deseeded

4 ripe tomatoes, halved

2 red onions, quartered

1 head garlic, cloves separated but unpeeled, plus 2 garlic cloves, chopped

3 tbsp olive oil

cayenne pepper

pepper to taste

For the pasta

50g (1¾oz) unsalted sunflower seeds

low-sodium soy sauce to taste

350g (12oz) wide noodles, such as reginette, lasagnette or pappardelle

3 tbsp tomato purée, or to taste

handful of fresh basil leaves or parsley, coarsely chopped

1 Preheat the oven to 190°C (375°F, gas mark 5). Arrange the aubergine, courgettes, red and green peppers, tomatoes, red onions and whole garlic cloves in a single layer in a large ovenproof dish or roasting tin. Sprinkle with about 2 tablespoons of the olive oil, a little cayenne pepper, half the chopped garlic, and some pepper to taste.

2 Roast for about 45 minutes or until the vegetables are tender but not soft and mushy, and are charred in places. Turn the vegetables once or twice during cooking.

3 Lightly brush a frying pan with just a few drops of olive oil, then heat the pan. Add the sunflower seeds, and toss and turn them for a few moments until they begin to toast. Shake in a few drops of soy sauce and turn the seeds quickly, letting the soy sauce evaporate as the seeds toast and brown lightly. This should take 4–5 minutes in total. Remove from the heat just before the seeds are crisp and leave them to cool in the pan. They will crisp up as they cool.

4 Cook the pasta in boiling water according to the packet instructions. Drain well and keep hot.

5 Using a knife and fork, cut the roasted vegetables into bite-size chunks. Toss the vegetables and garlic with the remaining raw chopped garlic, the tomato purée, and basil or parsley. Taste for seasoning and add more pepper if required.

6 Toss the pasta with the vegetables and serve immediately, sprinkled with the toasted sunflower seeds.

Some more ideas

• Crush a few saffron threads in a mortar using a pestle and add them to the roasted vegetables along with the tomato purée.

• Serve topped with sesame seeds instead of toasted sunflower seeds.

• Pumpkin seeds can also be used instead of sunflower seeds.

Health points

• As well as all the benefits from the excellent mixture of vegetables in this dish, the sunflower seeds provide a useful source of iron, vitamin B_1 and phosphorus.

photo, page 147

Each serving provides   Key nutrients 570kcals, 19g fat (of which 4g is saturated fat), 18g protein, 83g carbohydrate, 201mg sodium (0.5g salt), 9g fibre

Good source of potassium (1265mg)

Tagliatelle with mushroom medley

Choose a variety of exotic and wild mushrooms for this feast of fungi. Their flavours are complemented by red wine in a dish that will fit perfectly into a well-balanced diet.

Preparation time **15 minutes, plus 15 minutes soaking**   Cooking time **30 minutes**   *Serves 4*

10g (¼oz) dried porcini mushrooms

90ml (3fl oz) boiling water

1 tbsp olive oil

3 shallots, chopped

225g (8oz) button mushrooms, sliced

150ml (5fl oz) Marsala wine

1 garlic clove, finely chopped *(optional)*

450g (1lb) mixed mushrooms, such as chestnut, shiitake, oyster, or chanterelle or other wild mushrooms, sliced or halved

2 large tomatoes, skinned, deseeded and sliced

2 tsp fresh thyme leaves or 1 tsp dried thyme

2 tbsp chopped parsley

pepper to taste

To serve

450g (1lb) tagliatelle

1 Put the dried porcini mushrooms in a bowl and cover with the boiling water. Set aside to soak for 15 minutes, then drain, reserving the soaking liquid. Slice the rehydrated mushrooms, discarding any tough stalks.

2 Heat half the olive oil in a saucepan. Add the shallots and sauté for 3 minutes or until they are tender and golden. Add the button mushrooms and cook for 8–10 minutes or until all the juice from the mushrooms has evaporated.

3 Add the Marsala and the soaking liquid from the dried mushrooms. Simmer for about 10 minutes or until the liquid has reduced by half.

4 Meanwhile, cook the tagliatelle in a pot of boiling water according to the packet instructions.

5 About 5 minutes before the pasta is ready, heat the remaining oil in a large frying pan. Add the garlic, if using, and the mixed mushrooms. Cook over a moderate heat, shaking the pan often, for 3–5 minutes or until the mushrooms are lightly cooked.

6 Stir the tomatoes, thyme and parsley into the mushroom sauce and heat through for 1–2 minutes. Add the mixed mushrooms, season to taste and remove from the heat.

7 Drain the tagliatelle and divide it among four serving bowls. Spoon the mushroom sauce on top and serve.

Some more ideas

• For a creamy sauce, stir in 4 tbsp fromage frais or Greek-style yoghurt.

• White or red wine can be used in place of the Marsala.

Health points

• Mushrooms are a useful source of the B vitamins niacin, B_6 and folate. They also provide good amounts of copper, which is one of the all-important minerals that form part of a healthy diet.

• Most recipes use mushrooms in small quantities, so that the nutritional contribution they make to the diet is limited. However, this dish contains a substantial amount of fresh mushrooms, plus dried ones for additional flavour.

Each serving provides   Key nutrients 510kcals, 6g fat (of which 1g is saturated fat), 18g protein, 91g carbohydrate, 31mg sodium (0.08g salt), 6g fibre

Good source of potassium (997mg)

Tagliatelle with mushroom medley *p150*

Cold sesame noodles and vegetables *p152*

Spaghetti with chickpeas and
spicy tomato sauce *p153*

Linguine with no-cook sauce *p154*

Cold sesame noodles and vegetables

A long-time favourite at Chinese restaurants, cold sesame noodles make a great main or side dish. We've replaced hard-to-find sesame paste with peanut butter and sesame oil.

Preparation time **15 minutes**   Cooking time **1 hour 20 minutes**   *Serves 4*

225g (8oz) wholemeal linguine

For the sauce

15g (½oz) fresh coriander leaves

2 tbsp smooth peanut butter

2 tbsp low-sodium soy sauce

2½ tsp honey

1 tbsp rice vinegar or cider vinegar

1 tbsp toasted sesame oil

2 garlic cloves, peeled

¼ tsp cayenne pepper

2 carrots, slivered

1 red pepper, slivered

1 large celery stick, slivered

2 spring onions, slivered

1 Cook the linguine in a large pot of boiling water according to the packet instructions. Drain, reserving 125ml (4fl oz) of the cooking water.

2 While the pasta is cooking, combine the coriander, peanut butter, soy sauce, honey, vinegar, sesame oil, garlic and cayenne pepper in a food processor. Process until smooth. Transfer to a large bowl.

3 Whisk in the reserved pasta cooking water. Add the linguine, carrots, pepper, celery and spring onions, and toss. Chill for at least 1 hour before serving.

Some more ideas

• Add blanched cauliflower or broccoli florets to the pasta and vegetable mixture.

• Serve this dish warm by heating the sauce, then add cubes of cooked tofu.

Health points

• The pasta cooking water, which carries some of the pasta's starch, is used here to stretch the sauce. It's a traditional Italian technique for thinning or smoothing a sauce so that it coats the pasta evenly. And the water replaces what might otherwise be oil or other fat.

photo, page 151

Each serving provides   **Key nutrients** 310kcals, 8g fat (of which 2g is saturated fat), 10g protein, 49g carbohydrate, 300mg sodium (0.75g salt), 7g fibre

Useful source of potassium (471mg)

Spaghetti with chickpeas and spicy tomato sauce

Here's a colourful and easy pasta and bean dish that makes a satisfying main course all on its own. Garlic, olive oil, onion, Tabasco sauce and pecorino cheese add lots of sunny flavour.

Preparation and cooking time **20–25 minutes**   *Serves 4*

For the sauce

2 tbsp olive oil

1 onion, chopped

1 garlic clove, crushed

1 celery stick, finely chopped

1 can (about 400g) no-salt-added chopped tomatoes

For the pasta and beans

350g (12oz) spaghetti

2 cans (about 400g each) chickpeas, drained and rinsed

½ tsp Tabasco sauce, or to taste

175g (6oz) baby spinach leaves

pepper to taste

55g (2oz) pecorino cheese, freshly grated

fresh parsley leaves to garnish

1 To make the sauce, heat the olive oil in a heavy saucepan, add the onion and garlic, and cook over a moderate heat, stirring occasionally, for 3–4 minutes or until softened.

2 Add the celery and sauté, stirring, for 1–2 minutes, then stir in the chopped tomatoes with their juice and bring to the boil. Reduce the heat and leave to simmer gently, stirring occasionally, for about 15 minutes or until thick.

3 Meanwhile, cook the spaghetti in a large pan of boiling water according to the packet instructions.

4 When the sauce is cooked, stir in the chickpeas and Tabasco sauce. Add the spinach leaves and simmer, stirring, for 1–2 minutes or until the spinach wilts. Season with pepper to taste.

5 Drain the spaghetti and toss with the chickpeas and tomato sauce. Serve immediately, sprinkled with the pecorino cheese and parsley.

Some more ideas

Tagliatelle with cannellini beans Use tagliatelle or fettuccine instead of spaghetti, and replace the chickpeas with canned cannellini beans. Instead of spinach, add 225g (8oz) cooked asparagus spears, cut into 2.5cm (1in) lengths, to the sauce.

Health points

• Despite its name, the chickpea is not really a pea but a bean. Chickpeas contain good amounts of iron, manganese and folate, and are richer in vitamin E than most other beans.

• Cooking the spinach leaves in the sauce very briefly, just to wilt them, retains all their juices and the maximum nutrients.

photo, page 151

Each serving provides   Key nutrients 625kcals, 15g fat (of which 4g is saturated fat), 31g protein, 98g carbohydrate, 220mg sodium (0.55g salt), 11g fibre

Good source of potassium (1185mg)

Linguine with no-cook sauce

Of the hundreds of ways to dress linguine, this quick and easy sauce is bound to become the most requested in your house. It bursts with fresh-from-the-garden flavour.

Preparation time **20 minutes, plus standing**　　Cooking time **12 minutes**　　*Serves 4*

1.3kg (3lb) plum tomatoes, deseeded and chopped

25g (1oz) fresh basil, chopped

4 tbsp olive oil

4 tbsp chopped flat-leaf parsley

2 tbsp chopped fresh mint

2 tsp grated orange zest

3 garlic cloves, finely chopped

pepper to taste

To serve

350g (12oz) linguine or spaghetti

4 tbsp freshly grated Parmesan cheese

1 Mix together the tomatoes, basil, oil, parsley, mint, orange zest, garlic and pepper in a bowl. Leave to stand for at least 30 minutes, or up to 2 hours, at room temperature.

2 Cook the pasta in a large pot of boiling water according to the packet instructions. Drain well and put into a large pasta bowl. Top with the sauce and sprinkle with Parmesan.

Some more ideas

• Place the tomato topping on toasted rounds of ciabatta and serve as an appetiser.

• Spoon the tomato topping over any green salad.

• Use the tomato mixture to fill baked jacket potatoes.

Health points

• One serving of the fresh tomatoes in this dish supplies more than a day's requirement of vitamin C.

• Prolonged heating of foods can cause them to lose some of their nutrients. Only in rare cases does cooking enhance nutrition. In general, try to shorten your cooking times whenever possible. This recipe is a good example of how to preserve all the nutrients of fresh produce with no cooking.

photo, page 151

Each serving provides　**Key nutrients** 525kcals, 18g fat (of which 5g is saturated fat), 19g protein, 76g carbohydrate, 149mg sodium (0.37g salt), 6g fibre

Good source of potassium (1154mg)

Main dish salads

Oriental chicken salad

That old-fashioned chicken salad has adopted a new-fashioned Oriental accent. Grilled chicken is tossed with a healthy mix of oranges, spring onions, mangetout and lychees and is then crowned with a drizzle of smooth peanut dressing.

Preparation time **20 minutes**   Cooking time **10 minutes**   *Serves 4*

450g (1lb) cos or romaine lettuce

115g (4oz) mangetout

1 can (about 450g) lychees, drained and cut in half

1 large navel orange, peeled and cut into segments

1 red plum, stoned and sliced

4 spring onions, thinly sliced

350g (12oz) skinless, boneless chicken breasts

For the dressing

5 tbsp reduced-fat mayonnaise

3 tbsp smooth peanut butter

1 garlic clove, finely chopped

1 Finely shred the lettuce and put into a large salad bowl. Trim the mangetout and remove strings with your fingers. Cut the mangetout in half on the diagonal and add to the bowl. Add the lychees, orange, plum and spring onions, and toss to mix.

2 Coat a nonstick ridged grill pan with cooking spray and set over medium-high heat. After about 2 minutes, when the pan is really hot, lay the chicken breasts in the pan and cook for about 4 minutes on each side.

3 Meanwhile, whisk together the mayonnaise, peanut butter and garlic in a bowl until well blended. Cut the chicken into thin slices on the diagonal and add to the salad bowl. Drizzle the salad with the dressing, toss to coat and serve.

Some more ideas

• This salad works with other types of meat and seafood. In place of the chicken, grill the same amount of lamb leg steaks, turkey breast, pork tenderloin, fillet or rump steak, or peeled raw tiger prawns.

• Use spinach leaves in place of the lettuce, or a mixture.

Health points

• Lychees are a tropical fruit that originated in southern China. They have a relatively short growing season, so you'll only find them fresh in the shops occasionally, but canned lychees are available year-round. Lychees are high in vitamin C and potassium.

Each serving provides   Key nutrients 300kcals, 12g fat (of which 2.5g is saturated fat), 26g protein, 23g carbohydrate, 274mg sodium (0.68g salt), 3g fibre

Useful source of potassium (647mg)

Barley, black bean and avocado salad

We think of barley as a soup ingredient, but it's also a delicious main-dish grain, served hot or cold. When combined with black beans, tomato and avocado, it adds up to a salad that could hardly be more healthy or delicious.

Preparation time **10 minutes**   Cooking time **20 minutes**   *Serves 4*

225ml (8fl oz) carrot juice

½ tsp dried thyme

good pinch of cayenne pepper

100g (3½oz) quick-cooking pearl barley

3 tbsp fresh lemon juice

1 tbsp olive oil

1 can (about 450g) black beans, rinsed and drained

200g (7oz) diced fresh tomatoes

70g (2½oz) diced avocado

1 Combine the carrot juice, thyme and cayenne pepper in a medium saucepan. Bring to the boil over medium heat, then add the barley and reduce to a simmer. Cover and cook for about 15 minutes or until the barley is tender.

2 Meanwhile, whisk together the lemon juice and oil in a large bowl. Add the barley and any liquid remaining in the pan, and toss to coat.

3 Add the beans and tomatoes and toss to combine. Add the avocado and gently fold in. Serve at room temperature or chilled (for the best flavour, remove from the refrigerator about 20 minutes before serving).

Some more ideas

• Use 85g (3oz) long-grain brown rice in place of barley. Add 125ml (4fl oz) low-sodium chicken stock to the carrot juice mixture and cook the rinsed brown rice, covered, for 40–50 minutes or until it is tender.

• Replace the black beans with red kidney or pinto beans.

Health points

• This salad is a powerful combination of healthy foods. An exceptional amount of fibre comes from the barley and the beans. The avocado supplies vitamins A and E, and the beans and avocado are rich in the B vitamin, folate.

photo, page 161

Each serving provides   **Key nutrients** 290kcals, 7g fat (of which 1g is saturated fat), 12g protein, 46g carbohydrate, 37mg sodium (0.09g salt), 9g fibre

Good source of potassium (900mg)

Warm sesame chicken salad

Strips of chicken in a crisp coating of sesame seeds, breadcrumbs and cornflakes are served atop a crunchy vegetable salad dressed with a fresh herb vinaigrette. A little chilli powder in the coating gives a bit of a kick.

Preparation time **15 minutes**   Cooking time **15–20 minutes**   *Serves 4*

450g (1lb) skinless, boneless chicken breasts

75g (2½oz) fresh white breadcrumbs

50g (1¾oz) cornflakes, lightly crushed

4 tsp sesame seeds, plus extra to garnish

1 tsp hot chilli powder, or to taste

2 eggs

¼ white cabbage

½ frisée (curly endive)

2 heads chicory

For the dressing

1 tsp chopped parsley

1 tsp chopped fresh oregano

1 tbsp chopped fresh tarragon

1 tbsp white wine vinegar

4 tbsp olive oil

1 tsp clear honey

pepper to taste

1 Preheat the oven to 200°C (400°F, gas mark 6). Slice each chicken breast in half horizontally, then cut lengthways into strips.

2 Put the breadcrumbs, cornflakes, sesame seeds and chilli powder in a plastic bag and shake to mix well. Break the eggs into a shallow dish and beat together lightly.

3 Dip the chicken strips, one at a time, in the egg, then drop into the plastic bag. When a few pieces of chicken are in the bag, shake to coat evenly with the sesame seed mixture. As the chicken strips are coated, transfer to two nonstick baking trays, spreading out the pieces.

4 Bake the chicken strips for 15–20 minutes, turning the pieces over halfway through the baking time.

5 Meanwhile, make the salad. Finely shred the cabbage and place in a large mixing bowl. Pull the frisée and chicory leaves apart and tear any large ones into smaller pieces. Add to the mixing bowl.

6 In a small screw-top jar, shake together the dressing ingredients. Season to taste. Pour the dressing over the salad and toss well.

7 Divide the salad among four plates and pile the cooked chicken pieces on top. Garnish with a few more sesame seeds, then serve.

Some more ideas

Chinese-style chicken salad Beat 1 egg with 1 tbsp poppy seeds, 2 tbsp tomato purée, 2 tbsp dry sherry, 2 tbsp low-sodium soy sauce and 2 tsp five-spice powder in a bowl. Stir in the chicken strips. Lift them out and coat with the crumb mixture (made without the sesame seeds and chilli powder). Bake as in main recipe. Meanwhile, finely shred 1 head Chinese leaves. Place in a bowl and add 115g (4oz) bean sprouts and 1 bunch of spring onions, thinly sliced into rings. Toss with the dressing (made with 1½ tbsp each parsley and fresh coriander rather than parsley, oregano and tarragon). Serve the hot chicken strips on top of the salad.

Health points

• Cabbage belongs to a family of vegetables that contain phytochemicals that help protect against some cancers. Cabbage is also a source of folate.

photo, page 161

Each serving provides   **Key nutrients** 450kcals, 21g fat (of which 4g is saturated fat), 35g protein, 31g carbohydrate, 381mg sodium (0.95g salt), 2.5g fibre

Useful source of potassium (745mg)

Coronation chicken

This curry-flavoured salad with a fruity rice pilaf has become a traditional summer dish. Instead of using a cream and mayonnaise sauce, this version lightens up by reducing the mayonnaise and adding yoghurt.

Preparation time **about 1½ hours, plus cooling**   *Serves 6*

450g (1lb) skinless, boneless chicken breasts

1 onion, sliced

1 large carrot, chopped

1 celery stick, chopped

6 black peppercorns

1 bay leaf

375g (13oz) basmati rice, rinsed

40g (1½oz) raisins

40g (1½oz) ready-to-eat dried mango, chopped

1 large banana

70g (2½oz) pecan nuts

2 courgettes, cut into ribbons with a vegetable peeler

sprigs of fresh mint to garnish

For the dressing

150g (5½oz) plain low-fat yoghurt

4 tbsp reduced-fat mayonnaise

2 tbsp curry paste

grated zest of 1 large lemon

1 tbsp lemon juice

6 tbsp chopped mixed fresh herbs (chives, mint and parsley)

pepper to taste

1 Place the chicken breasts in a large saucepan and cover with water. Add the onion, carrot and celery, and bring almost to boiling point, skimming the surface as necessary. When bubbles begin to break through the surface, reduce the heat so the water is just simmering. Add the peppercorns, lightly crushed, and the bay leaf, and simmer for 15 minutes or until the juices run clear from the chicken.

2 Remove the chicken from the liquid and set aside to cool. Pour the cooking liquid through a fine sieve into a measuring jug. Discard the vegetables.

3 To make the pilaf, put the rice in a saucepan and add 600ml (1 pint) of the strained cooking liquid. Stir in the raisins and mango. Bring to the boil, then reduce the heat, cover and simmer for about 20 minutes or until all the liquid has been absorbed and the rice is tender.

4 Remove the rice from the heat and set aside, covered, for 5 minutes. Then transfer the rice to a bowl and leave to cool completely.

5 Meanwhile, make the dressing. Combine the yoghurt, mayonnaise, curry paste, and lemon zest and juice in a large mixing bowl and mix until well blended. Stir in the chives, mint, and parsley and pepper to taste.

6 When the chicken is completely cool, cut the meat into bite-size pieces. Fold them into the curry dressing. (If you like, cover the chicken and chill; remove from the refrigerator 15 minutes before serving.) Slice the banana and gently stir it into the chicken mixture.

7 Stir the pecans into the rice pilaf and spoon on to six plates. Arrange the courgette ribbons on the pilaf and top with the chicken mixture. Garnish with mint sprigs and serve.

Some more ideas

• Use halved seedless green grapes instead of sliced banana.

• Use skinless, boneless turkey in place of the chicken.

Health points

• Using the chicken stock to cook the rice ensures that you retain the water-soluble vitamins that seeped into the water while the chicken was being poached.

Each serving provides   Key nutrients 520kcals, 14g fat (of which 2g is saturated fat), 27g protein, 71g carbohydrate, 246mg sodium (0.61g salt), 3g fibre

Good source of potassium (878mg)

Coronation chicken *p160*

Barley, black bean and avocado salad *p158*

Warm sesame chicken salad *p159*

Marinated duck and kasha salad *p162*

Marinated duck and kasha salad

Kasha is toasted buckwheat grain. When you buy the grain plain, toast it yourself and then simmer it in stock, it develops a rich, nutty flavour. This works perfectly with griddled duck in a hearty main-dish salad.

Preparation and cooking time **50 minutes**   *Serves 4*

450g (1lb) skinless, boneless duck breasts

2 garlic cloves, chopped

juice of 1 lemon

12 sprigs of fresh thyme

1 tsp chopped fresh rosemary

2 tbsp olive oil

225g (8oz) plain buckwheat grain

750ml (1¼ pints) low-sodium chicken stock

125g (4½oz) green beans

200g (7oz) mixed salad greens

5 sprigs of fresh basil, finely shredded

½ red onion, thinly sliced

4 green olives, stoned (optional)

4 black olives, stoned (optional)

2 medium courgettes, thinly sliced lengthways

12 small spring onions

12 small tomatoes

1½ tbsp red wine vinegar, or a combination of sherry and balsamic vinegars

1 Remove all the fat from the duck breasts. With a sharp knife, score the flesh on both sides in a criss-cross pattern. Put the breasts in a bowl and add two-thirds of the garlic, the lemon juice, half of the thyme sprigs, the rosemary and 1 tablespoon of the oil. Turn to coat the breasts with the flavourings, then leave to marinate while you prepare the rest of the ingredients.

2 Put the grain in a heavy frying pan and toast over medium heat, stirring and tossing, for 4–5 minutes or until it has become slightly darker in colour. Remove from the heat.

3 Bring the stock to the boil in a saucepan. Add the toasted grain and bring back to the boil, then reduce the heat, cover and cook for 10–15 minutes or until the stock has been absorbed and the kasha is tender. Remove from the heat and set aside, still covered, until ready to use.

4 Heat a grill pan for 5 minutes. Meanwhile, drop the green beans into a saucepan of boiling water and blanch for 1–2 minutes. Drain and refresh under cold running water. Cut the beans in half and put into a salad bowl. Add the salad leaves, basil, red onion and olives, and toss to mix.

5 Remove the duck breasts from the marinade and place on the hot grill pan. Cook for 3 minutes on each side for rare (cook longer if you prefer it well done). Remove the duck to a board. Place the courgettes, spring onions and tomatoes on the grill pan and cook for 1–2 minutes or until lightly charred all over.

6 Combine the remaining garlic and oil with the vinegar in a small bowl. Add the leaves from the remaining thyme sprigs. Whisk together, then drizzle over the salad. Spoon on the kasha. Arrange the courgettes, spring onions and tomatoes on top. Slice the duck breasts, place over the salad and serve.

Some more ideas

Duck and pumpkin salad Rub the duck breasts with a mixture of 2 chopped garlic cloves, ½ tsp ground cumin, ¼ tsp ground cinnamon, and ½ tsp cocoa powder. Put in a mixing bowl. Add 150g (5½oz) peeled and seeded pumpkin or butternut squash, thinly sliced, and sprinkle over the juices of 1 lemon and 1 orange, and 1 tbsp extra virgin olive oil. Turn the ingredients to mix them, then leave to marinate for at least 30 minutes. Make the green bean and leaf salad, and sprinkle with 75g (2½oz) dried cherries and the segments of 1 orange. For the dressing, whisk the juice of 1 orange with 2 tbsp olive oil, 2 tsp caster sugar and ¼ tsp paprika. Griddle the duck breasts as in the main recipe, then slice. Griddle the pumpkin slices for 4–5 minutes. Pour the dressing over the salad, add the kasha, and arrange the duck and pumpkin slices on top.

photo, page 161

Each serving provides   **Key nutrients** 461kcals, 15g fat (of which 3g is saturated fat), 30g protein, 56g carbohydrate, 240mg sodium (0.6g salt), 4g fibre

Good source of potassium (1021mg)

Crab and grapefruit salad

Here's the surprise of the season: crab and grapefruit are the perfect partners for a quick, no-cook salad. The sweetness of the crabmeat and dressing contrast with the tartness of the grapefruit and the slight bitterness of the greens.

Preparation time **25 minutes**   *Serves 4*

4 grapefruits

2 tbsp reduced-fat mayonnaise

1 tbsp finely chopped mango chutney

2 tsp Dijon mustard

1 tsp toasted sesame oil

pepper to taste

350g (12oz) white crabmeat, picked over to remove any cartilage

125g (4½oz) watercress, tough stalks trimmed

1 head chicory, cut crossways into 1cm (½in) strips

1 soft, round lettuce, separated into leaves

1 With a small paring knife, peel the grapefruits. Working over a large bowl to catch the juice, separate the grapefruit segments from the membrane; reserve any juice that collects in the bowl.

2 In a medium bowl, whisk together the mayonnaise, chutney, mustard, sesame oil, pepper and 3 tablespoons of the reserved grapefruit juice.

3 Add the crabmeat, tossing to combine. Add the watercress, chicory and grapefruit segments, and toss. Serve the salad on a bed of lettuce leaves.

Some more ideas

• Crabmeat is a classic choice for this refreshing salad, but you could also use cooked prawns, lobster, scallops or chunks of poached chicken breast.

• Substitute oranges for the grapefruit.

Health points

• If you use pink or red grapefruit, not only will the salad have high amounts of vitamin C, but it will provide betacarotene too. Grapefruit of any colour is high in fibre and low in calories.

Each serving provides

Key nutrients 220kcals, 8g fat (of which 1g is saturated fat), 20g protein, 14g carbohydrate, 582mg sodium (1.45g salt), 3g fibre

Useful source of potassium (715mg)

Mango chicken salad

Here is a very special salad: new potatoes, slices of tender grilled chicken and asparagus tossed in a mellow fresh orange dressing and then mixed with juicy mango slices and baby salad leaves. It makes a well-balanced meal all on its own.

Preparation and cooking time **50 minutes, plus 15 minutes marinating**   *Serves 4*

1 garlic clove, crushed

1 tsp grated fresh root ginger

1 tbsp low-sodium soy sauce

2 tsp sunflower oil

2 skinless, boneless chicken breasts

800g (1¾lb) new potatoes, scrubbed

2 large sprigs of fresh mint

125g (4½oz) asparagus spears

1 mango, peeled and sliced

150g (5½oz) mixed baby salad leaves

For the dressing

½ tsp finely grated orange zest

1 tbsp orange juice

1 tsp Dijon mustard

1 tbsp sunflower oil

1 tbsp walnut oil

pepper to taste

1 Put the garlic, ginger, soy sauce and sunflower oil in a bowl and whisk together. Add the chicken breasts and turn to coat both sides, then leave to marinate for 15 minutes.

2 Put the potatoes in a saucepan, pour over boiling water to cover and add the mint sprigs. Cook for 15–20 minutes or until tender. At the same time, put the asparagus in a steamer basket or metal colander, cover and set over the pan of potatoes to steam. Cook thin spears for 4–5 minutes, thick spears for 8–10 minutes, or until just tender. Drain the potatoes (discard the mint) and leave until cool enough to handle, then slice thickly. Cut the asparagus diagonally into 6cm (2½in) lengths.

3 Preheat the grill to moderate. Remove the chicken from the marinade and place it on the grill rack. Grill, brushing frequently with the marinade and turning once, for about 15 minutes or until cooked through and the juices run clear when the chicken is pierced with the tip of a knife. Leave to rest for 3–4 minutes, then slice.

4 To make the dressing, put the orange zest and juice, mustard, and sunflower and walnut oils in a large serving bowl, and whisk together until slightly thickened. Season with pepper to taste.

5 Transfer the warm sliced chicken, potatoes and asparagus to the serving bowl and gently toss together to coat with the dressing. Add the mango and salad leaves and toss gently again. Serve immediately while still warm.

Some more ideas

• For a sharper citrus dressing, use lime zest and juice instead of orange.

Turkey and blueberry salad
Use turkey breast fillets, and marinate and grill as for the chicken in the main recipe. Cut 900g (2lb) new potatoes into 2cm (¾in) dice and cook in boiling water for about 10 minutes or until just tender. Drain well and toss with the warm turkey slices in the fresh orange dressing. Put 150g (5½oz) blueberries in a small saucepan with 1 tbsp balsamic vinegar and 2 tsp clear honey. Gently bubble for 3–4 minutes or until the blueberries soften. Add the salad leaves to the turkey and potato mixture and toss together, then drizzle over the blueberries.

Health points

• Mango is an excellent source of antioxidants that help to protect against damage by free radicals. Mango is also a good source of vitamin A.

Each serving provides Key nutrients 330kcals, 10g fat (of which 1.5g is saturated fat), 23g protein, 39g carbohydrate, 195mg sodium (0.49g salt), 4g fibre

Good source of potassium (1164mg)

Mango chicken salad *p164*

Indian-style rice with turkey *p166*

Marinated duck salad with bulghur *p167*

Pork and pear salad with pecans *p168*

Indian-style rice with turkey

The spicy aromas of this satisfying salad make it tempting fare at any time of year. The rice, with its slightly chewy texture and Indian spicing, provides the perfect backdrop for the turkey, vegetables, grapes and nuts.

Preparation time **50 minutes, plus cooling**   *Serves 6*

1 tbsp sunflower oil

375g (13oz) brown basmati rice, well rinsed

1 onion, finely chopped

1 tsp grated fresh root ginger

¼ tsp garam masala

¼ tsp ground coriander

½ tsp curry powder

750ml (1¼ pints) hot low-sodium chicken stock

1 bay leaf

3 large celery sticks, chopped

4 spring onions, chopped

1 large carrot, grated

140g (5oz) seedless red grapes, halved

450g (1lb) skinless cooked turkey breast meat, cubed

3 tbsp chopped parsley

Oak Leaf lettuce leaves

75g (2½oz) toasted pecans, coarsely chopped

For the dressing

4 tbsp orange juice

2 tsp lime juice

4 tsp sunflower oil

1 tbsp snipped fresh chives

1 Heat the oil in a large saucepan over moderate heat. Add the rice and stir to coat thoroughly, then cook, stirring frequently, for 1 minute. Add the onion, ginger, garam masala, coriander and curry powder, and continue cooking, stirring, for 3–4 minutes or until the onion starts to soften.

2 Add the hot stock and bay leaf, and bring to the boil. Reduce the heat, cover and simmer for 25 minutes or until the rice is tender. Discard the bay leaf and transfer the rice to a large bowl to cool.

3 Meanwhile, to make the dressing, whisk together the orange and lime juices, oil and chives. Season with pepper to taste.

4 Add the celery, spring onions and carrot to the cooled rice. Reserve half the grapes and add the remainder to the rice together with the turkey and parsley. Drizzle over the dressing and turn the salad gently to combine everything.

5 Arrange a bed of lettuce leaves on each of four plates and pile the rice salad on top. Scatter the remaining grapes and the pecans over the salad and serve.

Some more ideas

Herbed brown rice salad with salmon Cook the rice with the onion as in the main recipe, but omit the ginger and spices. Leave to cool, then stir in 1 tbsp chopped fresh dill or tarragon, 2 tbsp snipped fresh chives and 4 tbsp chopped parsley. Fold in ½ cucumber, peeled, quartered lengthways and sliced; 1 large grated carrot; 3 sliced celery sticks; and 5 radicchio leaves, torn into thin ribbons. Add the dressing and toss gently. Heat 1 tsp olive oil in a small frying pan and sauté 450g (1lb) skinless salmon fillet for about 3 minutes on each side or until just cooked through. Break into large flakes and fold gently into the rice salad. Garnish with halved cherry tomatoes.

• Peel 3 oranges and divide into segments, working over a bowl to catch the juice. Use the juice in the dressing and garnish the salads with the orange segments.

photo, page 165

Each serving provides   **Key nutrients** 510kcals, 20g fat (of which 3g is saturated fat), 28g protein, 59g carbohydrate, 170mg sodium (0.42g salt), 3g fibre

Useful source of potassium (677mg)

Marinated duck salad with bulghur wheat

The contrast of sweet citrus, spicy chilli, earthy grains, tangy basil and tender duck is marvellous. This seems like an ambitious, unusual dish but, if you buy the ingredients in advance, it comes together quickly. It's worth the effort!

Preparation time **45 minutes**   Cooking time **10 minutes**   *Serves 4*

150g (5½oz) bulghur wheat

4 small boneless duck breasts, about 500g (1lb 2oz) in total

3 garlic cloves, chopped

1½ tbsp mild chilli powder

1½ tsp ground cumin

4 tbsp finely shredded fresh basil

grated zest of 1 orange

juice of 3 oranges

juice of 1½ lemons

2 tbsp olive oil

16 kumquats

1½ tbsp sugar

175ml (6fl oz) water

3 spring onions, thinly sliced

3 tbsp chopped fresh coriander

pepper to taste

225g (8oz) mixed salad greens

2 tsp balsamic vinegar, or to taste

¼ cucumber, finely diced

½ large tomato, finely diced

1 Place the bulghur wheat in a bowl and cover with boiling water. Leave to soak for about 30 minutes.

2 Meanwhile, remove skin and fat from the duck breasts. Put the breasts in a dish and add half of the garlic, chilli powder, cumin and basil, the orange zest, juice of 1 orange, juice of ½ lemon and ½ tablespoon of olive oil. Mix well and turn the breasts to coat, then set aside to marinate.

3 To prepare the kumquats, cut a small slit in each one (do not cut all the way through). Place the kumquats in a saucepan with the juice of 1 orange, the sugar and water. Bring to the boil and simmer over a moderate heat, turning the kumquats so that they cook evenly, for 15–20 minutes or until they are just tender and the liquid has reduced by about half. Remove from the heat and leave to cool in the liquid.

4 Drain the soaked bulghur wheat and return it to the bowl. Add the spring onions, the remaining garlic, chilli powder, cumin, lemon juice and orange juice, 1 tablespoon of the remaining olive oil, and the coriander. Season to taste.

5 Heat a large nonstick frying pan. Remove the duck from its marinade and brown on both sides over a high heat. Cook for a further 4–5 minutes, turning the breasts frequently so that they don't stick. The meat will be rosy in colour in the centre (cook a little longer if you prefer it well done). Remove the breasts to a carving board and slice very thinly against the grain.

6 Arrange the salad leaves and remaining basil on four plates and add 4 kumquats to each. Drizzle with the remaining olive oil, the balsamic vinegar and a little of the kumquat cooking liquid. Place the bulgur wheat salad in the centre and arrange the duck slices around it. Scatter over the cucumber and tomato, and serve immediately.

Some more ideas

• Instead of bulghur wheat, use quinoa, a nutty little grain that comes from Peru. Rinse 75g (2½oz) quinoa well (it is coated with a sticky substance), then place in a saucepan and add 125ml (4fl oz) boiling water. Bring to the boil, then cover and simmer for 10 minutes or until the grains are just tender and have absorbed the liquid. Fluff up with a fork, then dress as for the bulghur wheat.

• Add a North African flavour to the marinade for the duck breasts. In addition to the spices above, add ¼ tsp each ground ginger, cinnamon and coriander and ¼ tsp mild or medium curry powder. Double the amount of lemon juice.

Health points

• Oranges and kumquats are both excellent sources of vitamin C. They also contain compounds called coumarins, which are believed to help thin the blood, thus helping to prevent stroke and heart attacks.

photo, page 165

Each serving provides   **Key nutrients** 430kcals, 15g fat (of which 3g is saturated fat), 30g protein, 46g carbohydrate, 154mg sodium (0.38g salt), 3g fibre

Good source of potassium (903mg)

Pork and pear salad with pecans

This is a simple yet substantial salad with lots of interesting ingredients that you wouldn't ordinarily think of combining. The dressing is delicately flavoured with ginger juice, squeezed from fresh root ginger.

Preparation time **35 minutes**   *Serves 4*

55g (2oz) pecan nuts

900g (2lb) new potatoes, scrubbed

115g (4oz) red radishes, cut into quarters

2 pears

1 Oak Leaf lettuce, separated into leaves

100g (3½oz) watercress, tough stalks discarded

350g (12oz) cooked roast pork loin, fat removed and thinly sliced

For the dressing

2.5cm (1in) piece peeled fresh root ginger

2 tsp coarse mustard

2 tsp white wine vinegar

2 tbsp olive oil

2 tsp hazelnut oil

pepper to taste

1 Heat a frying pan and toast the pecans over moderate heat for 6–7 minutes. Cool, then chop roughly. Set aside.

2 Cook the potatoes in a saucepan of boiling water for about 15 minutes or until tender. Drain. When cool enough to handle, cut into quarters. Place in a mixing bowl.

3 To make the dressing, first put the ginger in a garlic crusher and press to squeeze out the juice (this will have to be done in batches). You need 2 teaspoons of ginger juice. Put the ginger juice, mustard, vinegar, olive and hazelnut oils and pepper to taste in a screw-top jar. Shake well to mix. Pour about one-third of the dressing over the warm potatoes and toss gently to coat. Leave to cool.

4 Meanwhile, in another bowl, toss the red radishes with half of the remaining dressing, to prevent them from browning. Halve the pears lengthways and scoop out the cores, then cut into long wedges. Toss with the radishes.

5 Arrange the lettuce leaves and watercress in a shallow salad bowl. Add the radish mixture to the potatoes and gently mix together. Pile on to the salad leaves, and arrange the pork slices on top.

6 Stir the toasted pecans into the remaining dressing and drizzle over the top of the salad. Serve immediately.

Some more ideas

• Instead of pears, use other fresh fruit, such as 2 peaches or 4 apricots.

Pork and apple salad with hazelnuts Replace the pears with red-skinned apples. Add 2 carrots, cut into matchstick strips. Finish with toasted hazelnuts instead of pecans.

Health points

• Radishes offer useful amounts of fibre and vitamin C and, in common with other members of the cruciferous family, they contain phytochemicals that may help to protect against cancer. Most of the enzymes responsible for the hot taste are found in the skin. If you find the taste over-powering, peeling will help to reduce the heat.

photo, page 165

Each serving provides   Key nutrients 520kcals, 23g fat (of which 4g is saturated fat), 35g protein, 46g carbohydrate, 144mg sodium (0.36g salt), 5g fibre

Good source of potassium (1441mg)

Garden pasta salad

This Italian salad (known in its homeland as insalata alla giardiniera) uses the freshest produce from the vegetable garden to provide it with a wonderful mix of colours, flavours and nutrients. It stores well and is even better the next day.

Preparation time **30 minutes, plus marinating**   Cooking time **25 minutes**   *Serves 6*

350g (12oz) broccoli florets

1 large red pepper, cut into thin strips

1 yellow courgette, thinly sliced

1 small red onion, chopped

280g (10oz) radiatore pasta

175g (6oz) yellow or red baby plum tomatoes, halved

For the dressing

150ml (5fl oz) cider vinegar

4 tbsp extra virgin olive oil

5 tbsp finely chopped parsley

2 tbsp finely chopped fresh dill

pepper to taste

1 Set out large bowl of iced water. Bring a large pot of water to the boil over high heat. Put the broccoli, red pepper, courgette and onion in a large metal sieve. Immerse in the water and blanch for about 2 minutes or just until the colours brighten. Lift out and drain, then plunge into the iced water.

2 Cook the pasta in the boiling water until al dente. Drain and put into a large pasta bowl. Drain the vegetables and add to the pasta together with the tomatoes.

3 Put the vinegar, oil, parsley, dill and pepper to taste in a screw-top jar and shake until combined. Pour over the salad and toss gently to coat. Cover and refrigerate for at least 8 hours, or overnight. Toss again before serving.

Some more ideas

• White wine vinegar or tarragon vinegar can be used instead of cider vinegar.

• Replace the broccoli with asparagus tips.

• For more fibre, use wholemeal radiatore or another pasta shape.

Health points

• This salad gives you four servings of vegetables, getting you most of the way towards the goal of eating at least five servings of fruit and vegetables every day. Add a couple of pieces of fruit as snacks, and you will have had a truly healthy day of eating.

Each serving provides   Key nutrients 270kcals, 9g fat (of which 1.5g is saturated fat), 9g protein, 40g carbohydrate, 15mg sodium (0.03g salt), 4g fibre

Useful source of potassium (540mg)

Roast beef and rice salad

This family-style salad is packed with vitamins, minerals and fibre. It is an excellent way of using up leftover roast beef, and the vegetables can be varied to suit all tastes. It makes a hearty meal in itself.

Preparation time **about 1 hour**   *Serves 4*

450g (1lb) lean roast beef, cut into 1cm (½in) pieces

55g (2oz) rehydrated dry-pack sun-dried tomatoes

4 spring onions, thinly sliced

2 tbsp snipped fresh chives

250g (9oz) basmati rice, rinsed

1 celery stick, thinly sliced

1 carrot, coarsely grated

1 courgette, coarsely grated

85g (3oz) button mushrooms, thinly sliced

4 tbsp chopped parsley

radicchio or other salad leaves *(optional)*

For the dressing

1½ tsp dry mustard

½ tsp caster sugar

2 tbsp cider vinegar

3 tbsp olive oil

pepper to taste

1 First make the dressing. Put the dry mustard and sugar in a large mixing bowl and stir in the vinegar until smooth. Whisk in the oil until thoroughly blended. Season with pepper to taste.

2 Add the beef, sun-dried tomatoes, spring onions and chives to the bowl and stir to coat all the ingredients with the dressing. Cover and refrigerate for at least 30 minutes (or up to 8 hours).

3 Meanwhile, cook the rice in a saucepan of boiling water for 8–10 minutes or until just tender. Drain well and spread out on a tray to cool completely.

4 When the rice is cool, transfer it to a bowl and stir in the celery, carrot, courgette, mushrooms and parsley. Cover and chill until needed.

5 About 10 minutes before serving, remove the marinated beef and the rice salad from the refrigerator. If you like, line four plates with radicchio or other salad leaves. Add the marinated beef mixture to the rice salad and gently stir together until well mixed. Spoon on to the bed of leaves and serve.

Some more ideas

Chicken, peach and rice salad Use cubes of roast chicken instead of beef. Replace the sun-dried tomatoes and spring onions with 2 sliced peaches, and the chives with chopped parsley. In the rice salad, instead of celery, carrot, courgettes and mushrooms, use 200g (7oz) thawed frozen sweetcorn kernels, 2 thinly sliced leeks and 200g (7oz) chopped fennel.

• For extra texture, add some alfalfa sprouts.

Health points

• Beef is now much leaner than it used to be. Cuts of beef, such as topside, can contain less than 3 per cent fat.

• Vinegar has been used in the kitchen, for preserving and cooking, as well as in cleaning and for healing, for more than 10,000 years.

Each serving provides

Key nutrients 590kcals, 22g fat (of which 7g is saturated fat), 43g protein, 54g carbohydrate, 80mg sodium (0.2g salt), 1.5g fibre

Useful source of potassium (688mg)

Roast beef and rice salad *p170*

Tabbouleh with goat's cheese *p172*

Tropical beef and rice salad *p173*

Lemony lentil and vegetable salad *p174*

Tabbouleh with goat's cheese

Tabbouleh is a classic Middle Eastern salad made with bulghur wheat. While the wheat is soaking, you have just enough time to chop the vegetables and herbs, and make the dressing. Serve with pitta bread.

Preparation time **about 30 minutes**   *Serves 4*

280g (10oz) bulghur wheat

1 yellow pepper, deseeded and chopped

20 cherry tomatoes, quartered

1 small red onion, finely chopped

1 small cucumber, deseeded and chopped

1 large carrot, grated

5 tbsp chopped parsley

2 tbsp chopped fresh coriander

2 tbsp chopped fresh mint

1 small fresh red chilli, deseeded and finely chopped *(optional)*

pepper to taste

lettuce leaves

200g (7oz) soft goat's cheese, crumbled

12 radishes, sliced

For the dressing

¼ tsp ground cumin

1 small garlic clove, very finely chopped

1 tbsp lemon juice

3 tbsp olive oil

1 Put the bulghur wheat in a mixing bowl, pour over enough boiling water to cover and stir well. Leave to soak for 15–20 minutes.

2 Meanwhile, make the dressing. Whisk together the cumin, garlic and lemon juice in a small bowl, then whisk in the olive oil.

3 Drain the bulghur wheat in a sieve, pressing out excess water, then return it to the bowl. Add the yellow pepper, tomatoes, onion, cucumber, carrot, parsley, coriander and mint, plus the chilli, if using. Pour the dressing over the top and season with pepper to taste. Fold gently to mix well.

4 Arrange lettuce leaves on four plates or a serving platter. Pile the bulghur salad on the leaves and sprinkle the goat's cheese over the top. Garnish with the radishes.

Some more ideas

Spicy tabbouleh with chicken Replace the goat's cheese with 2 cooked skinless, boneless chicken breasts, about 280g (10oz) in total, cut into cubes. Mix the soaked bulghur wheat with the chicken, pepper, onion, carrot and parsley (omit the other vegetables and herbs). For the dressing, gently warm 3 tbsp olive oil in a small frying pan with 1 finely chopped garlic clove. Add ½–1 tsp each of ground cumin, ground coriander, dry mustard and curry powder, and cook for 1 minute. Stir in 2 tbsp lemon juice. Season to taste. Pour the dressing over the salad and stir gently to combine. Garnish with sliced cucumber rounds. Serves 6.

Health points

• Goat's cheese is a tasty source of protein and calcium and lower in fat than cheeses such as Cheddar and Parmesan.

photo, page 171

Each serving provides   **Key nutrients** 530kcals, 23g fat (of which 10g is saturated fat), 19g protein, 62g carbohydrate, 322mg sodium (0.8g salt), 3g fibre

Useful source of potassium (697mg)

Tropical beef and rice salad

Ginger, honey, orange and chilli add exciting flavours to this colourful salad. It is perfect for a relaxed lunch, as it can be mostly prepared ahead. To finish, add the papaya and salad leaves, and sprinkle with toasted sesame seeds.

Preparation and cooking time **about 45 minutes**   *Serves 4*

350g (12oz) fillet steak, cut into 2cm (¾in) slices

280g (10oz) mixed basmati and wild rice

1 papaya, peeled and sliced

6 spring onions, sliced

55g (2oz) mixed salad leaves

1 tbsp sesame seeds, toasted

For the marinade

3 tbsp sherry vinegar

1 large garlic clove, crushed

2 tsp sunflower oil

1 tsp finely chopped fresh root ginger

grated zest of 1 orange

1 tsp light brown sugar

pepper to taste

For the dressing

2 tbsp sunflower oil

2 tbsp orange juice

2 tsp red wine vinegar

1 tsp clear honey

1 tsp finely chopped fresh root ginger

1 large fresh red chilli, deseeded and finely chopped

1 Put all the ingredients for the marinade in a large shallow dish. Add pepper to taste and mix well. Place the steak in the marinade, then cover and chill for 30 minutes, turning the slices over after 15 minutes so that both sides absorb the flavours.

2 Meanwhile, put the rice in a pan, add 750ml (1¼ pints) water and bring to the boil. Cover and simmer very gently for about 20 minutes or until the rice is tender and has absorbed all the water. Remove from the heat.

3 While the rice is cooking, put all the ingredients for the dressing in a large salad bowl and whisk to combine. Season to taste. When the rice is cooked, add it to the bowl and stir gently to mix with the dressing.

4 Preheat the grill to medium. Remove the steak slices from the marinade and place on the rack of the grill pan. Grill for 5–6 minutes or until cooked to your taste, turning over halfway through the cooking and brushing with any remaining marinade. Transfer the steak to a board and cut the slices across the grain into narrow strips. Add to the rice. (Cool and chill, if you like.)

5 Just before serving, add the papaya, spring onions and salad leaves, and toss gently together. Sprinkle with the sesame seeds and serve.

Some more ideas

• Substitute skinless, boneless chicken breasts for the steak. Marinate and grill the chicken for 5–6 minutes on each side.

Health points

• Not long ago, tropical fruits like papaya were considered exotic and strange. But with widespread distribution, people are discovering how delicious and versatile they are. Papaya is extremely healthy too, with lots of nutrients good for blood pressure, such as vitamin C, potassium, fibre, folate and carotenoids.

• Sesame seeds can provide useful amounts of calcium.

photo, page 171

Each serving provides Key nutrients 490kcals, 15g fat (of which 4g is saturated fat), 25g protein, 63g carbohydrate, 30mg sodium (0.07g salt), 1.5g fibre

Useful source of potassium (471mg)

Lemony lentil and vegetable salad

This is a deliciously healthy and filling Middle Eastern salad. The lentils are cooked with lemon and spices, then dressed while warm. Vegetables add colour, and dried apricots, goat's cheese and sunflower seeds complete the feast.

Preparation and cooking time **about 50 minutes**   *Serves 4*

250g (9oz) green lentils, rinsed

1 garlic clove, peeled

good pinch of ground cumin

1 slice of lemon

1 small red onion, finely chopped

85g (3oz) ready-to-eat dried apricots, roughly chopped

3 small peppers (1 red, 1 green and 1 yellow), deseeded and cut into 2cm (¾in) squares

115g (4oz) broccoli, broken into small florets

25g (1oz) goat's cheese

2 tbsp toasted sunflower seeds

For the dressing

juice of 1 lemon

3 tbsp olive oil

2 tbsp finely chopped fresh coriander

pepper to taste

1 Put the lentils in a large saucepan, cover with water and bring to the boil, skimming off any scum. Add the garlic, cumin and lemon slice, then reduce the heat and simmer for about 30 minutes or until the lentils are tender.

2 Meanwhile, to make the dressing, put the lemon juice, oil, coriander and pepper to taste into a large salad bowl, and whisk together.

3 Drain the lentils, discarding the lemon and garlic, and add them to the salad bowl. Toss gently to mix with the dressing.

4 Add the onion, apricots, peppers and broccoli florets, and mix gently. Crumble the cheese over the top, scatter over the sunflower seeds and serve immediately.

Some more ideas

• Instead of goat's cheese, top the salad with slices of hard-boiled eggs.

Health points

• Lentils are a good source of soluble fibre, which can help to reduce blood cholesterol levels. Lentils also offer protein and B vitamins.

• The sunflower was first brought to Europe around 1510 as a decorative plant, but it wasn't until the 18th century that sunflowers began to be grown as a crop for the production of sunflower oil. Sunflower seeds are rich in healthy polyunsaturated fats and they are a good source of the antioxidant vitamin E, which helps to protect cell membranes from damage by free radicals and vitamin B_1. They also provide useful amounts of the minerals zinc, iron, copper, phosphorus, selenium and magnesium.

photo, page 171

Each serving provides   Key nutrients 427kcals, 17g fat (of which 4g is saturated fat), 23g protein, 49g carbohydrate, 50mg sodium (0.1g salt), 10g fibre

Good source of potassium (1345mg)

Turkey salad with red cabbage

This is a lovely, crunchy salad for winter, full of contrasting tastes and tossed with an unusual dressing made from cranberry sauce and walnut oil. Red cabbage tends to stain the other ingredients, so serve the salad as soon as it's made.

Preparation time **about 20 minutes**   *Serves 4*

55g (2oz) pecan nuts, coarsely chopped

½ tsp caraway seeds

350g (12oz) cold roast turkey meat, without skin, diced

200g (7oz) red cabbage, finely shredded

3 celery sticks, sliced

2 carrots, grated

25g (1oz) sultanas or raisins

For the dressing

2 tbsp cranberry sauce

1 tbsp olive oil

1 tbsp walnut oil

2 tbsp red wine vinegar

pepper to taste

1 Put all the ingredients for the dressing into a salad bowl and whisk together until well blended and starting to emulsify.

2 Place the pecans and caraway seeds in a small frying pan and toast over a low heat, stirring occasionally, for 3–5 minutes or until the pecans are golden and you can smell the nutty fragrance. Put into a bowl and leave to cool slightly.

3 Add the turkey, red cabbage, celery, carrots and sultanas to the bowl with the dressing. Add the toasted pecans and caraway seeds, and mix until all the ingredients are well coated with the dressing. Serve immediately.

Some more ideas

Summer turkey salad Make the dressing with 3 tbsp olive oil, 2 tsp Dijon mustard, 1 tbsp clear honey, 2 tbsp lemon juice, 2 tsp finely grated fresh root ginger and seasoning to taste. Stir the diced turkey into the dressing. Steam 225g (8oz) asparagus, cut into bite-size pieces, 225g (8oz) small sugarsnap peas and 225g (8oz) sliced new potatoes. Toss the vegetables with the turkey and dressing while still hot. Fold in 2 tbsp snipped fresh chives. Serve warm or at room temperature.

• Use white cabbage instead of red, and substitute apples for the carrots and sultanas.

Health points

• Cranberries contain a compound that helps to prevent *E. coli* bacteria from causing urinary tract infections.

• Red cabbage provides the B vitamin folate, vitamin C and potassium, making it a potent food for healthier blood pressure.

Each serving provides **Key nutrients** 350kcals, 19g fat (of which 3g is saturated fat), 30g protein, 14g carbohydrate, 110mg sodium (0.27g salt), 3.5g fibre

Useful source of potassium (729mg)

Fresh artichoke and crab salad

This salad is a real treat when globe artichokes are in season. The large outer leaves are removed and the succulent, meaty bottom part, or heart, is cooked, then served with fresh crabmeat in a lemony dressing.

Preparation time **1½ hours, plus cooling**   *Serves 4*

4 large globe artichokes

2 lemons, halved

For the dressing

1 tbsp lemon juice

3 tbsp olive oil

pepper to taste

1 tbsp finely chopped fresh chervil or parsley

1 tbsp finely chopped fresh chives

For the crab salad

2 tbsp plain low-fat yoghurt

2 tbsp reduced-fat mayonnaise

½ tsp grated lemon zest

1 tsp lemon juice

1½ tbsp chopped fresh chives

450g (1lb) fresh crabmeat, preferably white

Little Gem lettuce leaves to serve

1 To prepare each artichoke, cut off the top two-thirds and trim the stalk level with the base. Rub the cut surfaces with lemon juice as you work. Pull off the large outer leaves, starting from the bottom, to expose the soft, pale inner leaves. Holding the artichoke in one hand, trim the top edge to form a rounded shape, and trim around the sides and base to remove all the green parts and expose the pale yellow flesh. Drop the artichoke into a bowl of water with the juice of half a lemon added to it. Prepare the remaining artichokes in the same way.

2 Put the artichokes in a saucepan large enough to hold them in a single layer, cover with boiling water and add the juice of half a lemon. Cover the pan and simmer for about 40 minutes or until a leaf can be pulled away easily and the hearts are tender. Remove from the pan and leave to drain upside down until cool.

3 To make the dressing, put the lemon juice in a bowl, whisk in the olive oil and season with pepper to taste. Stir in the chervil or parsley and chives.

4 Quarter the artichokes and use a teaspoon to scoop out the fuzzy choke just underneath the centre leaves. Add the artichoke pieces to the dressing and turn to coat.

5 For the crab salad, put the yoghurt, mayonnaise, lemon zest and juice, and chives in a mixing bowl and stir to combine. Add the crab and mix in gently. Taste and add more lemon juice if you wish.

6 Arrange 2–3 lettuce leaves on each of four plates to form a small bed or cup and spoon on the crab salad. Add the artichoke quarters with their dressing, and serve at once.

Some more ideas

Artichoke, mushroom and chicken salad Replace the crabmeat with 225g (8oz) sliced button mushrooms and 280g (10oz) cooked skinless chicken breast, cut into thin slivers. Use 1 tsp grated lemon zest and 2 tsp Dijon mustard in the dressing. Cut the artichokes into eighths, and instead of tossing them in the dressing, fold them into the mushroom and chicken salad. Pile on to lettuce leaves and garnish with a good sprinkling of chopped fresh chives and chervil or parsley.

Health points

• Crab, like other shellfish, is a good source of low-fat protein. It also provides useful amounts of vitamin B_2, potassium and zinc.

• Chives are a member of the same family as onions and garlic, and share the same antibiotic healing powers.

• Globe artichokes are rich in cynarin, a phytochemical that is believed to help reduce high blood cholesterol levels.

Each serving provides

Key nutrients 260kcals, 16g fat (of which 2g is saturated fat), 25g protein, 4g carbohydrate, 575mg sodium (1.4g salt), 1g fibre

Useful source of potassium (665mg)

Sweet-and-sour duck salad *p178*

Fresh artichoke and crab salad *p176*

Steakhouse salad *p179*

Prawns with dill dressing *p181*

Sweet-and-sour duck salad

With ripe nectarines, red grapes, peppery lettuces and slices of tender grilled duck, this is a particularly pretty salad. The unusual dressing complements and brings together all the ingredients.

Preparation time **about 1 hour, plus cooling**   *Serves 4*

250g (9oz) mixed basmati and wild rice

450g (1lb) skinless, boneless duck breasts

2 tsp olive oil

85g (3oz) watercress, tough stalks discarded

140g (5oz) seedless green grapes, halved

4 spring onions, thinly sliced

3 celery sticks, thinly sliced

4 nectarines

8 radicchio leaves or other red salad leaves

3 tbsp toasted pumpkin seeds

For the dressing

1 tsp grated fresh root ginger

1 small garlic clove, very finely chopped

1 tbsp apricot jam

2 tsp raspberry vinegar or white wine vinegar

2 tbsp hazelnut oil

pepper to taste

1 Cook the rice in a saucepan of boiling water for about 20 minutes or until tender. Drain, then transfer to a bowl and allow to cool.

2 Heat a ridged grill pan. Meanwhile, remove all excess fat from the duck breasts, and brush them on both sides with the olive oil. Place on the grill pan and cook over moderately high heat for 3 minutes on each side (the meat will be rare, so cook longer if you prefer it well done). Allow the duck breasts to cool.

3 To make the dressing, put the ginger, garlic, apricot jam, vinegar and hazelnut oil in a small bowl and stir to combine. Season with pepper to taste.

4 Chop half the watercress and add to the rice together with the grapes, spring onions and celery. Drizzle over half the dressing and mix gently.

5 Cut the duck breasts into thin slices. Thinly slice the nectarines. Arrange the radicchio and reserved watercress leaves on four plates and divide the rice salad among them. Arrange the duck and nectarine slices on top, drizzle over the remaining dressing and sprinkle with the pumpkin seeds.

Some more ideas

Grilled duck, sweet potato and apple salad Cook 675g (1½lb) peeled and cubed sweet potatoes in enough boiling water to cover for 6–8 minutes or until tender. Drain well and cool slightly. For the dressing, stir 2½ tbsp each reduced-fat mayonnaise and plain low-fat yoghurt with 1 tbsp Dijon mustard in a small bowl. Core and chop 1 large dessert apple and toss with 2 tbsp lemon juice in a large mixing bowl. Add 3 celery sticks and 4 spring onions, all thinly sliced, and stir in the dressing. Fold in the sweet potatoes and the hot sliced duck. Serve warm, on a bed of salad leaves.

• Use 4 peaches instead of the nectarines.

Health points

• Nectarines are high in vitamin C, fibre and beta-carotene (the darker the colour of the flesh, the higher the carotenoid content). They also offer B-complex vitamins.

photo, page 177

Each serving provides Key nutrients 610kcals, 20g fat (of which 4g is saturated fat), 32g protein, 74g carbohydrate, 155mg sodium (0.38g salt), 3g fibre

Good source of potassium (907mg)

Steakhouse salad

How can steak be part of a smart diet? Very easily! Grill the finest and leanest of steaks – fillet – and arrange it atop fresh greens and plenty of vegetables to make a delicious 'composed' salad.

Preparation time **20 minutes**   Cooking time **16 minutes**   *Serves 4*

4 medium red peppers

280g (10oz) well-trimmed fillet steak

1 garlic clove

450g (1lb) green beans

pepper to taste

For the dressing

3 tbsp balsamic vinegar

2 tsp extra virgin olive oil

1 garlic clove

2 tbsp finely chopped shallot

To serve

115g (4oz) mixed baby salad leaves

6 medium tomatoes, cut into 5mm (¼in) wedges

1 Preheat the grill. Put the red peppers on the grill rack and grill for about 10 minutes or until the skins are blistered and blackened, turning frequently. Put them in a plastic bag, seal tightly and steam for 10 minutes. Then peel away the blackened skins from the peppers, deseed and cut into chunks.

2 Lay the steaks flat on a cutting board and slit horizontally three-quarters of the way through. Open like a book and press flat. Sprinkle with pepper. Cut 1 garlic clove in half and rub the cut sides all over the steak. Grill the steak for about 3 minutes on each side for medium, or until done to your taste. Thinly slice the beef.

3 Cook the beans in boiling water for about 5 minutes or until just tender. Drain and rinse with cold water.

4 Finely chop the remaining garlic clove. Whisk together the vinegar, oil, garlic, shallot and pepper to taste in a small bowl. Divide the salad leaves among plates and arrange the steak, red peppers, beans and tomatoes on top. Drizzle over the dressing.

Some more ideas

• Use other lean steaks such as sirloin or rump, well-trimmed, in place of fillet.

• Use yellow or orange peppers instead of red ones.

• Make a herb dressing. To the vinegar and oil mixture, add 2 tsp finely chopped fresh thyme and basil.

Health points

• Choosing the right cuts and controlling your portion sizes are the secrets to making beef a part of a healthy diet. Beef can range widely in its fat content – 85g (3oz) of minced beef, for example, has 14g of fat, while the same amount of topside has 4g of fat. Beef is rich in potassium, zinc and vitamin B$_{12}$, as well as protein.

photo, page 171

Each serving provides **Key nutrients** 211kcals, 6g fat (of which 2g is saturated fat), 20g protein, 19g carbohydrate, 63mg sodium (0.15g salt), 7g fibre

Good source of potassium (1221mg)

Peachy cottage cheese salad

This fresh-tasting salad combines luscious, sweet peaches and crisp green vegetables with a generous portion of creamy cottage cheese. It is quick and easy to put together, taking only a little longer to make than a sandwich.

Preparation time **about 30 minutes**   *Serves 4*

250g (8½oz) frozen broad beans

175g (6oz) mange-tout, halved

115g (4oz) rocket

40g (1½oz) lamb's lettuce

4 ripe peaches, stoned and thinly sliced

450g (1lb) low-fat cottage cheese

4 tbsp toasted flaked almonds

cayenne pepper

sprigs of fresh dill to garnish

For the dressing

2 tbsp olive oil

grated zest and juice of 1 lemon

1 tsp Dijon mustard

2 tsp clear honey

2 tbsp chopped fresh dill

black pepper to taste

1 Plunge the broad beans into a saucepan of boiling water and cook for 4 minutes. Add the mange-tout and cook for a further minute. Drain and refresh under cold water.

2 To make the dressing, put the oil, lemon zest and juice, mustard, honey, chopped dill and black pepper in a mixing bowl. Whisk well.

3 Add the beans, peas, rocket and lamb's lettuce to the dressing and toss to coat well.

4 Divide the dressed vegetables among four serving plates. Scatter over the peach slices and top with the cottage cheese. Sprinkle with the flaked almonds and a little cayenne pepper. Garnish with dill sprigs and serve.

Some more ideas

• Top this salad with nectarines or fresh apricots in place of peaches.

• Use ricotta instead of cottage cheese.

• Serve with warmed sunflower seed, walnut or pumpkin bread for a well-balanced lunch.

Health points

• In 100g (3½oz) of low-fat cottage cheese there are 78kcals and 1.4g of fat, compared to 98kcals and 3.9g of fat in the same weight of regular cottage cheese. All cottage cheese is a great source of B vitamins.

• Fresh peaches are a good source of vitamin C and provide some beta-carotene.

Each serving provides

Key nutrients 327kcals, 17g fat (of which 3g is saturated fat), 25g protein, 21g carbohydrate, 358mg sodium (0.9g salt), 8g fibre

Useful source of potassium (678mg)

Prawns with dill dressing

In this good-looking salad, tiger prawns are served piled on a mixture of aromatic basmati and wild rice, crunchy broccoli florets, mangetout and yellow pepper tossed in a fresh dill and lime juice dressing.

Preparation time **40 minutes, plus cooling**   *Serves 4*

250g (9oz) mixed basmati and wild rice, rinsed

thinly pared zest and juice of 1 lime

2 tbsp sunflower oil

2 tsp toasted sesame oil

1 tbsp low-sodium soy sauce

pepper to taste

225g (8oz) broccoli, broken into small florets

225g (8oz) mangetout, halved lengthways

450g (1lb) peeled raw tiger prawns, tails left on

1 small yellow pepper, deseeded and thinly sliced

3 spring onions, sliced

4 tbsp coarsely chopped fresh dill

1 Cook the rice with the lime zest in a saucepan of boiling water for about 20 minutes or until tender. Drain the rice and put it into a wide salad bowl. Discard the lime zest.

2 Whisk together 1 tablespoon of the lime juice, 1 tablespoon of the sunflower oil, the sesame oil, soy sauce and pepper to taste in a small bowl. Drizzle this dressing over the rice and stir to mix. Leave to cool.

3 Meanwhile, put the broccoli in a steamer basket set over a pan of boiling water and steam for 4 minutes. Add the mangetout and steam for a further 2 minutes or until the vegetables are just tender. Drain the vegetables in a colander and refresh under cold running water.

4 Heat the remaining sunflower oil in a large frying pan. Add the prawns and cook over a high heat for 1–2 minutes on each side or until pink and cooked through. Remove from the heat and sprinkle with the remaining lime juice.

5 Add the yellow pepper, spring onions and 3 tablespoons of the dill to the rice and stir gently to mix. Pile the prawns on top and scatter over the remaining dill to garnish.

Some more ideas

• The salad can be made in advance and refrigerated until needed. Allow it to stand at room temperature for about 30 minutes before serving.

• For a high-fibre salad, use brown long-grain rice instead of basmati and wild rice.

• Replace the broccoli and mangetout with asparagus tips and sliced courgettes.

• To save time, use cooked peeled prawns and simply toss them in the lime juice.

• Instead of prawns, use 16 scallops, searing them in the hot oil for about 1 minute on each side or until golden brown.

Health points

• Prawns are low in fat and calories. They contain a useful amount of vitamin B_{12}, which is essential for the formation of red blood cells and maintaining a healthy nervous system. They also provide good amounts of copper, phosphorus, iodine and the antioxidant selenium.

photo, page 177

Each serving provides   Key nutrients 447kcals, 9g fat (of which 1.5g is saturated fat), 35g protein, 56g carbohydrate, 500mg sodium (1.25g salt), 3g fibre

Useful source of potassium (678mg)

Sweetcorn and whole grain salad

Grains of wholewheat have a distinctive sweet, nutty flavour and slightly chewy texture. Here they are mixed with grilled fresh sweetcorn, toasted walnuts and crisp vegetables in a fragrant orange dressing to make a nutritious salad.

Preparation and cooking time **35 minutes, plus cooling**   *Serves 4*

300g (10½oz) pre-cooked wholewheat grains

900ml (1½ pints) boiling water

1 bay leaf

2 corn on the cob, peeled and silk removed

½ tbsp sunflower oil

70g (2½oz) walnuts, coarsely chopped

1 red pepper, deseeded and diced

115g (4oz) button mushrooms, sliced

½ cucumber, cut into small chunks

1 tbsp chopped fresh mint

1 egg, hard-boiled and sliced

sprigs of fresh mint to garnish

For the dressing

1 tsp Dijon mustard

½ tsp finely grated orange zest

1 tbsp orange juice

1 tbsp sunflower oil

1 tbsp walnut oil

pepper to taste

1 Put the wholewheat grains in a medium saucepan and add the boiling water and the bay leaf. Simmer for 15–20 minutes or until the grain is tender and all the liquid has been absorbed. Discard the bay leaf and turn the grains into a mixing bowl.

2 Preheat the grill to medium-high. Brush the corn cobs all over with the sunflower oil, then put them on the rack of the grill pan. Grill, turning frequently, for 10 minutes or until tender and lightly charred in places. Set aside to cool slightly.

3 Meanwhile, spread out the walnuts in a baking sheet. Put them under the grill and toast lightly for 2–3 minutes, turning them frequently and watching them all the time, as they burn easily. Set aside.

4 When the sweetcorn is cool enough to handle, cut the kernels off the cobs with a sharp knife. Add them to the wholewheat grains.

5 To make the dressing, whisk together the mustard, orange zest and juice, and sunflower and walnut oils. Season with pepper to taste. Drizzle the dressing over the warm grains mixture and toss well. Leave to cool completely.

6 Add the red pepper, mushrooms, cucumber, mint and toasted walnuts to the grains mixture and toss gently. Serve at room temperature, garnished with slices of hard-boiled egg and sprigs of mint.

Some more ideas

Barley and egg salad Heat 2 tsp sunflower oil in a large saucepan, add 300g (10½oz) pearl barley and 1 crushed garlic clove, and cook gently for about 1 minute. Add a bay leaf and pour in 1.2 litres (2 pints) boiling low-sodium vegetable stock. Bring to the boil, then reduce the heat and simmer for 35–40 minutes or until the barley is tender. Drain off any excess stock, then turn the barley into a bowl and leave to cool. Mix in 175g (6oz) each broccoli florets and cauliflower florets, 1 deseeded and sliced yellow pepper and a bunch of spring onions, sliced. For the dressing, whisk together 2 tbsp sunflower oil, 1 tsp toasted sesame oil, 2 tsp sherry vinegar, 2 tsp low-sodium soy sauce and pepper to taste. Drizzle over the salad. Add 2 tbsp toasted sunflower seeds and 1 tbsp toasted sesame seeds and toss together. Gently mix in 4 hard-boiled eggs, cut into wedges, just before serving at room temperature.

Each serving provides   Key nutrients 400kcals, 23g fat (of which 6g is saturated fat), 11g protein, 33g carbohydrate, 40mg sodium (0.1g salt), 3g fibre

Good source of potassium (1061mg)

Avocado and prawn cups p184

Sweetcorn and whole grain salad p182

Warm kasha and seafood salad p188

Pasta salad with cucumber salsa p187

Avocado and prawn cups

Here, lettuce-lined salad bowls are filled with a popular mix of ingredients, then topped with creamy yoghurt for a real hot and cold taste explosion. Serve for lunch with wholemeal bread.

Preparation time **25 minutes, plus cooling**   *Serves 4*

450g (1lb) new potatoes, scrubbed and diced

2 tbsp sunflower oil

1 small red onion, thinly sliced

1 garlic clove, crushed

1 fresh mild red chilli, deseeded and finely chopped

1 tsp coriander seeds, roughly crushed

1 tsp cumin seeds, roughly crushed

1 large avocado

450g (1lb) peeled cooked prawns, thawed if frozen

juice of 2 limes

pepper to taste

6 tbsp plain low-fat bio yoghurt

3 tbsp chopped fresh coriander

round lettuce leaves

1 Cook the potatoes in a saucepan of boiling water for 8 minutes or until just tender. Drain and refresh under cold running water. Dry in a clean tea towel.

2 Heat the oil in a large frying pan, add the onion and fry for 5 minutes or until softened and lightly browned. Add the garlic, chilli, and crushed coriander and cumin seeds, and cook for 1 more minute, stirring. Stir in the potatoes and cook over a high heat for 3 minutes. Remove from the heat and leave to cool.

3 Peel the avocado, remove the stone and cut the flesh into cubes. Add to the potato mixture together with the prawns and lime juice. Season with pepper to taste and toss gently.

4 Mix together the yoghurt and chopped coriander. Arrange 2 lettuce leaves in each of four bowls. Spoon the salad into them and top with the coriander yoghurt.

Some more ideas

Avocado, potato and tofu salad Replace the prawns with 225g (8oz) plain tofu, drained and cubed. Add the tofu in step 2 with the garlic and spices.

• Use just 280g (10oz) of potatoes, and spoon the salad into 4 warmed round Arab flat breads or chapattis. Top each with shredded lettuce and a spoonful of the yoghurt and coriander mixture.

Health points

• Substances in avocados stimulate the production of collagen, which is why they have a reputation for being good for the skin.

• Coriander and cumin seeds are particularly healthy spices. Both appear to have anti-bacterial properties. Coriander also contains limonene, a flavonoid thought to help fight cancer. Cumin is being studied for potential antioxidant and anti-cancer effects.

photo, page 183

Each serving provides   Key nutrients 350kcals, 16g fat (of which 3g is saturated fat), 24g protein, 23g carbohydrate, 244mg sodium (0.6g salt), 3g fibre

Good source of potassium (1061mg)

Creamy turkey salad with grapes and pecans

With its wonderfully contrasting tastes and textures, this salad makes a satisfying main course that is luxurious without containing a lot of saturated fat. It is the perfect recipe for roast turkey leftovers.

Preparation time **25 minutes, plus cooling**   *Serves 4*

225g (8oz) fusilli pasta

150g (5½oz) plain low-fat yoghurt

3 tbsp reduced-fat mayonnaise

1 tsp white wine vinegar

2 tsp Dijon mustard

3 tbsp chopped fresh tarragon

250g (9oz) skinless, boneless roast turkey, cubed

2 celery sticks, cut into thin strips

115g (4oz) seedless black grapes, or a mixture of black and green grapes, halved

55g (2oz) pecan nuts, toasted and coarsely chopped

pepper to taste

sprigs of fresh tarragon to garnish

1 Cook the pasta in boiling water according to the packet instructions. Drain and leave to cool.

2 Meanwhile, mix the yoghurt with the mayonnaise, white wine vinegar, mustard and tarragon in a large bowl. Stir until all the ingredients are combined and the dressing is smooth.

3 Add the pasta, turkey, celery, grapes, toasted pecans and pepper to taste. Toss until the ingredients are all evenly coated with the dressing.

4 Transfer to a serving dish or plates and garnish with sprigs of tarragon.

Some more ideas

• For a spicy Indian flavour, stir 2 tbsp curry paste (or to taste) with the yoghurt. Garnish with chopped fresh coriander instead of the tarragon.

• Replace the pecan nuts with roasted unsalted cashews, and the grapes with 2 cored and chopped dessert apples. Add 55g (2oz) sultanas.

• Try 225g (8oz) firm tofu instead of the turkey, to make a vegetarian salad.

Health points

• Grapes are high in sugar and relatively low in vitamins when compared with other fruits. However, they contain unusually large amounts of bioflavonoids, the antioxidants that help to protect against the damaging effects of free radicals linked with cancer and heart disease. They also have ample amounts of potassium, an important mineral for healthy blood pressure.

• Naturopaths consider grapes to have healing powers.

Each serving provides   Key nutrients 453kcals, 16g fat (of which 2g is saturated fat), 28g protein, 57g carbohydrate, 262mg sodium (0.66g salt), 3g fibre

Useful source of potassium (602mg)

Apple and date salad

A crunchy salad of fruit, vegetables and nuts in a creamy yoghurt-based dressing, this is attractively presented on chicory leaves. The bitterness of the chicory provides a good contrast to the sweet fruit.

Preparation time **15 minutes**   *Serves 4*

55g (2oz) hazelnuts, chopped

2 green dessert apples, cored and roughly chopped

175g (6oz) fresh dates, stoned and roughly chopped

1 small red pepper, deseeded and chopped

2 celery sticks, sliced

115g (4oz) seedless green grapes, halved

2 heads red or white chicory

2 tbsp chopped parsley (optional)

For the dressing

150g (5½oz) plain low-fat yoghurt

4 tbsp reduced-fat mayonnaise

1 tbsp lemon juice

1 tsp caster sugar

pepper to taste

1 Put the hazelnuts into a small frying pan and toast over moderate heat, stirring, for about 3 minutes or until you can smell the nutty fragrance. Turn the nuts into a bowl and set aside.

2 To make the dressing, put the yoghurt, mayonnaise, lemon juice and sugar into a large bowl with pepper to taste, and mix well.

3 Add the apples to the dressing and stir until the pieces are well coated. Add the dates, red pepper, celery and grapes, and stir to mix.

4 Separate the heads of chicory into leaves, trimming off the hard bases. Slice the bottom half of the leaves and add to the salad. Pile the salad on a large plate or in a shallow serving dish and arrange the tops of the chicory leaves around the edge. Sprinkle over the toasted nuts and parsley, if using.

Some more ideas

• Use 85g (3oz) sultanas in place of the dates.

• You could dress the salad with a vinaigrette instead of the mayonnaise and yoghurt mixture. Mix together 3 tbsp olive oil, 1 tbsp red wine vinegar or lemon juice, ¼ tsp Dijon mustard, ¼ tsp caster sugar, and salt and pepper to taste.

Health points

• This recipe provides plenty of fibre from apples with their skins, celery, chicory and, of course, dates.

• Radicchio, a member of the chicory family, has deep red-and-white, tightly packed leaves. The red pigment means this vegetable is high in beta-carotene.

Each serving provides

Key nutrients 265kcals, 14g fat (of which 2g is saturated fat), 5g protein, 32g carbohydrate, 188mg sodium (0.47g salt), 4g fibre

Useful source of potassium (651mg)

Pasta salad with cucumber salsa

Snail-shaped pasta traps a herby yoghurt and tomato dressing so that each piece is full of flavour. A refreshing vegetable and fruit salsa brings extra nutritional value as well as exciting taste and texture contrast.

Preparation time **40–50 minutes, plus cooling and 1 hour chilling**   *Serves 4*

225g (8oz) lumache (pasta snails) or other hollow shapes

4 tbsp chopped parsley

4 tbsp chopped fresh mint

4 tbsp snipped fresh chives

2 tbsp fresh tarragon leaves

4 tomatoes, skinned, deseeded and chopped

pepper to taste

200g (7oz) plain low-fat yoghurt

1 avocado

sprigs of fresh mint to garnish

For the salsa

4 celery sticks finely diced

1 green pepper, deseeded and finely diced

½ cucumber, diced

4 spring onions, finely chopped

grated zest of 1 lime *(optional)*

50g (1¾oz) watercress, coarsely chopped

1 tsp olive oil

1 crisp dessert apple, such as Braeburn or Jonagold

1 Cook the pasta in boiling water according to the packet instructions. Meanwhile, mix the parsley, mint, chives and tarragon with the tomatoes in a large bowl (the bowl should be large enough to take the cooked pasta too). Add a little seasoning, then stir in the yoghurt.

2 Drain the cooked pasta thoroughly, shaking the shapes in a colander to make sure that there is no cooking water trapped in them. Add the hot pasta to the yoghurt dressing and use a large spoon to turn them until they are thoroughly coated. Cover and set aside to cool until just warm. (Or leave to cool completely, then chill for 1 hour.)

3 Meanwhile, mix together the celery, green pepper, cucumber and spring onions. Stir in the lime zest, if using, and the watercress. Cover and set aside.

4 Shortly before serving, stir the oil into the cucumber mixture with pepper to taste. Quarter, core and finely dice the apple, leaving its peel on. Add to the cucumber salsa and stir well.

5 Halve the avocado and remove the stone, then cut it lengthways into quarters and peel off the skin. Dice the flesh and fold it into the pasta salad.

6 Serve the cucumber salsa as an accompaniment to the pasta so that it can be added to taste. (The hot pasta absorbs its yoghurt dressing, becoming quite dry as it cools, so the cucumber salsa acts as a second dressing.) Garnish the pasta with sprigs of mint before serving.

Some more ideas

• Use wholemeal pasta for a dish that is higher in fibre.

• Add a finely chopped garlic clove to the yoghurt dressing.

• Make the yoghurt dressing green and the salsa red: omit the tomatoes from the yoghurt dressing and instead add them to the salsa. Use red pepper instead of green, and a red-skinned apple. Season the salsa with a little paprika to enhance the colour.

Health points

• Vitamin C in vegetables and fruit is easily destroyed during cooking, so eating them raw ensures they provide their maximum vitamin content.

• With roughly a dozen fresh fruits, vegetables and herbs in this recipe, you'll be certain to get a wonderful cross-section of vitamins, minerals and phytochemicals.

photo, page 183

Each serving provides   **Key nutrients** 355 kcals, 10g fat (of which 2g is saturated fat), 13g protein, 56g carbohydrate, 91mg sodium (0.2g salt), 6.4g fibre

Good source of potassium (1042mg)

Warm kasha and seafood salad

Kasha, or toasted buckwheat grains, makes a pleasant change from rice and pasta. Add seafood and raw vegetables and you have an unusual – and unusually good-tasting – main-dish salad.

Preparation and cooking time **1½ hours**   *Serves 4*

250g (9oz) kasha (toasted buckwheat)

600ml (1 pint) low-sodium chicken or vegetable stock

2 tsp sunflower oil

1 packet (about 400g) frozen mixed seafood, thawed

1 cucumber, diced

225g (8oz) sugarsnap peas, sliced

1 bulb fennel, halved and thinly sliced

115g (8oz) radishes, thinly sliced

For the dressing

1 tbsp olive oil

1 tbsp white wine vinegar

1 tsp Dijon mustard

2 tbsp chopped fresh mixed herbs

pepper to taste

1 Put the kasha in a nonstick saucepan, pour over the stock and bring to the boil. Cover and simmer for 5 minutes or until the kasha has absorbed all the stock.

2 Stir in half the oil, cover and cook for 10 minutes. Then remove the lid and fork up the kasha, tossing and turning to separate the grains. Cook over a very low heat, uncovered, for a further 1 hour, tossing the kasha with a fork every 10 minutes to separate the grains.

3 Meanwhile, make the dressing. Put all the ingredients in a bowl and whisk together until thoroughly mixed.

4 Heat the remaining 1 teaspoon of oil in a wok or large frying pan. Add the seafood and stir-fry over a moderate heat for 2–3 minutes or until hot. Add the hot seafood to the kasha together with the cucumber, sugarsnap peas, fennel and radishes. Drizzle over the dressing and toss gently to mix.

Some more ideas

• Use green beans in place of sugarsnap peas.

• Instead of mixed seafood, use 450g (1lb) skinless, boneless chicken or turkey breast, or lean beef or lamb steak, cut into thin strips. Stir-fry until cooked and lightly browned, then toss with the dressed kasha and vegetables.

Health points

• Sugarsnap peas are a good source of vitamin C, and they contain more dietary fibre than ordinary peas. This is because the edible pod contributes to the fibre content.

• Buckwheat is a wonderfully healthy grain, containing lots of plant protein and significant amounts of the important amino acid lysine. Buckwheat is also an excellent source of iron and magnesium.

photo, page 183

Each serving provides Key nutrients 390 kcals, 7g fat (of which 1g is saturated fat), 27g protein, 59g carbohydrate, 482mg sodium (1.2g salt), 4g fibre

Useful source of potassium (709mg)

Side dishes

Asparagus with confetti vinaigrette

Fresh asparagus was once just a spring vegetable, but these days it is available year-round. When it's sprinkled with a light and colourful vinaigrette, its uniquely sweet flavour shines through.

Preparation time **10 minutes**   Cooking time **10 minutes**   *Serves 4*

675g (1½lb) asparagus

2 large red peppers, finely chopped

2 large yellow peppers, finely chopped

4 spring onions, thinly sliced

2 tsp fresh thyme or ½ tsp dried thyme

5 tbsp low-sodium chicken stock

3 tbsp white wine vinegar

pepper to taste

1 Bring 5cm (2in) of water to a simmer in a large frying pan over medium-high heat. Add the asparagus and simmer for 3–4 minutes or until the asparagus is tender. Transfer to a platter. Keep warm.

2 Wipe the pan dry. Coat it with cooking spray or a teaspoon of olive oil and set over a medium-high heat. Add the red and yellow peppers, and sauté for about 4 minutes or until tender. Stir in the spring onions and thyme, and cook for a further 1 minute.

3 Stir in the stock and vinegar, and bring to a simmer. Sprinkle with pepper and pour over the asparagus.

Some more ideas

• Make this dish using florets of broccoli or cauliflower, steamed until tender, instead of asparagus.

• Use the pepper confetti mixture to top grilled chicken breasts or salmon.

Health points

• Asparagus is loaded with nutrients such as beta-carotene, vitamin C, folate and potassium. It is also rich with blood-pressure-friendly fibre. During the 17th and early 18th centuries, the French king Louis XIV had such a liking for asparagus that it became the rage throughout France. Its popularity continues today.

photo, page 193

Each serving provides   Key nutrients 100kcals, 1.5g fat (of which 0.5g is saturated fat), 7g protein, 14g carbohydrate, 35mg sodium (0.08g salt), 5g fibre

Useful source of potassium (704mg)

Side dishes

Asparagus with confetti vinaigrette

Fresh asparagus was once just a spring vegetable, but these days it is available year-round. When it's sprinkled with a light and colourful vinaigrette, its uniquely sweet flavour shines through.

Preparation time **10 minutes**   Cooking time **10 minutes**   *Serves 4*

675g (1½lb) asparagus

2 large red peppers, finely chopped

2 large yellow peppers, finely chopped

4 spring onions, thinly sliced

2 tsp fresh thyme or ½ tsp dried thyme

5 tbsp low-sodium chicken stock

3 tbsp white wine vinegar

pepper to taste

1 Bring 5cm (2in) of water to a simmer in a large frying pan over medium-high heat. Add the asparagus and simmer for 3–4 minutes or until the asparagus is tender. Transfer to a platter. Keep warm.

2 Wipe the pan dry. Coat it with cooking spray or a teaspoon of olive oil and set over a medium-high heat. Add the red and yellow peppers, and sauté for about 4 minutes or until tender. Stir in the spring onions and thyme, and cook for a further 1 minute.

3 Stir in the stock and vinegar, and bring to a simmer. Sprinkle with pepper and pour over the asparagus.

Some more ideas

• Make this dish using florets of broccoli or cauliflower, steamed until tender, instead of asparagus.

• Use the pepper confetti mixture to top grilled chicken breasts or salmon.

Health points

• Asparagus is loaded with nutrients such as beta-carotene, vitamin C, folate and potassium. It is also rich with blood-pressure-friendly fibre. During the 17th and early 18th centuries, the French king Louis XIV had such a liking for asparagus that it became the rage throughout France. Its popularity continues today.

photo, page 193

Each serving provides   Key nutrients 100kcals, 1.5g fat (of which 0.5g is saturated fat), 7g protein, 14g carbohydrate, 35mg sodium (0.08g salt), 5g fibre

Useful source of potassium (704mg)

Country-style mashed potatoes

A topping of crumbled, crisp turkey rashers and beautiful brown sautéed onions brings out the personality in these mashed potatoes. This is a side dish that could steal the show.

Preparation time **20 minutes**   Cooking time **20 minutes**   *Serves 6*

675g (1½lb) floury potatoes such as King Edwards, peeled and cut into pieces

4 turkey rashers, coarsely chopped

1 small red onion, chopped

1 tsp chopped fresh thyme

5 tbsp semi-skimmed milk

25g (1oz) butter, cut into pieces

pepper to taste

2 spring onions (green parts only), very thinly sliced

1 Put the potatoes in a saucepan of boiling water and cook for about 10 minutes or until tender. Drain and return to the empty pan. Shake the potatoes in the pan over low heat until dry. Remove from the heat, cover and keep hot.

2 Sauté the turkey rashers and onion in a medium nonstick frying pan over a medium-high heat for about 7 minutes or until the rashers are crisp and the onions are browned. Stir in the thyme.

3 While the turkey rashers and onions are cooking, heat the milk and butter in a small saucepan over a medium heat until the butter has melted and the milk is hot and beginning to bubble. Pour over the potatoes. Add pepper to taste, and mash with a potato masher (do not use an electric mixer or food processor). Keep the mash a bit chunky. Stir in the spring onions. Spoon the turkey rashers and onions over the potatoes and serve.

Some more ideas

• Instead of semi-skimmed milk, you could use some of the potato cooking water, low-sodium chicken or beef stock, buttermilk, low-fat plain yoghurt or fromage frais.

• Spice up the cooking water by adding peeled cloves of garlic, fresh thyme sprigs, slivers of onion, or a grinding of freshly ground black pepper.

Health points

• Butter contains more saturated fat than margarine, but if you are not using a lot of saturated fat elsewhere in your diet, it is safe to use butter. If you have raised cholesterol levels, use a cholesterol-lowering spread, such as Flora Proactiv and Benecol, instead of butter.

Each serving provides   Key nutrients 164kcals, 7g fat (of which 3g is saturated fat), 4g protein, 21g carbohydrate, 269mg sodium (0.7g salt), 2g fibre

Useful source of potassium (510mg)

Orange-glazed carrots

Did Mother Nature colour oranges and carrots similarly to tip us off to what a tasty combination they make? Here the carrot-orange combo is divinely enhanced with Moroccan seasonings.

Preparation time **15 minutes**   Cooking time **25 minutes**   *Serves 8*

900g (2lb) carrots, halved lengthways and cut into 5cm (2in) lengths

175ml (6fl oz) orange juice concentrate, thawed if frozen

2½ tsp ground coriander

175ml (6fl oz) water

15g (½oz) butter

5 tbsp chopped fresh mint

1 Combine the carrots, orange juice concentrate and ground coriander in a large frying pan. Add the water and bring to the boil over a medium heat. Reduce to a simmer, cover and cook for about 15 minutes or until the carrots are almost tender but still firm.

2 Uncover the pan, increase the heat to high and cook for a further 7 minutes or until the carrots are tender.

3 Add the butter and cook for 1 minute, swirling the liquid in the pan, until the carrots are glossy and the sauce is creamy. Stir in the mint.

Some more ideas

• To save preparation time, make this dish with peeled baby carrots.

• If you can't find fresh mint, use fresh basil, coriander or dill instead.

Health points

• Carrots contain a unique type of soluble fibre called calcium pectate, which is believed to lower LDL ('bad') cholesterol.

• Carrots may not directly help your eyesight, as the old saying claims, but they are indeed an important source of the antioxidant beta-carotene, which the body converts into vitamin A.

Each serving provides

Key nutrients 62kcals, 2g fat (of which 1g is saturated fat), 1g protein, 11g carbohydrate, 42mg sodium (0.1g salt), 3g fibre

Orange-glazed carrots *p192*

Asparagus with confetti vinaigrette *p190*

Mangetout with apples and ginger *p194*

Pan-roasted new potatoes with garlic *p195*

Mangetout with apples and ginger

Garlic, ginger...and apples? You bet! Slices of firm apple, briefly stir-fried, have the same crunch as water chestnuts, so they work very well with crisp, fresh mangetout.

Preparation time **10 minutes**   Cooking time **10 minutes**   *Serves 4*

2 tsp olive oil

2 tbsp finely slivered fresh root ginger

3 garlic cloves, finely chopped

450g (1lb) mangetout, strings removed

2 crisp red dessert apples, unpeeled, cut into thin wedges

1 Heat the oil in a large nonstick frying pan over low heat. Add the ginger and garlic, and cook for about 2 minutes.

2 Add the mangetout and apples to the pan and cook, stirring frequently, for about 7 minutes or until the mangetout are just tender. Serve hot.

Some more ideas

• For an unusual main-dish salad, fold the cooled mangetout and apple mixture into cooked and cooled brown rice, together with cubes of cooked chicken breast or lean pork loin.

• Use sugarsnap peas or asparagus tips in place of the mangetout.

Health points

• Apples contain anthocyanins, natural pigments in apple skin that may help to improve cardiovascular health. The soluble fibre pectin, abundant in apples, also assists in lowering harmful cholesterol levels. So 'an apple a day' *is* good advice.

• Bright green vegetables such as mangetout and other peas contain chlorophyll, which studies suggest may deter certain chemicals from causing DNA damage to cells.

photo, page 193

Each serving provides   Key nutrients 72kcals, 2g fat (of which 0.2g is saturated fat), 4g protein, 10.5g carbohydrate, 3mg sodium (0.007g salt), 3g fibre

Pan-roasted new potatoes with garlic

The old way to roast potatoes was in a pan with fatty meat. The fresher, tastier way is to roast them separately with olive oil and fragrant spices. Here, roasted garlic cloves are a flavour bonus.

Preparation time **10 minutes**   Cooking time **35 minutes**   *Serves 4*

1 tbsp olive oil

8 large garlic cloves, unpeeled

3 thick slices fresh root ginger, unpeeled

1½ tsp fennel seeds

1½ tsp cumin seeds

1½ tsp turmeric

675g (1½lb) small red-skinned potatoes, cut into 1cm (½in) chunks

4 tbsp water

1 tbsp fresh lemon juice

1 Heat the oil in a large nonstick frying pan over low heat. Add the garlic, ginger, fennel, cumin and turmeric. Cook for 1 minute.

2 Add the potatoes and shake the pan to coat them with the spice mixture. Cook for about 5 minutes or until they begin to turn golden brown. Add the water, cover the pan and cook, shaking pan occasionally, for about 30 minutes or until the potatoes are tender.

3 Remove and discard the ginger. Sprinkle the lemon juice over the potatoes. Serve the garlic cloves in their skins; each diner can then squeeze the roasted garlic from its skin onto the potatoes.

Some more ideas

Italian roasted potatoes Omit the ginger, fennel, cumin and turmeric, and instead use 1½ tsp each dried oregano and basil and 1 tsp dried thyme. Add ½ tsp freshly ground black pepper with the garlic in step 1.

• Use Pink Fir Apple or other new potatoes instead of red-skinned potatoes.

Health points

• It is no coincidence that garlic and ginger are integral to the diet of the world's healthiest cultures. Both contain phyto-chemicals that fight disease and aid the body. Note that among vegetables, herbs and spices, bold colours and strong flavours are often an indication of healthy chemistry.

• Don't let all the talk of low-carb diets scare you away from potatoes. Particularly when eaten with their skins, potatoes are filled with vitamin C, potassium and many phytochemicals.

photo, page 193

Each serving provides   Key nutrients 150kcals, 3g fat (of which 0.5g is saturated fat), 3.5g protein, 28g carbohydrate, 19mg sodium (0.04g salt), 2g fibre

Useful source of potassium (582mg)

Sesame stir-fried asparagus and peas

When asparagus comes into season, run – don't walk – to the nearest greengrocer or farmers' market and buy a big bunch (or two). Toasted sesame seeds add a nutty aroma to this festive dish.

Preparation time **10 minutes**　　Cooking time **15 minutes**　　*Serves 4*

2 tsp sesame seeds

550g (1¼lb) asparagus

1 tsp olive oil

115g (4oz) finely chopped red onion

1 garlic clove, slivered

140g (5oz) frozen peas

1 Toast the sesame seeds in a small, heavy frying pan over low heat, stirring frequently, for 3 minutes or until golden brown. Transfer to a plate.

2 Cut the asparagus on a diagonal into 5cm (2in) lengths. Coat a large nonstick frying pan with cooking spray or a teaspoon of olive oil. Add the oil and heat over medium heat. Add the onion and garlic, and cook, stirring, for 5 minutes or until the onion is tender.

3 Add the asparagus and peas to the pan and cook, stirring frequently, for 5 minutes or until the asparagus is just tender and the peas are hot.

4 Sprinkle the sesame seeds over the asparagus and peas, and toss to combine.

Some more ideas

Sesame vegetable pasta
To serve 4, cook 350g (12oz) pasta shapes, then toss with the hot asparagus and pea mixture and a good spoonful of fromage frais.

• Serve with roast turkey breast and steamed brown rice, and follow with a dessert of low-fat frozen yoghurt topped with shreds of crystallised ginger.

Health points

• One of the many phyto-chemicals in asparagus is rutin. This antioxidant flavonoid works hand-in-hand with vitamin C to maintain blood-vessel health.

Each serving provides　Key nutrients 90kcals, 3g fat (of which 0.5g is saturated fat), 7g protein, 8g carbohydrate, 4mg sodium (0.01g salt), 5g fibre

Useful source of potassium (484mg)

Balsamic baked tomatoes with Parmesan crumbs

The complex flavour of balsamic vinegar is the result of its being aged in a succession of barrels, each made from a different kind of wood. This fruity vinegar is the perfect complement to a hearty cheese, like Parmesan, and firm, deep-red tomatoes.

Preparation time **5 minutes**   Cooking time **25 minutes**   *Serves 8*

4 large tomatoes, about 225g (8oz) each

55g (2oz) whole-grain bread

3 tbsp freshly grated Parmesan cheese

1 tsp olive oil

For the glaze

5 tbsp balsamic vinegar

2 tbsp light brown sugar

2 tbsp water

1 Preheat the oven to 200°C (400°F, gas mark 6). Core the tomatoes and cut in half horizontally. Place the tomato halves, cut-side up, in a ceramic or glass baking dish large enough to hold them in a single layer.

2 Place the bread in a food processor and pulse to fine crumbs. Combine the crumbs, Parmesan and oil in a small bowl. Sprinkle the tomatoes with the crumb mixture.

3 Bake for about 25 minutes or until the crumb topping is just beginning to brown and the tomatoes are hot.

4 Meanwhile, combine the vinegar, brown sugar and water in a small frying pan. Bring to the boil over high heat and cook for about 3 minutes or until syrupy. Drizzle the glaze over the baked tomatoes and serve.

Some more ideas

• Drizzle the balsamic vinegar glaze over cooked fish such as grilled salmon.

• Parmesan is a flavour-packed cheese that holds up well when combined with other strong flavours. To enjoy it at its best, buy a chunk and grate it yourself. Pre-grated cheeses are never as robust.

Health points

• To keep the saturated-fat levels in this dish low, the proportions of a typical cheese and crumb topping are swapped here from mostly cheese to mostly crumbs.

photo, page 199

Each serving provides   Key nutrients 80kcals, 3g fat (of which 1.3g is saturated fat), 4g protein, 10g carbohydrate, 109mg sodium (0.27g salt), 1.5g fibre

Lemony sugarsnap peas

The very essence of early summer, emerald-green sugarsnaps are so tender you can eat them pods and all.
No fussy sauces or flourishes are needed, just delicate flavourings like these.

Preparation time **10 minutes**   Cooking time **10 minutes**   *Serves 4*

675g (1½lb) sugarsnap peas

2 tsp olive oil

3 shallots, thinly sliced

1 garlic clove, finely chopped

1 tbsp grated lemon zest

1 Remove strings from both sides of the sugarsnap peas, if necessary. Heat the oil in a large nonstick frying pan over medium heat. Add the shallots and garlic, and cook, stirring, for about 3 minutes or until the shallots are softened.

2 Add the sugarsnaps and lemon zest, and cook, stirring, for about 4 minutes or until the sugarsnaps are just tender.

Some more ideas

• Rather than grating lemon zest for this recipe with a box grater, try making tendrils of zest. To do this, either use a citrus zester, or remove wide strips of zest with a vegetable peeler and then cut the strips into very fine slivers.

• For a simple, heart-smart meal, serve the sugarsnaps with grilled chicken breasts and steamed Jersey Royal potatoes – another early summer delicacy.

Health points

• Sugarsnap peas and other edible-podded peas (such as mangetout) supply three times as much vitamin C as shelled peas. To get the most vitamin C, eat the peas raw or cook them only briefly, as in this recipe.

Each serving provides **Key nutrients** 80kcals, 2g fat (of which 0.2g is saturated fat), 6g protein, 10g carbohydrate, 7mg sodium (0.01g salt), 3g fibre

Balsamic baked tomatoes with Parmesan crumbs *p197*

Lemony sugarsnap peas *p198*

Crispy cauliflower with Parmesan and almonds *p201*

Curried mushrooms, peas and potatoes *p200*

Curried mushrooms, peas and potatoes

India's vegetarian cooks turn humble ingredients like potatoes, peas, lentils and rice into amazingly flavourful, utterly satisfying meals; the secret is in the tantalising medley of spices.

Preparation time **15 minutes**   Cooking time **30 minutes**   *Serves 4*

1 small onion, cut into chunks

3 garlic cloves, peeled

2 tbsp sliced fresh root ginger

3 tbsp plus 225ml (8fl oz) water

2 tsp olive oil

225g (8oz) fresh shiitake mushrooms, stalks discarded and caps quartered

2 tsp curry powder, preferably Madras

350g (12oz) small red-skinned potatoes, cut into wedges

140g (5oz) frozen peas

150g (5½oz) plain low-fat yoghurt

1 Combine the onion, garlic, ginger and 3 tablespoons of water in a blender and purée.

2 Heat the oil in a large nonstick frying pan over medium heat. Add the onion purée and cook for 5 minutes or until the liquid has evaporated. Add mushrooms and cook, stirring frequently, for about 3 minutes or until tender.

3 Stir in the curry powder. Add the potatoes and stir until the potatoes are coated with the spice and onion mixture. Add the remaining 225ml (8fl oz) water and bring to the boil. Reduce to a simmer, cover and cook for about 15 minutes or until the potatoes are tender.

4 Stir in the peas and cook for a further 2 minutes or until they are hot. Remove from the heat and stir in the yoghurt.

Some more ideas

• If you cannot find shiitake mushrooms, use white button or chestnut mushrooms. These are milder in flavour than shiitake, which have a slightly peppery finish.

• In the summer, use fresh peas. Keep the peas, in their pods, in the refrigerator so that their sugar content doesn't turn to starch.

Health points

• Peas are an excellent source of carbohydrate and fibre, and also provide potassium. Make canned peas your last choice, since they are higher in sodium and lower in nutrients than either frozen or fresh peas.

• Shiitake mushrooms contain an immune-boosting compound called lentinan, which may help to lower blood pressure.

photo, page 199

Each serving provides   Key nutrients 141kcals, 3g fat (of which 0.5g is saturated fat), 7g protein, 23 carbohydrate, 52mg sodium (0.13g salt), 4g fibre

Useful source of potassium (674mg)

Crispy cauliflower with Parmesan and almonds

Baking cauliflower at high heat with a crunchy coating of breadcrumbs, almonds and Parmesan notches up this vegetable's appeal. Raisins add sweetness, colour and surprise.

Preparation time **10 minutes**   Cooking time **30 minutes**   *Serves 4*

1 large cauliflower, about 675g (1½lb), cut into florets

75g (2½oz) raisins

5 tbsp fine dried breadcrumbs

2 tbsp freshly grated Parmesan cheese

1 tbsp flaked almonds

2 tsp olive oil

2 tbsp fresh lemon juice

1 Preheat the oven to 200°C (400°F, gas mark 6). Line a large roasting tin with foil and coat the foil with cooking spray. Steam the cauliflower for about 5 minutes or until just tender but still firm.

2 Meanwhile, stir together the raisins, breadcrumbs, Parmesan, almonds and oil in a bowl.

3 Transfer the cauliflower to the roasting tin and sprinkle with the breadcrumb mixture. Put into the oven and bake for about 20 minutes or until the crumb topping is golden brown. Drizzle the lemon juice over the top and bake for a further 5 minutes. Serve hot or at room temperature.

Some more ideas

• Shop-bought breadcrumbs are usually made from white bread. For healthier fibre-rich crumbs use wholemeal bread. Place slices of bread on a baking tray and bake them at 150°C (300°F, gas mark 2) until they are completely dried out but not browned. Allow the slices to cool, then process them to fine crumbs in a food processor or blender.

• Use sultanas instead of raisins.

• Use the crumb mixture to top steamed carrots or broccoli florets.

Health points

• Cauliflower is an excellent source of folate, vitamin C and potassium. All three nutrients play a role in the prevention of heart disease and help improve high blood pressure.

• Since cauliflower loses more of its B vitamins (including folate) when cooked in water, it is steamed for this recipe rather than boiled.

photo, page 199

Each serving provides   Key nutrients 246kcals, 8g fat (of which 2g is saturated fat), 12g protein, 33g carbohydrate, 251mg sodium (0.63g salt), 4g fibre

Good source of potassium (908mg)

Tex-Mex sweetcorn bake

Something like a soufflé in texture, but easier to make and far more flavourful and colourful, this side dish will really perk up even the simplest of meals!

Preparation time **10 minutes**   Cooking time **50 minutes**   *Serves 6*

4 tbsp skimmed milk powder

2 tbsp plain flour

225ml (8fl oz) semi-skimmed milk

55g (2oz) diced red pepper

1 tbsp mild chilli powder

2 tsp sugar

½ tsp ground cumin

1 large egg plus 1 large egg white

450g (1lb) frozen sweetcorn kernels, thawed

3 spring onions, thinly sliced

1 Preheat the oven to 190°C (375°F, gas mark 5). Stir the milk powder and flour together in a medium saucepan. Whisk in the semi-skimmed milk. Bring to a simmer over medium heat. Add the red pepper, chilli powder, sugar and cumin, and cook, stirring constantly, for 5 minutes or until thick enough to coat the back of a spoon.

2 Beat the egg with the egg white in a small bowl. Whisk in a ladleful of the hot sauce. Remove the pan of sauce from the heat and stir in the egg mixture, then stir in two-thirds of the sweetcorn and the spring onions. Purée the remaining sweetcorn in a food processor. Stir into the mixture.

3 Transfer to a shallow baking dish set in a roasting tin. Pour hot water into the tin to come halfway up the sides of the baking dish. Bake for 35–45 minutes or until set and the top is light golden brown.

Some more ideas

• Make this dish spicier by adding 1 diced jalapeño or other fresh green chilli. If you prefer, remove the seeds from the chilli, to reduce the heat.

• Serve this side dish with grilled turkey burgers and roast asparagus.

Health points

• By using a whole egg and an egg white rather than 2 whole eggs, you'll save 5g fat and 200mg cholesterol.

• Mixing skimmed milk powder with semi-skimmed milk adds about 50mg of calcium.

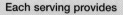

Each serving provides   **Key nutrients** 133kcals, 3g fat (of which 1g is saturated fat), 7g protein, 22g carbohydrate, 42mg sodium (0.1g salt), 1.5g fibre

Squash and aubergine casserole

This colourful vegetable casserole is transformed into a feast for the eye and palate with a fresh and punchy mixture of parsley, garlic, lemon zest and toasted almonds, and can be served with polenta or potato and carrot purée.

Preparation time **about 20 minutes**   Cooking time **about 45 minutes**   *Serves 4*

1 tbsp olive oil

1 large onion, cut into 8 wedges

12 baby corn

1 small or ½ large butternut squash, about 600g (1lb 5oz), peeled, quartered lengthways, deseeded and cut across into 2.5cm (1in) slices

1 aubergine, halved lengthways and cut across into 2.5cm (1in) slices

1 red pepper, deseeded and cut into 1cm (½in) pieces

125ml (4fl oz) dry white wine

450ml (16fl oz) low-sodium vegetable stock

pepper to taste

For the topping

2 tbsp slivered almonds

1 garlic clove, finely chopped

finely shredded or coarsely grated zest of 1 lemon

5 tbsp chopped parsley

1 Heat the oil in a flameproof casserole. Add the onion and baby corn, and sauté over medium heat for 5 minutes, stirring. Preheat the oven to 180°C (350°F, gas mark 4).

2 Add the slices of butternut squash to the casserole and toss them in the oil, then stir in the aubergine and red pepper. Cover and leave to cook over low to medium heat, turning the vegetables twice, for 10 minutes or until they are lightly tinged golden brown. Pour in the wine and let it bubble, then stir in the stock. Bring to the boil and add pepper to taste. Cover the casserole and cook in the oven for 30 minutes.

3 Meanwhile, make the topping. Preheat the grill to high. Spread the slivered almonds on a baking tray and toast under the grill until they are lightly browned. Watch them closely and shake the tray occasionally to ensure the nuts are evenly toasted. Place in a small bowl and mix in the remaining topping ingredients.

4 Serve as a vegetable accompaniment or a tasty vegetarian main meal, ladled over polenta or a potato and carrot purée (see Some more ideas).

Some more ideas

• Polenta makes a good accompaniment. Bring a litre of water to the boil and stir in 200g (7oz) instant polenta. Whisk until all the water is absorbed and then let it simmer, stirring, for 5–10 minutes. Beat in 25g (1oz) freshly grated Parmesan cheese and about 2 tbsp chopped fresh oregano.

• Serve it with a potato and carrot purée instead. Cook 450g (1lb) potatoes with 225g (8oz) sliced carrots in boiling water until tender, then drain well. Mash with 5 tbsp semi-skimmed milk. Stir in 25g (1oz) grated reduced-fat Cheddar cheese and 2–4 tbsp chopped parsley.

Health points

• Butternut squash is a good source of beta-carotene, which the body converts into vitamin A. Cooking the squash with a small amount of fat makes it easier for the body to absorb the beta-carotene.

photo, page 205

Each serving provides   Key nutrients 190kcals, 8g fat (of which 1g is saturated fat), 6g protein, 20g carbohydrate, 118mg sodium (0.3g salt), 6g fibre

Good source of potassium (898mg)

Sweetcorn fritters

In this recipe, juicy sweetcorn kernels are added to a thick batter flavoured with fresh coriander, and then pan-fried in big spoonfuls. Piled on a bed of watercress and drizzled with a yoghurt sauce, the fritters are delicious and quick.

Preparation and cooking time **30 minutes**   *Serves 6*

140g (5oz) plain flour

½ tsp baking powder

150ml (5fl oz) skimmed milk

2 large eggs, lightly beaten

400g (14oz) frozen sweetcorn kernels, thawed and drained

3 spring onions, finely chopped

1 fresh red chilli, deseeded and finely chopped

3 heaped tbsp chopped fresh coriander

pepper to taste

1 tbsp sunflower oil

115g (4oz) watercress

For the sauce

225g (8oz) plain low-fat yoghurt

4 spring onions, finely chopped

2 tbsp chopped fresh mint

grated zest and juice of 1 lime

1 First make the yoghurt sauce. Put the yoghurt in a serving bowl and stir in the spring onions, mint and lime zest. Cover and refrigerate while you make the fritters (keep the lime juice for use later).

2 Sift the flour and baking powder into a bowl. Make a well in the centre and add the milk and eggs. Using a wooden spoon, mix together the milk and eggs, then gradually draw in the flour from around the edges. Beat with the spoon to make a smooth, thick batter. Alternatively, the batter can be made in a food processor: put the milk and eggs in the container first, spoon the flour and baking powder on top and process for a few seconds to blend.

3 Add the sweetcorn kernels, spring onions, chilli and coriander to the batter, and season with pepper to taste. Mix well.

4 Heat a griddle or large, heavy frying pan, then brush with a little of the oil. Drop large spoonfuls of the fritter batter on to the pan – make about 4 fritters at a time – and cook over moderate heat for about 2 minutes or until golden and firm on the underside.

5 Turn the fritters over, using a spatula, and cook on the other side for 2 minutes or until golden brown. Remove the fritters from the pan and drain on kitchen paper. Keep warm while cooking the rest of the fritters in the same way, adding more oil to the pan as necessary.

6 Arrange the watercress on six plates and sprinkle with the lime juice. Arrange the sweetcorn fritters on top and serve hot, with the yoghurt sauce to be drizzled over.

Some more ideas

• Instead of chilli and coriander, flavour the batter with 2 tsp green Thai curry paste.

Pea fritters Replace the sweetcorn with frozen peas and use chopped fresh basil in place of coriander.

Health points

• Sweetcorn is a good source of fibre as well as vitamins A and C and folate. It is generally a popular food with children, and this recipe makes a healthy dish they are sure to love.

• Watercress, like other dark green, leafy vegetables, contains folate, one of the B vitamins, which recent research suggests may help to protect the body against heart disease and prevent Alzheimer's disease.

Each serving (2 fritters) provides

Key nutrients 226kcals, 6g fat (of which 1g is saturated fat), 10g protein, 34g carbohydrate, 132mg sodium (0.33g salt), 2.5g fibre

Useful source of potassium (441mg)

Sweetcorn fritters *p204*

Squash and aubergine casserole *p203*

Sweet-and-sour cabbage *p206*

Boston baked beans *p207*

Sweet-and-sour cabbage

Cabbage, carrots, red pepper and red onion – all packed wih healthy nutrients – join together to brighten this variation on a traditional German favourite.

Preparation time **15 minutes**   Cooking time **25 minutes**   *Serves 4*

2 tsp olive oil

1 large red onion, cut into small chunks

2 carrots, cut into matchsticks

1 red pepper, cut into small chunks

1 small green cabbage, thickly shredded

2 tbsp light brown sugar

pepper to taste

¼ tsp dried sage

4 tbsp rice vinegar or cider vinegar

1 Heat the oil in a large nonstick frying pan over medium heat. Add the onion and cook for about 5 minutes or until softened. Add the carrots and red pepper, and cook, stirring frequently, for about 5 minutes or until just tender.

2 Stir in the cabbage. Sprinkle the brown sugar, pepper and sage over the cabbage, and cook, stirring frequently, for about 10 minutes or until the cabbage is wilted.

3 Add the vinegar, increase the heat to medium-high and cook for a further 3 minutes, stirring to mix. Serve warm or at room temperature.

Some more ideas

• Red cabbage can be used as a colourful substitute for green cabbage in this recipe. Add 5 minutes to the cooking time in step 2. Red cabbage has more vitamin C than green.

• In place of sage, try using dried thyme.

• Serve this cabbage dish over cooked brown rice and add sautéed tofu cubes, to make a satisfying vegetarian meal.

Health points

• In this nutritious dish, immunity-boosting vitamin C is supplied by the pepper and the cabbage, and beta-carotene is provided by the carrots.

photo, page 205

Each serving provides   Key nutrients 110 kcals, 2g fat (of which 0.5g is saturated fat), 2g protein, 19g carbohydrate, 21mg sodium (0.05g salt), 4g fibre

Useful source of potassium (400mg)

Boston baked beans

Baked beans aren't just popular in Boston – they're big all over the world! It could be because beans are perfect cold-weather food, or it could be that this rich, sweet contemporary version and others like it are sweeping the globe.

Preparation time **15 minutes plus soaking**   Cooking time **2 hours**   *Serves 8*

225g (8oz) dried haricot beans, rinsed, drained and picked over

2 turkey rashers, cut crossways in half

1 large onion, chopped

4 tbsp light brown sugar

4 tbsp no-salt-added tomato ketchup

4 tbsp light molasses

1 tbsp dry mustard

pepper to taste

1 Put the beans in a large saucepan and add water to cover by 5cm (2in). Bring to the boil and boil for 3 minutes. Remove from the heat, cover and leave for 1 hour. Drain the beans and rinse with cold water. Return to the saucepan.

2 Pour in enough fresh water to cover the beans by 5cm (2in). Bring to the boil, then reduce the heat to medium-low, cover and cook for about 1½ hours or until the beans are tender. Add hot water during cooking, if necessary, to keep the beans covered by 5cm (2in). Drain the beans, reserving 350ml (12fl oz) of the cooking liquid. Transfer the beans and liquid to a large casserole.

3 While the beans are cooking, preheat the oven to 150°C (300°F, gas mark 2). Coat a medium nonstick frying pan with cooking spray or a teaspoon of olive oil, and set over a medium-high heat. Cook the turkey rashers until crisp. Transfer with a slotted spoon to kitchen paper to drain, then crumble. Sauté the onion in the pan drippings for 5 minutes or until soft.

4 Stir the brown sugar, ketchup, molasses, mustard, onion and half of the turkey rashers into the beans in the casserole. Season with pepper to taste. Sprinkle the remaining turkey rashers on top. Cover and place in the oven. Cook for about 30 minutes or until hot and bubbling, stirring once.

Some more ideas

• Serve this side dish with barbecued chicken, grilled mixed vegetables and a tossed green salad.

Health points

• By using no-salt-added ketchup, this dish is lower in sodium than the usual baked beans, making it a good choice for people with high blood pressure. And by using turkey rashers instead of salt pork or bacon, you cut the calories too.

• All dried beans need soaking – either a quick soaking (as described in step 1) or long soaking (for at least 6 hours). Longer soaking can help to eliminate more of the wind-producing sugars in beans, cutting down on flatulence.

photo, page 205

Each serving provides   Key nutrients 161kcals, 2g fat (of which 0.5g is saturated fat), 8g protein, 30g carbohydrate, 138mg sodium (0.35g salt), 5g fibre

Useful source of potassium (503mg)

Black-eyed beans with sweet peppers

In the southern United States, black-eyed beans are said to bring their eaters good luck. Turkey rashers add a smoky flavour to this traditional New Year's Day dish from the American South.

Preparation time **15 minutes**   Cooking time **40 minutes**   *Serves 8*

2 tsp olive oil

3 turkey rashers, thinly sliced crossways

1 medium onion, finely chopped

2 mixed colour peppers (red, yellow, green or orange), cut into 1cm (½in) squares

2 garlic cloves, finely chopped

1 can (about 400g) black-eyed beans (no-salt variety), drained and rinsed

55g (2oz) long-grain white rice

pepper to taste

225ml (8fl oz) water

1½ tbsp red wine vinegar

1 tsp Tabasco sauce

1 Heat the oil in a nonstick flameproof casserole over medium heat. Add the turkey rashers and cook for about 5 minutes or until crisp.

2 Add the onion and cook, stirring frequently, for 5 minutes or until tender. Add the peppers and garlic, and cook, stirring frequently, for about 4 minutes or until the peppers are tender but still firm.

3 Stir in the black-eyed beans, rice, pepper and water, and bring to the boil. Reduce to a simmer, cover and cook for 20 minutes or until the rice is tender and has absorbed all the liquid. Stir in the vinegar and Tabasco sauce.

Some more ideas

• For more fibre, substitute brown rice for the white rice.

• Try this with turkey burgers and a mixed salad, with sliced strawberries for dessert.

Health points

• Black-eyed beans provide both soluble and insoluble fibre and protein, and are high in potassium, iron, vitamin B$_1$ and folate. Even using canned beans does not compromise their outstanding nutritional value.

Each serving provides   **Key nutrients** 100kcals, 2g fat (of which 0.5g is saturated fat), 5g protein, 15g carbohydrate, 100mg sodium (0.25g salt), 3.5g fibre

Vegetable stir-fry with spicy garlic sauce

This lively stir-fry will rekindle your love of vegetables. Crisp broccoli, bright red peppers and tender baby corn are tossed with tantalising Asian seasonings for a speedy and exotic side dish.

Preparation time **15 minutes**   Cooking time **14 minutes**   *Serves 4*

1½ tsp groundnut or vegetable oil

1–2 garlic cloves, crushed

3 tbsp finely chopped fresh root ginger

200g (7oz) broccoli florets

300g (10½oz) baby corn

1 large red pepper, cut into thin strips

1 can (about 250g) sliced water chestnuts, drained

1 tbsp sesame seeds, toasted, to garnish

For the sauce

350ml (12fl oz) low-sodium chicken stock

2 tbsp low-sodium soy sauce, or to taste

2 tbsp cornflour

½ tsp Thai chilli paste *(optional)*

1 First make the sauce. Combine 4 tablespoons of the stock, the soy sauce, cornflour and chilli paste (if using) in a small bowl, mixing until smooth. Set aside.

2 Coat a large nonstick wok or deep frying pan with cooking spray or a teaspoon of olive oil. Add the oil and set the wok over a high heat. When it is hot but not smoking, add the garlic and ginger, and stir-fry for 1 minute or until fragrant. Remove with a slotted spoon and set aside.

3 Add the broccoli and corn to the wok and stir-fry for about 4 minutes or just until they begin to soften. Transfer to a bowl. Add the red pepper and water chestnuts, and stir-fry for 3 minutes or just until they begin to soften. Return the broccoli and corn to the wok and add the remaining stock.

4 Cover the wok and cook for about 3 minutes or until all the vegetables are tender but still firm. Whisk the cornflour mixture again, then add to the wok together with the ginger and garlic. Stir-fry for 1 minute or just until the sauce thickens and boils. Sprinkle with the sesame seeds and serve.

Some more ideas

• To turn this into a main dish add some tofu. In step 3, before adding the broccoli and corn, stir-fry 450g (1lb) cubed extra-firm tofu for 3–4 minutes or until lightly browned; remove and set aside. Return the tofu to the wok after the sauce is added in step 4 and toss gently to coat the tofu with the sauce.

• Use 5cm (2in) pieces of asparagus instead of broccoli.

Health points

• Stir-frying remains one of the simplest and healthiest ways to cook. Use a wok if possible as its small cooking base and wide sides allow you to conserve on the amount of oil needed. The high heat helps preserve the food's nutrients, crunch and colour.

• You'll never need table salt to provide flavour in stir-fries. Ingredients such as garlic, ginger and soy sauce will provide lots of taste without the sodium.

photo, page 211

Each serving provides   Key nutrients 151kcals, 7g fat (of which 1g is saturated fat), 6g protein, 16g carbohydrate, 371mg sodium (0.9g salt), 2.5g fibre

Useful source of potassium (367mg)

Spicy red cabbage parcels

In this updated version of stuffed cabbage, mellow-flavoured red cabbage leaves are filled with a hearty mixture of turkey, lentils, rice and cashews and baked in a simple tomato sauce.

Preparation time **40 minutes**   Cooking time **30 minutes**   *Serves 4*

55g (2oz) long-grain rice

300ml (10fl oz) water

8 large red cabbage leaves

1 tbsp sunflower oil

1 onion, finely chopped

1½ tsp cumin seeds

1 tsp ground coriander

1 tsp ground cinnamon

3 tbsp mango chutney

45g (1½oz) unsalted cashew nuts, coarsely chopped

1 can (about 420g) green lentils (no-salt variety), drained and rinsed well

225g (8oz) cooked turkey or chicken, without skin, diced

4 tbsp chopped parsley

pepper to taste

200ml (7fl oz) tomato juice

sprigs of parsley to garnish

1 Place the rice and water in a small saucepan and bring to the boil. Stir once, then reduce the heat to low and cover the pan. Cook for 15 minutes. Remove from the heat and leave the rice to stand, without removing the lid, for 10 minutes.

2 Meanwhile, preheat the oven to 200°C (400°F, gas mark 6). Trim off the tough stalk from the base of each cabbage leaf. Bring a large saucepan of water to the boil. Add half the leaves, bring back to the boil and blanch for 30 seconds. Remove the leaves and plunge them into a large bowl of cold water to stop them cooking. Repeat with the remaining leaves. Drain the leaves well and spread out on a tea towel to dry.

3 Heat the sunflower oil in a large pan and sauté the onion for 2–3 minutes or until softened. Add the cumin seeds and ground coriander and cinnamon, and cook for a further 2–3 minutes. Remove from the heat.

4 Add 2 tablespoons of the mango chutney to the onion mixture together with the cashews, well-rinsed lentils, turkey or chicken, parsley and pepper to taste, and mix well. Stir in the rice until thoroughly combined.

5 Lay a cabbage leaf flat on the work surface, with the stalk end towards you. Place some of the rice mixture on the leaf. Fold the base of the leaf over the filling, then fold in the sides and roll up the leaf to enclose the filling in a neat parcel. Repeat with the remaining leaves and filling.

6 Mix the remaining 1 tablespoon of mango chutney with the tomato juice. Pour about one-quarter of this sauce into a large baking dish. Pack the cabbage parcels into the dish and pour the rest of the sauce over them. Cover loosely with foil and bake for about 30 minutes or until the leaves are tender. Garnish with parsley.

Some more ideas

Chinese-style cabbage parcels Use blanched Chinese leaves instead of red cabbage, and replace the lentils with 150g (5½oz) baby corn, sliced and cooked in boiling water for 4–5 minutes. Add 1 tbsp finely chopped fresh root ginger and 1 large garlic clove, crushed, to the onion. Use plum sauce instead of mango chutney and add 25g (1oz) toasted sesame seeds to the rice mixture.

• Experiment with different types of rice. Try basmati or a mixture of wild rice and white rice. For more fibre, use brown rice, but remember that it requires longer to cook than white rice, so follow the packet instructions.

• Cooked lean roast pork or beef can be used instead of the turkey or chicken.

Health points

• Lentils are low in fat, high in protein and provide good amounts of folate. They are rich in soluble fibre – the kind that helps to reduce cholesterol levels.

Each serving provides

Key nutrients 360kcals, 14g fat (of which 3g is saturated fat), 26g protein, 35g carbohydrate, 285mg sodium (0.7g salt), 3g fibre

Useful source of potassium (638mg)

Vegetable stir-fry with spicy garlic sauce *p209*

Spicy red cabbage parcels *p210*

Stuffed jacket-baked potatoes *p214*

Indian-style okra with potatoes *p212*

Indian-style okra with potatoes

This makes a wonderful accompaniment to a spicy main dish. It is also good as a vegetarian main course for two, especially when served with Indian-style lentil dishes and warm naan bread.

Preparation time **15 minutes**   Cooking time **35–40 minutes**   *Serves 4*

1 large onion, quartered

4 garlic cloves

5cm (2in) piece fresh root ginger, peeled

2 tbsp sunflower oil

1 fresh red or green chilli, deseeded and finely chopped

1 tsp black mustard seeds

2 tsp ground coriander

1 tsp ground cumin

1 tsp turmeric

450ml (16fl oz) low-sodium vegetable stock

1 can (about 400g) no-salt-added chopped tomatoes

225g (8oz) fresh okra, trimmed and sliced

450g (1lb) potatoes, peeled and cut into large chunks

1 red, green or yellow pepper, deseeded and cut into chunks

4 tbsp raisins

pepper to taste

3 tbsp chopped fresh coriander plus extra to garnish

1 Put the onion, peeled garlic and ginger in a food processor or blender and purée. Alternatively, finely chop the ingredients and mix well together. Heat the oil in a saucepan. Add the onion purée and the chilli, and sauté over low heat for 6–7 minutes or until the mixture is beginning to turn golden brown in places.

2 Add the mustard seeds, ground coriander, cumin and turmeric, and stir to form a paste. Gradually pour in the stock and tomatoes with their juice, stirring well. Bring to the boil, then reduce the heat and cover the pan. Simmer over low heat for 10 minutes or until the spices are cooked and their flavours blended.

3 Add the okra, potatoes, pepper, raisins and pepper to taste. Stir well, then cover again and simmer over low heat for 15–20 minutes or until the potatoes are tender.

4 Stir in the chopped coriander and serve at once, sprinkled with extra coriander to garnish.

Some more ideas

• If you are serving this as a vegetarian main dish, plain or spiced basmati rice tossed with chopped almonds or cashews is a tasty partner.

Health points

• In addition to the delicious spiciness it brings to the dish, ginger also aids digestion.

• Chillies are a good source of vitamin C. Also, red chillies contain more beta-carotene than their green counterparts.

photo, page 211

Each serving provides Key nutrients 230kcals, 7g fat (of which 1g is saturated fat), 6g protein, 38g carbohydrate, 157mg sodium (0.4g salt), 5g fibre

Useful source of potassium (1074mg)

Braised cabbage, apple and caraway

For versatility, it's hard to beat cabbage. It can be braised, steamed, boiled or eaten raw in salads. In this recipe, caraway seeds offer pungency, and walnuts add both flavour and crunch.

Preparation time **15 minutes**   Cooking time **15 minutes**   *Serves 6*

2 tsp vegetable oil

1 small onion, finely chopped

1 tsp caraway seeds

450g (1lb) green cabbage, cored and thinly sliced

1 tbsp cider vinegar

2 small crisp red apples such as Gala, Braeburn or Empire, cored and cut into small cubes

1 tsp clear honey

2 tbsp chopped walnuts, toasted *(optional)*

1 Heat the oil in a large nonstick frying pan over medium heat. Add the onion and caraway seeds. Sauté for about 5 minutes or until the onion is softened.

2 Stir in the cabbage and vinegar. Cover and cook for 4 minutes or just until the cabbage wilts. Uncover the pan and increase the heat to high. Add the apples and honey. Cook, stirring frequently, for 4–6 minutes or until the apples are tender but crisp and most of the liquid has evaporated. Transfer to a serving dish and top with the walnuts, if using.

Some more ideas

• Substitute red cabbage for the green. Red cabbage is usually cooked longer than green, but for this dish you might want to keep it crunchy. In step 2, increase the wilting time to 8–10 minutes.

• Instead of the apples, use 2 small firm Conference or other pears, cored and cut into small cubes.

Health points

• Cabbage is nutritionally excellent, given its levels of vitamin C and fibre, and it is even richer in bioflavonoids and other phytochemicals believed to prevent cancer.

• Caraway, which is part of the carrot family, contains a phytochemical called limonene that may prevent cancer.

Each serving provides   **Key nutrients** 86kcals, 5g fat (of which 0.5g is saturated fat), 2.5g protein, 9g carbohydrate, 5mg sodium (0.01g salt), 3g fibre

Stuffed jacket-baked potatoes

A steaming hot baked potato is perfect comfort food. This tasty vegetarian filling combines marinated mushrooms and courgettes. And there's another satisfying filling to try: roasted garlic and tomato.

Preparation time **15–20 minutes**   Cooking time **1¼ hours**   *Serves 4*

4 medium baking potatoes

2 tbsp olive oil

225g (8oz) small open-cup mushrooms, stalks trimmed

1 large courgette, sliced

1 tsp red wine vinegar

1 tsp Dijon mustard

pepper to taste

4 tbsp chopped parsley

1 Preheat the oven to 200°C (400°F, gas mark 6). Push a metal skewer through each potato or push the potatoes on to a potato roasting rack. (The metal skewer helps to conduct heat through to the centre of the potatoes so that they cook more quickly.) Place the potatoes directly on the shelf in the oven and bake for about 1¼ hours or until they are tender.

2 Make the filling when you first put the potatoes in the oven so that it has time to marinate. Alternatively, it can be made just before the potatoes are cooked, and served hot. Heat a large ridged grill pan or frying pan. Drizzle half the oil over the pan and cook the mushrooms and courgette slices for 10–15 minutes or until they are tender and well browned in places and have released their juices.

3 Transfer the vegetables to a bowl with all their juices and add the remaining oil, the vinegar and mustard. Add pepper to taste and mix well, then leave to marinate until the potatoes are cooked.

4 Split open the baked potatoes, then press gently to part the halves, keeping them joined at the base. Stir the parsley into the marinated vegetables, then pile them into the potatoes. Serve immediately.

Some more ideas

Roasted garlic and cherry tomato filling Trim the tough stalk off a whole bulb of garlic, then wrap it in foil. Bake with the potatoes for 45 minutes. Cool the garlic slightly, then squeeze the pulp from each clove into a bowl. Add 1 large bunch fresh basil, tough stalks discarded and leaves torn; 1 tbsp olive oil; and seasoning to taste. Stir in 450g (1lb) cherry tomatoes, quartered. Preheat the grill to moderate. Scoop some flesh out of the potatoes, leaving a thick layer. Break up the scooped-out flesh coarsely with a fork. Stir into the tomato mixture, then spoon the filling back into the potato shells. Sprinkle each with 1 tbsp freshly grated Parmesan cheese. Brown under the grill and serve.

Health points

• Potatoes are an excellent source of vitamin C when cooked in their skins, as the vitamin is stored just beneath the skin.

photo, page 211

Each serving provides   Key nutrients 252kcals, 6.5g fat (of which 1g is saturated fat), 7g protein, 44g carbohydrate, 35mg sodium (0.09g salt), 4g fibre

Good source of potassium (1216mg)

Brussels sprouts and potatoes with caraway-mustard sauce

Horseradish adds a bold bite to the warm, creamy dressing that brings this delicious combination of Brussels sprouts, red potatoes, celery, spring onions and apples together.

Preparation time **20 minutes**   Cooking time **15 minutes**   *Serves 4*

225g (8oz) small red potatoes, quartered

280g (10oz) Brussels sprouts, quartered

1 red dessert apple, cut into 1cm (½in) chunks

2 celery sticks, thinly sliced

3 spring onions, thinly sliced

For the dressing

125ml (4fl oz) apple juice

5 tbsp cider vinegar

2 tbsp plain flour

1 tbsp spicy brown or Dijon mustard

1 tbsp grated horseradish

1 tsp olive oil

½ tsp caraway seeds

1 Cook the potatoes in a large pan of boiling water for 5 minutes. Add the Brussels sprouts and continue cooking for 5–8 minutes or until the potatoes and sprouts are tender but not soft. Drain and place in a serving bowl with the apple, celery and spring onions.

2 Whisk together the apple juice, vinegar, flour, mustard, horseradish, oil and caraway seeds in a small saucepan. Bring to a simmer over medium heat, whisking constantly. Simmer for 2 minutes.

3 Pour the hot dressing over the vegetables and toss to combine. Serve warm or at room temperature.

Some more ideas

• You can use frozen sprouts. Thaw them first. Cook the potatoes for 8 minutes before you add the sprouts, then cook together for 3–5 minutes

• Use new potatoes in place of red potatoes. Leave whole if they are small; cut larger ones into small cubes.

• Serve this as a side dish with lean roast meat, particularly beef, or poultry.

Health points

• A single serving of Brussels sprouts supplies more than a day's requirement of vitamin C. These tiny members of the cabbage family are also good sources of vitamin B_6, folate and potassium – all key ingredients for fighting heart disease.

Each serving provides   **Key nutrients** 128kcals, 2g fat (of which 0.5g is saturated fat), 4.5g protein, 25g carbohydrate, 37mg sodium (0.09g salt), 4g fibre

Useful source of potassium (716mg)

Avocado salad with raspberries

Avocados do contain a great deal of fat, but it is the good, monounsaturated type. In this salad, the creaminess of avocado is complemented by fresh raspberries and a fruity vinaigrette.

Preparation time **about 10 minutes**   *Serves 4*

2 avocados

175g (6oz) mixed salad greens

100g (3½oz) raspberries

sprigs of fresh mint to garnish

For the vinaigrette

2 tbsp olive oil

1½ tbsp raspberry vinegar

1 tbsp single cream

finely grated zest of ½ orange

½ tsp orange juice

pinch of caster sugar

pepper to taste

1 Put all the ingredients for the raspberry vinaigrette in a large salad bowl, adding pepper to taste, and whisk to mix.

2 Halve the avocados and remove the stone, then peel back the skin and dice the flesh. Add to the dressing immediately and tumble to coat, to prevent the avocados from turning brown.

3 Add the salad leaves to the bowl and toss gently with the avocados. Scatter over the raspberries and garnish with mint sprigs. Serve at once.

Some more ideas

Tropical avocado and mango salad Line four plates with romaine lettuce leaves. Cut each avocado half horizontally into thin slices and arrange on the plates with 1 thinly sliced, large ripe mango. Scatter 3 chopped spring onions over the top. Drizzle each salad with 1 tbsp olive oil and 1–2 tbsp orange juice, and dust lightly with cayenne pepper.

Italian-style avocado and mozzarella salad Thickly slice each avocado half horizontally and arrange on four plates with 25g (1oz) sliced mozzarella cheese per person. Sprinkle each with 1 tbsp sliced sun-dried tomatoes, then drizzle over 1 tbsp olive oil. Season with pepper and garnish with fresh basil leaves.

Health points

• Avocados help to lower levels of LDL ('bad') cholesterol while raising levels of HDL ('good') cholesterol. One avocado provides half the recommended daily intake of vitamin B_6.

Each serving provides   Key nutrients 238kcals, 23g fat (of which 5g is saturated fat), 2.5g protein, 4g carbohydrate, 8mg sodium (0.02g salt), 3.5g fibre

Useful source of potassium (480mg)

Hot cabbage and grape coleslaw *p218*

Avocado salad with raspberries *p216*

Crunchy nut coleslaw *p220*

Oriental sprouted salad *p219*

Hot cabbage and grape coleslaw

Crunchy, lightly cooked white cabbage is perfectly complemented by juicy fruit, walnuts and herbs in this well-balanced salad. It is a good example of how a combination of familiar ingredients can be elevated into a sophisticated side dish.

Preparation time **about 25 minutes**   Cooking time **7–8 minutes**   *Serves 4*

200g (7oz) mixed salad leaves

3 tbsp chopped fresh herbs, preferably chives, tarragon and parsley

1 tbsp walnut oil

2 tsp olive oil

125g (4½oz) celeriac

1 tbsp lemon juice

1 Asian pear

5 shallots, chopped

200g (7oz) white cabbage, finely shredded

4 tbsp red wine vinegar

pepper to taste

115g (4oz) seedless green grapes, halved

115g (4oz) seedless red grapes, halved

25g (1oz) walnut pieces

1 Combine the salad leaves with the herbs in a bowl. Add the walnut oil and 1 teaspoon of the olive oil and toss well. Arrange the dressed leaves on a serving platter or plates.

2 Peel the celeriac and cut it into matchstick strips. Toss with the lemon juice. Core the Asian pear and cut it into similar-sized strips. Toss with the celeriac and lemon juice, then scatter the celeriac and pear over the salad leaves.

3 Heat the remaining 1 teaspoon of olive oil in a large frying pan. Add the shallots and cook, stirring from time to time, for 4–5 minutes or until lightly browned. Add the cabbage and toss for 1 minute, then pour in the vinegar and boil until the vinegar has reduced by about half. Add pepper to taste and remove from the heat.

4 Add the green and red grapes and walnuts to the hot cabbage salad. Spoon the cabbage salad and its juices over the dressed leaves, celeriac and pear, and serve immediately.

Some more ideas

• Use a firm, ripe dessert pear instead of the Asian pear.

• For a main dish, add 225g (8oz) cooked cubed chicken breast with the cabbage. Serve with crusty bread.

• For a simple but delicious lunch or midweek supper, increase the amount of walnuts and serve the salad with jacket-baked potatoes.

Health points

• Cabbage belongs to a family of vegetables that contain a number of different phyto-chemicals which may help to protect against breast cancer. Cabbage is also a good source of vitamin C and is among the richest vegetable sources of folate.

photo, page 217

Each serving provides   Key nutrients 163kcals, 9g fat (of which 1g is saturated fat), 3g protein, 18g carbohydrate, 36mg sodium (0.09g salt) 4.5g fibre

Useful source of potassium (639mg)

Oriental sprouted salad

The Chinese-style dressing for this vibrant side salad, with zesty tones of ginger and coriander, complements the fresh flavours of sprouted beans and seeds, apple and vegetables.

Preparation time **10 minutes**   *Serves 4*

1 carrot

1 celery stick

1 large dessert apple

100g (3½oz) mung bean sprouts

50g (1¾oz) sprouted sunflower seeds

45g (1½oz) alfalfa sprouts

For the dressing

1 tbsp lime juice

1 tbsp finely chopped fresh coriander

2 tbsp sunflower oil

½ tsp toasted sesame oil

½ tsp low-sodium soy sauce

1 tsp grated fresh root ginger

pepper to taste

1 Cut the carrot into 4cm (1½in) lengths. Slice thinly lengthways, then cut into very fine matchsticks. Cut the celery into matchsticks the same size as the carrot. Core the apple and cut into 8 wedges, then thinly slice the wedges crossways to make fan-shaped pieces.

2 Combine the carrot, celery, apple, mung bean sprouts, sunflower sprouts and alfalfa sprouts in a mixing bowl.

3 To make the dressing, whisk together all the ingredients, seasoning with pepper to taste. Pour the dressing over the salad, toss well to coat evenly and serve.

Some more ideas

• If you don't have time to sprout your own beans and seeds, you can use sprouts bought from supermarkets and health food shops. Look for bags of mixtures such as sprouted aduki beans, lentils and chickpeas.

• For a more substantial salad, to serve as a light main dish, replace the mung bean sprouts with sprouted green or brown lentils, and stir in 225g (8oz) diced tofu.

Health points

• Sprouted beans and seeds are a good source of vitamin C and folate, as well as several phytochemicals including lutein, coumarins and xanthophylls.

photo, page 217

Each serving provides   Key nutrients 161kcals, 12g fat (of which 1.5g is saturated fat), 4g protein, 9g carbohydrate, 14mg sodium (0.014g salt), 2g fibre

Crunchy nut coleslaw

Everyone loves coleslaw. This crowd-pleaser is made with white cabbage, carrot and radishes, flecked with spring onions, sweet sultanas and roasted peanuts, and tossed with a creamy dressing that is tasty, yet low in fat.

Preparation time **15 minutes**   *Serves 4*

200g (7oz) white cabbage, finely shredded

1 large carrot, coarsely grated

50g (1¾oz) sultanas

4 spring onions, finely chopped, with the white and green parts kept separate

2 tbsp reduced-fat mayonnaise

150g (5½oz) plain low-fat yoghurt

pepper to taste

6 radishes, sliced

50g (1¾oz) unsalted roasted peanuts

3 tbsp chopped parsley or snipped fresh chives, or a mixture of the two *(optional)*

1 Mix together the cabbage, carrot, sultanas and white parts of the spring onions in a large bowl.

2 Stir the mayonnaise and yoghurt together and season with pepper to taste. Stir this dressing into the cabbage mixture and toss to coat all the ingredients.

3 Just before serving, stir in the radishes and peanuts, and sprinkle with the chopped green parts of the spring onions and the parsley or chives.

Some more ideas

• For a celeriac coleslaw, use 250g (9oz) peeled celeriac, cut into matchstick strips, instead of the cabbage. Flavour the dressing with 2 tsp whole-grain mustard and 1 tbsp mango chutney.

• Toss 1 cored and diced red dessert apple with 2 tbsp lemon juice, then stir into the coleslaw with 1 tsp caraway seeds.

• Add 100g (3½oz) canned or thawed frozen sweetcorn.

• Lightly toast 1 tbsp pumpkin seeds and 2 tbsp sunflower seeds, and use to garnish the coleslaw in place of the herbs.

Health points

• Roasted peanuts are a nutri-tious addition to a coleslaw. New research suggests that a daily intake of peanuts, peanut butter or peanut (groundnut) oil may help to lower levels of total cholesterol, harmful LDL cholesterol and triglyceride, to protect against heart disease.

photo, page 217

Each serving provides   Key nutrients 174kcals, 9g fat (of which 1.5g is saturated fat), 7g protein, 19g carbohydrate, 16mg sodium (0.29g salt), 3g fibre

Useful source of potassium (539mg)

Soups & stews

Asparagus and pea soup

This green version of classic vichyssoise is enriched with yoghurt rather than cream. Traditionally served chilled, the soup can also be served hot, so is ideal for days when the weather is changeable.

Preparation time **10 minutes, plus at least 1 hour chilling**   Cooking time **about 20 minutes**   *Serves 4*

1 tbsp sunflower oil

175g (6oz) potato, peeled and diced

1 medium leek, coarsely chopped

300g (10½oz) asparagus, trimmed and chopped

225g (8oz) sugarsnap peas, chopped

1.2 litres (2 pints) low-sodium chicken stock

1 tbsp finely snipped fresh chives or chopped fresh chervil

125g (4½oz) plain low-fat yoghurt

white pepper to taste

snipped fresh chives or sprigs of fresh chervil to garnish

1 Heat the oil in a large saucepan, add the potato and leek, and stir well. Cover and cook over low heat, stirring occasionally, for 5 minutes or until the leek has softened but not browned.

2 Stir in the asparagus and sugarsnap peas, then pour in enough of the stock to cover the vegetables. Bring to the boil, then cover and reduce the heat. Simmer gently for 5–7 minutes or until all the vegetables are tender.

3 Cool for a few minutes, then purée the vegetables with their cooking liquid in a blender or food processor. Pour into a bowl. Stir in the remaining stock, the chives or chervil and half of the yoghurt. Season to taste with white pepper. Leave to cool completely, then chill for at least 1 hour.

4 Taste and adjust the seasoning, if necessary. Ladle the soup into bowls and top each portion with a spoonful of the remaining yoghurt. Garnish with chives or chervil and serve immediately.

Some more ideas

Chilled cucumber soup
Replace the asparagus and sugarsnap peas with 1 cucumber, chopped, and the chives or chervil with 1 tbsp very finely chopped fresh mint. Cucumber contains a lot of water, so use only 600ml (1 pint) of stock. Garnish with shreds of fresh mint.

• The soup freezes well, but do not add the yoghurt before freezing: stir in the yoghurt when the soup is thawed but still chilled, then season, garnish and serve.

Health points

• Asparagus is an excellent source of folate. It also provides vitamins C and E as well as beta-carotene. In addition, asparagus has a mild laxative effect.

photo, page 225

Each serving provides   Key nutrients 122kcals, 4g fat (of which 0.5g is saturated fat), 8g protein,15g carbohydrate, 213mg sodium (0.5g salt), 3g fibre

Useful source of potassium (593mg)

Cream of courgette soup

This silky-smooth vitamin-rich soup tastes as good as it looks. Top this lively green soup with a pretty swirl of yoghurt and you've made a delightful summer lunch dish or a beautiful beginning for a summer dinner.

Preparation time **20 minutes**   Cooking time **25 minutes**   *Serves 8*

1 tbsp olive oil

1 large onion, coarsely chopped

2 garlic cloves, finely chopped

900ml (1½ pints) low-sodium vegetable stock

225g (8oz) potatoes, peeled and diced

450g (1lb) courgettes, trimmed and thinly sliced

70g (2½oz) parsley leaves

225ml (8fl oz) semi-skimmed milk

pepper to taste

225g (8oz) plain low-fat yoghurt

1 In a large saucepan, heat the oil over moderate heat. Add the onion and garlic with about 4 tablespoons of the stock. Sauté until softened but not browned. Add the potatoes and stir to coat. Pour in the remaining stock and bring to the boil.

2 Add the courgettes and simmer, partially covered, for 10 minutes or until all vegetables are very tender.

3 Remove from the heat and stir in the parsley. Strain the soup liquid into a large bowl. Purée the vegetables in a blender or food processor until very smooth.

4 Stir the purée into the liquid and allow to cool. Stir in the milk and pepper, and chill the soup until ready to serve. Top each bowl of soup with a large spoonful of yoghurt. With the tip of a spoon, gently draw the yoghurt out in a circle to make an attractive swirl.

Some more ideas

Chilled cream of carrot soup Substitute 4 large carrots, peeled and diced, for the courgettes.

• For a richer-tasting soup, use evaporated skimmed milk in place of the fresh semi-skimmed milk.

Health points

• Courgettes supply good amounts of vitamins B_1, C and folate. Adding the milk and yoghurt helps to boost the calcium level and gives the soup a rich, creamy taste without adding too much fat.

Each serving provides   **Key nutrients** 80kcals, 2.5g fat (of which 1g is saturated fat), 4.5g protein, 11g carbohydrate, 128mg sodium (0.3g salt), 1g fibre

Useful source of potassium (444mg)

Cool blueberry soup

Start off a light summer supper in Scandinavian style, with this deep-blue-coloured soup. And you don't even have to wait for summer to make it, because you can use fresh or frozen blueberries.

Preparation time **5 minutes**   Cooking time **2 minutes**   *Serves 4*

3 tbsp sugar

1 tsp grated lemon zest

good pinch of ground allspice

225ml (8fl oz) water

550g (1¼lb) fresh or frozen blueberries

300g (10½oz) plain low-fat yoghurt

2 tbsp fresh lemon juice

1 Combine the sugar, lemon zest, allspice and water in a small frying pan over medium heat. Bring to the boil and boil for 1 minute to dissolve the sugar.

2 Put the blueberries, 225g (8oz) of the yoghurt and the lemon juice in a food processor or blender. Remove the syrup from the heat and add to the food processor. Purée until smooth.

3 Allow to cool, then chill until ready to serve. Top each serving with 1 tablespoon of yoghurt.

Some more ideas

Berry granita Freeze the berry mixture in an ice cube tray, then briefly whiz the frozen cubes in a food processor until slushy. Serve immediately.

• Follow the blueberry soup with grilled salmon, steamed sugarsnap peas and pan-roasted new potatoes, and serve biscotti for dessert.

Health points

• Blueberries supply a type of heart-healthy soluble fibre called pectin. Scientists believe that pectin helps to lower LDL cholesterol levels by binding cholesterol in the intestine and pulling it out of the body before it can be absorbed.

Each serving provides   Key nutrients 121kcals, 1g fat (of which 0.5g is saturated fat), 6g protein, 24g carbohydrate, 67mg sodium (0.17g salt), 3g fibre

Useful source of potassium (432mg)

Cool blueberry soup *p224*

Asparagus and pea soup *p222*

Peach soup with almonds *p226*

Cream of leek and potato soup *p227*

Peach soup with almonds

Buttermilk and nutmeg combine with the fresh peaches to create a thick, creamy soup that's not too tart and not too sweet. It's a great way to enjoy one of your daily servings of fruit.

Preparation time **20 minutes plus chilling**   Cooking time **20 minutes**   *Serves 4*

675g (1½lb) fresh peaches

225ml (8fl oz) water

thinly pared zest of 1 lemon, cut in wide strips

2 tbsp sugar

450m (16fl oz) buttermilk or semi-skimmed milk

pinch of grated nutmeg

225ml (8fl oz) peach nectar

25g (1oz) flaked almonds

1 Bring a large saucepan of water to the boil. Add the peaches and return to the boil. Immediately transfer the peaches to a bowl of cold water. When cool enough to handle, peel the peaches. Cut into chunks, discarding the stones.

2 Put the water, lemon zest and sugar in the empty saucepan and bring to the boil. Add the peaches. Cover and simmer, stirring occasionally, for 5–8 minutes or until very soft. Remove from the heat, and discard the lemon zest.

3 Pour half of the buttermilk or semi-skimmed milk into a food processor or blender. Using a slotted spoon, transfer the peaches from their syrup to the food processor; reserve the syrup. Whiz the peaches to a purée. Turn into a large bowl. Add the remaining buttermilk or milk, the nutmeg and peach nectar. Stir in the reserved syrup. Cover and chill for at least 1 hour.

4 Preheat the oven to 180°C (350°F, gas mark 4). Spread the almonds on a baking tray and toast in the oven for about 10 minutes or until golden. Cool. Sprinkle the almonds on the soup before serving.

Some more ideas

• You can make this soup with many other summer fruits. Nectarines and plums are excellent choices. Try mango juice instead of peach for a more tropical flavour.

Health points

• Peaches are an excellent source of vitamin A and a good source of vitamin C. Their moderate amounts of fibre can also help lower cholesterol.

photo, page 225

Each serving provides   Key nutrients 187kcals, 4g fat (of which 0.5g is saturated fat), 7g protein, 32g carbohydrate, 73mg sodium (0.18g salt), 3 g fibre

Useful source of potassium (548mg)

Cream of leek and potato soup

Leeks are closely related to onions – which accounts for their wonderful similarity in flavour. A pinch of freshly chopped chives and a swirl of fromage frais add just the right contrasting touches to this classic soup.

Preparation time **15 minutes**   Cooking time **45 minutes**   *Serves 6*

1 tbsp olive oil

225g (8oz) leeks, white part only, thickly sliced

1 large onion, coarsely chopped

900ml (1½ pints) low-sodium chicken stock

450g (1lb) potatoes, peeled and diced

white pepper to taste

5 tbsp fromage frais

chopped fresh chives to garnish

1 Heat the oil in a large saucepan over moderate heat. Stir in the leeks and onion with 175ml (6fl oz) of the stock. Cover and cook, stirring frequently, for 10 minutes or until soft but not browned. Add the potatoes and stir to mix.

2 Pour in half of the remaining stock and bring to the boil. Simmer, partially covered, for 15–20 minutes or until the potatoes are very soft. Remove from the heat. Transfer to a blender or food processor and purée until very smooth.

3 Pour the remaining stock into the pan. Add the vegetable purée and bring the soup to a simmer, stirring constantly. Season with white pepper to taste.

4 Remove from the heat and stir in the fromage frais. Ladle into soup bowls and garnish with chives.

Some more ideas

• Add small cubes of cooked chicken breast to the soup in step 3 as the soup simmers.

• You can make other 'cream' soups in this fashion. Use asparagus, broccoli or carrots in place of, or in addition to, the potatoes.

Health points

• Instead of the traditional double cream used in these kinds of soups, this equally delicious version is enriched with fromage frais. This saves on total fat content as well as on saturated fat.

photo, page 225

Each serving provides   Key nutrients 108kcals, 3.5g fat (of which 1g is saturated fat), 4g protein, 17g carbohydrate, 34mg sodium (0.08g salt), 2g fibre

Useful source of potassium (423mg)

Mediterranean roasted vegetable soup

A Mediterranean sweetness from a bounty of roasted and caramelised vegetables makes each bowl of this soup a treasured memory. Carrot juice in place of stock powers up the nutrition as well as the flavour.

Preparation time **25 minutes**   Cooking time **40 minutes**   *Serves 4*

1 tbsp olive oil

5 garlic cloves, peeled

350g (12oz) potatoes, unpeeled, cut into 1cm (½in) chunks

2 peppers (1 green and 1 yellow), cut into 1cm (½in) squares

2 tsp finely chopped fresh rosemary

1 large yellow or green courgette, halved lengthways, then cut crossways into 1cm (½in) pieces

1 large red onion, cut into 1cm (½in) chunks

350ml (12fl oz) carrot juice

350g (12oz) plum tomatoes, diced

1 tsp fresh tarragon

175ml (6fl oz) water

1 Preheat the oven to 230°C (450°F, gas mark 8). Combine the oil and garlic in a roasting tin and heat in the oven for 5 minutes or until the oil begins to sizzle. Add the potatoes, peppers and rosemary, and toss to coat with the oil. Roast for 15 minutes or until the potatoes begin to colour and soften.

2 Add the courgette and onion, and continue roasting for 15 minutes or until the courgette is tender.

3 Mix together the carrot juice, tomatoes and tarragon in a large saucepan and bring to the boil over medium heat. Spoon the roasted vegetables into the pan.

4 Pour the water into the roasting tin and scrape up any browned bits. Pour these juices into the saucepan. Cook, stirring, for 2 minutes or until heated through.

Some more ideas

• When they're in season, use Jersey Royal or other new potatoes. Or try sweet potatoes.

• Substitute patty pan squash for the courgette. Depending on their size, use 2–4 patty pans.

Health points

• Intensely coloured vegetables like peppers and tomatoes provide potent, disease-fighting carotenoids, such as beta-carotene and lycopene.

photo, page 231

Each serving provides   **Key nutrients** 170kcals, 4g fat (of which 0.5g is saturated fat), 5g protein, 30g carbohydrate, 63mg sodium (0.16g salt), 4g fibre

Good source of potassium (1085mg)

Cheddar cheese and broccoli soup

With the creaminess of your favourite comfort food, this recipe delivers a satisfying bowl of goodness – silky-smooth, yet still full of vegetable flavour. The Cheddar cheese brings it all together.

Preparation time **15 minutes**   Cooking time **23 minutes**   *Serves 6*

450g (1lb) broccoli

1 tbsp olive oil

1 onion, chopped

1 celery stick, chopped

2 tbsp plain flour

400ml (14fl oz) low-sodium chicken stock

1 can (about 400g) evaporated skimmed milk

350g (12oz) reduced-fat Cheddar cheese, grated

¼ tsp grated nutmeg

pepper to taste

1 Trim and peel the broccoli stalks. Cut off 12 small florets. Coarsely chop the remaining broccoli (with the peeled stalks). Blanch the chopped broccoli and florets in boiling water for 2 minutes or until bright green. Drain and set aside.

2 Heat the oil in a medium saucepan over medium heat. Add the onion and celery, and sauté for 5 minutes or until soft. Whisk in the flour and cook for 1 minute. Add the stock and milk. Cook, stirring constantly, for 5 minutes or until the mixture simmers and thickens.

3 Add the blanched chopped broccoli, cheese, nutmeg and pepper to taste. Stir over low heat for about 3 minutes or until the cheese melts and the soup is heated through; do not boil. Serve garnished with the broccoli florets.

Some more ideas

Cheddar cheese and asparagus soup Replace the broccoli with 450g (1lb) asparagus spears, coarsely chopped. Use the asparagus tips to garnish. The switch from broccoli to asparagus increases the folate content of the soup. Folate helps protect against heart disease.

Health points

• Cheddar cheese is a very good source of calcium, a mineral that is vital for the development and maintenance of healthy bones and teeth.

Each serving provides   **Key nutrients** 290kcals, 14g fat (of which 7g is saturated fat), 28g protein, 13g carbohydrate, 480mg sodium (1.2g salt), 2.5g fibre

Useful source of potassium (565mg)

Old-fashioned chicken noodle soup

Anyone can make a wonderful bowl of chicken soup. The trick is to start with a fresh broth, using good-quality chicken. Add a few vegetables and noodles to the broth, and you'll see why this is known as a restorative.

Preparation time **about 45 minutes**   Cooking time **1 hour 15 minutes**   *Serves 4*

For the broth

1 chicken, about 1.35kg (3lb) skinned and jointed, or 4 chicken quarters, skinned

2 onions, halved, the inner layer of skin left on

3 carrots, chopped

3 celery sticks, chopped

1 bouquet garni

4 black peppercorns

For the soup

115g (4oz) spaghetti or linguine, broken into 5cm (2in) pieces

1 carrot, halved lengthways and thinly sliced

1 celery stick, thinly sliced

55g (2oz) small broccoli florets

200g (7oz) frozen sweetcorn, thawed

pepper to taste

2 tbsp finely chopped parsley

2 tsp fresh thyme leaves

1 First make the broth. Put the chicken joints in a large, heavy stockpot or saucepan. Add the onions, carrots and celery, then pour in about 2 litres (3½ pints) cold water to cover the ingredients. Bring to the boil, skimming the surface constantly until all grey scum is removed.

2 Reduce the heat to low immediately after the liquid boils. Add the bouquet garni and peppercorns. Partially cover the pan and simmer for 1 hour, skimming as necessary. Test the chicken joints after 30–40 minutes; remove them as soon as they are cooked (the juices will run clear when the joints are pierced with the tip of a knife). Set aside.

3 Line a large colander or sieve with dampened muslin and place it over a large heatproof bowl. Strain the broth through this. Discard the vegetables and flavouring ingredients. Return 1.5 litres (2¾ pints) of broth to the cleaned pan. Skim off any excess fat on the surface. (Cool and freeze the leftover broth to use as a chicken stock in other recipes.)

4 When the chicken is cool enough to handle, remove and discard all the bones. Cut 225g (8oz) meat into bite-size pieces for use in the soup. Reserve the remaining chicken for sandwiches or other recipes.

5 Bring the broth to the boil, then reduce the heat so the broth is simmering. Add the spaghetti or linguine and the carrot, and simmer for 4 minutes. Add the celery, broccoli and sweetcorn, and continue cooking for 5 minutes or until the pasta and all the vegetables are just tender.

6 Stir in the chicken with pepper to taste and heat through. Sprinkle in the parsley and thyme, and serve the soup at once.

Some more ideas

• Increase the fibre content by using wholemeal spaghetti. Alternatively, add 1 can (about 400g) butter beans, drained and rinsed. Stir in the beans with the chicken and just heat through.

• Vary the vegetables to suit the season. Small cauliflower florets, finely diced celeriac, sliced mushrooms or diced green, red and yellow peppers are all ideal. The fresher the better!

Health points

• Unlike the majority of vegetables, which are most nutritious when eaten raw, carrots are a better source of beta-carotene when they are cooked. Cooking breaks down their cell membranes, making it easier for the body to convert their beta-carotene into vitamin A.

Each serving provides   Key nutrients 233kcals, 3g fat (of which 0.5g is saturated fat), 18g protein, 31g carbohydrate, 295mg sodium (0.7g salt), 2g fibre

Useful source of potassium (481mg)

Old-fashioned chicken noodle soup *p230*

Mediterranean roasted vegetable soup *p228*

New England clam chowder *p232*

Soup of leafy greens and herbs *p233*

New England clam chowder

This rich, creamy American soup is all that you'd want a chowder to be – hearty with potatoes and chunky with lots of plump, juicy clams. It's substantial enough to make a meal on its own.

Preparation time **15 minutes**   Cooking time **30 minutes**   *Serves 4*

900g (2lb) clams in shell, scrubbed

450ml (16fl oz) water

4 turkey rashers, cut into 1cm (½in) pieces

1 large onion, chopped

2 tbsp plain flour

450g (1lb) potatoes, peeled and cut into 1cm (½in) cubes

450 ml (16fl oz) semi-skimmed milk

2 tsp fresh thyme leaves

1 bay leaf

pinch of cayenne pepper

4 tbsp chopped fresh flat-leaf parsley

1 Put the clams and water in a large saucepan and bring to the boil over high heat. Reduce the heat, cover and cook for 5 minutes or until the clams open (discard any that remain stubbornly closed). Transfer the clams with a slotted spoon to a bowl. Strain the clam broth, adding water to make 350ml (12fl oz), if necessary; set aside. Wipe out the saucepan.

2 Lightly coat the saucepan with cooking spray and set over medium heat. Add the turkey rashers and onion, and sauté for 7 minutes or until the onion is golden. Sprinkle in the flour and cook, stirring constantly, for 1 minute or just until bubbling but not browned.

3 Add the potatoes, milk, reserved clam broth, thyme, bay leaf and cayenne pepper. Bring to a simmer and cook, stirring occasionally, for about 10 minutes or until the potatoes are tender (do not allow to boil).

4 Meanwhile, remove the clams from their shells and cut into bite-size pieces, if necessary. Stir the clams into the chowder and cook for a further 2 minutes or until heated through. Discard the bay leaf. Ladle into bowls and sprinkle with the parsley.

Some more ideas

Manhattan clam chowder
Omit the milk and instead use 1 can (about 400g) no-salt-added chopped tomatoes, with their liquid, and 225ml (8fl oz) low-sodium chicken stock.

• If fresh clams aren't available you can use 3 cans (about 200g each) of clams. Drain, rinse very well to remove the salty brine and drain again.

Health points

• This lighter version of clam chowder uses a small amount of turkey rashers to add a smoky bacon flavour. It is also made with semi-skimmed milk whisked with a little flour rather than with cream. Both of these give the chowder an authentic flavour without the fat.

photo, page 231

Each serving (2 cups per bowl) provides   **Key Nutrients** 261kcals, 6g fat (of which 2g is saturated fat), 19g protein, 34g carbohydrate, 466mg sodium (1.1g salt), 2g fibre

Useful source of potassium (755mg)

Soup of leafy greens and herbs

Hearty but not too heavy, this is a wonderful dish for summer and autumn, when so many vegetables are at the peak of flavour. You can use all sorts of greens – simply adjust the cooking time accordingly. So be creative!

Preparation time **20–25 minutes**   Cooking time **about 30 minutes**   *Serves 4*

2 tbsp olive oil

1 leek, white part only, cut into thin strips

1 small onion, chopped

½ carrot, thinly sliced

4 garlic cloves, chopped

½ tsp fennel seeds

2 tbsp chopped parsley

55g (2oz) cooked ham, trimmed of fat, then cut into thin strips or chopped

115g (4oz) Swiss chard or spinach, very finely shredded

3 small ripe tomatoes or no-salt-added canned whole tomatoes, diced

1.5 litres (2¾ pints) low-sodium chicken or vegetable stock

pinch of crushed dried chillies *(optional)*

pepper to taste

225g (8oz) small pasta shapes, such as conchigliette (shells) or ditalini (small thimbles)

55g (2oz) fresh basil, stalks discarded, thinly sliced or torn

2 tbsp freshly grated Parmesan cheese

1 Heat the oil in a large saucepan. Add the leek and onion, and cook for 5 minutes or until slightly softened. Add the carrot, garlic, fennel seeds, parsley and ham. Continue cooking for about 5 minutes, stirring occasionally.

2 Stir in the shredded greens and the tomatoes, and cover the pan. Cook for 2 minutes or until the greens are slightly softened, then pour in the stock. Add the crushed chillies, if using. Season to taste with pepper. Bring to the boil, then simmer over a medium-high heat for 5 minutes or until the shredded greens are just tender.

3 Meanwhile, cook the pasta in a big pan of boiling water according to the packet instructions. Drain well.

4 Divide the pasta among four serving bowls. Ladle the soup into the bowls and sprinkle with the basil and grated Parmesan. Serve immediately.

Some more ideas

Middle Eastern leafy green soup Omit the ham and use vegetable stock. Stir 150g (5½oz) plain low-fat yoghurt into the soup, off the heat. Add 3 tbsp chopped fresh coriander and the juice of ½ lemon (or to taste). Serve hot, sprinkled with paprika and cayenne pepper to taste.

• For a Chinese-style soup, omit the fennel seeds, parsley, ham, basil and Parmesan, and spice the soup with 1–2 tbsp finely chopped fresh root ginger and low-sodium soy sauce to taste. Add 85g (3oz) firm tofu, cut into small cubes.

• Other greens that are good in this soup include pak choy, Chinese leaves, kale and watercress. Coarser leaves, such as kale, will take a little more time to cook.

Health points

• Dark green, leafy vegetables provide good amounts of beta-carotene, as well as the B vitamins niacin, folate and B$_6$.

photo, page 231

Each serving provides   **Key nutrients** 350kcals, 11g fat (of which 3g is saturated fat), 15g protein, 52g carbohydrate, 379mg sodium (0.96g salt), 4g fibre

Useful source of potassium (671mg)

Minestrone with meatballs

In Italian, a 'minestra' is a soup, but a 'minestrone' is a BIG soup – a meal in itself. Tender and moist turkey meatballs and a host of seasonal herbs and vegetables enhance the depth of flavour in this one-bowl meal.

Preparation time **15 minutes**   Cooking time **20 minutes**   *Serves 4*

1 tsp olive oil

1 small onion, finely chopped

3 garlic cloves, finely chopped

225g (8oz) skinless, boneless turkey breast, cut into chunks

3 tbsp rolled oats

4 tbsp semi-skimmed milk

25g (1oz) Parmesan cheese, freshly grated

25g (1oz) fresh basil, chopped

450ml (16fl oz) low-sodium chicken stock

1 can (about 400g) no-salt-added canned chopped tomatoes

450ml (16fl oz) water

75g (2½oz) farfallini (small bow-tie pasta) or other small soup pasta shapes

280g (10oz) kale, shredded

1 yellow or green courgette, quartered lengthways and thickly sliced

1 Heat the oil in a medium nonstick saucepan over low heat. Add the onion and garlic, and cook, stirring frequently, for about 5 minutes or until the onion is tender. Transfer to a medium bowl and cool to room temperature.

2 Meanwhile, place the turkey in a food processor and pulse on and off until finely minced. Transfer the turkey to the bowl with the onion mixture.

3 Add the oats, milk, 2 tablespoons of the Parmesan and 2 tablespoons of the basil, and mix to combine. Gently shape the mixture into 24 small meatballs.

4 Combine the stock, tomatoes and water in a large saucepan and bring to the boil over high heat. Add the pasta and kale, and cook for 5 minutes.

5 Reduce to a simmer. Add the remaining basil and the meatballs, and cook for 1 minute. Add the courgette, cover and simmer for about 5 minutes or until the meatballs are cooked through and the kale is tender. Serve sprinkled with the remaining Parmesan.

Some more ideas

• Make the meatballs using chicken breast instead of turkey. Or combine 115g (4oz) each lean minced beef and turkey or chicken.

• Substitute spinach leaves for the kale. Kale contains more vitamin C than spinach, but spinach has a higher amount of beta-carotene.

Health points

• Kale is an often forgotten leafy green, even though it is mild enough to be acceptable to most palates. It is rich in fibre and calcium, and can nicely substitute for spinach in many recipes.

Each serving provides   Key nutrients 271kcals, 7g fat (of which 2g is saturated fat), 25g protein, 30g carbohydrate, 210mg sodium (0.53g salt), 4.5g fibre

Good source of potassium (944mg)

Minestrone with meatballs *p234*

Beefy mushroom and barley soup *p236*

Speedy two-bean chilli *p240*

Moroccan vegetable tagine *p239*

Beefy mushroom and barley soup

Visions of cauldrons of soup cooked on an open fire come to mind with each spoonful of this robust soup. One-dish meals like this are all the rage now, and it's easy to see how they have satisfied generations.

Preparation time **20 minutes**   Cooking time **1 hour**   *Serves 6*

350g (12oz) lean stewing steak, cut into 2.5cm (1in) cubes

3 medium onions, coarsely chopped

280g (10oz) mushrooms, sliced

3 large carrots, sliced

100g (3½oz) pearl barley

1.5 litres (2¾ pints) low-sodium beef stock

225ml (8fl oz) dry red wine or tomato juice

pepper to taste

140g (5oz) frozen peas

2 tsp fresh lemon juice

1 Coat a large heavy saucepan with cooking spray or a teaspoon of olive oil and set over medium-high heat until hot. Add the beef cubes and sauté until brown on all sides. Transfer with a slotted spoon to a double layer of kitchen paper to drain.

2 Sauté the onions and mushrooms in the pan drippings for about 7 minutes or until the onions are golden. Return the beef to the pan. Stir in the carrots, barley, stock, wine and pepper to taste, and bring to the boil.

3 Reduce the heat to medium-low and simmer, partially covered, for about 45 minutes or until the beef and barley are tender. Stir in the peas and cook, uncovered, for a further 5 minutes or until they are hot. Remove from the heat, stir in the lemon juice and serve.

Some more ideas

Beefy mushroom and brown rice soup Instead of pearl barley, use 175g (6oz) rinsed long-grain brown rice

• Substitute 350g (12oz) cubed boneless, skinless chicken thighs for the stewing steak.

Health points

• The barley and vegetables, full of nutritious complex carbohydrates, balance out the beef in just the right proportions. Barley is a fair source of the B vitamins needed for energy production.

photo, page 235

Each serving provides   **Key nutrients** 207kcals, 3g fat (of which 1g is saturated fat), 18g protein, 21g carbohydrate, 84mg sodium (0.2g salt), 2.5g fibre

Useful source of potassium (594mg)

Tomato and lentil soup

Lentils and dried mushrooms bring a robust, earthy flavour to this soul-soothing lunch or light supper dish. Pungent ginger and sweet tarragon add complexity.

Preparation time **10 minutes**   Cooking time **55 minutes**   *Serves 4*

25g (1oz) dried porcini mushrooms

225ml (8fl oz) hot water

1 tbsp olive oil

1 large onion, finely chopped

3 garlic cloves, finely chopped

1 can (about 400g) no-salt-added chopped tomatoes

1 tsp ground ginger

1 tsp dried tarragon

450ml (16fl oz) cold water

100g (3½oz) green or brown lentils, picked over and rinsed

1 Combine the mushrooms and hot water in a small bowl. Leave to soak for 20 minutes or until rehydrated. With a slotted spoon, scoop out the mushrooms. Strain the liquid and set aside. Coarsely chop the mushrooms.

2 Heat the oil in a large saucepan over medium heat. Add the onion and garlic, and cook, stirring frequently, for about 7 minutes or until the onion is golden.

3 Stir in the mushrooms with their soaking liquid, the tomatoes with their juice, the ginger, tarragon and cold water. Add the lentils and bring to the boil. Reduce to a simmer, then cover and cook for about 30 minutes or until the lentils are tender. Serve hot. (The soup can be cooled and refrigerated; reheat gently for serving, adding 1–2 tablespoons of water if it is too thick.)

Some more ideas

Tomato and yellow split pea soup Simply replace the lentils with yellow split peas. Cook for the same length of time.

• Serve the soup with wholegrain bread, with fresh fruit for dessert.

• Use low-sodium chicken stock instead of water.

Health points

• Dried mushrooms are loaded with blood-pressure-lowering potassium. Another way to use them is to grind them into a powder and then use the powder to flavour and thicken sauces and stews.

Each serving provides   **Key nutrients** 141kcals, 3.5g fat (of which 0.5g is saturated fat), 8g protein, 21g carbohydrate, 47mg sodium (0.11g salt), 3g fibre

Useful source of potassium (597mg)

Chickpea soup with asparagus

Adding orzo, a rice-shaped pasta, to this tasty soup makes it deliciously filling. For a main meal, serve with a little strong-flavoured cheese and some warm, crusty bread.

Preparation time **15 minutes**   Cooking time **about 40 minutes**   *Serves 4*

1 can (about 400g) chickpeas (no-added-salt variety), drained and rinsed

1 onion, coarsely chopped

2 garlic cloves, chopped

1 litre (1¾ pints) low-sodium chicken or vegetable stock

150g (5½oz) asparagus, trimmed and cut into bite-size pieces

175g (6oz) orzo or other soup pasta

pepper to taste

finely pared zest of 1 lemon, in shreds

2 tbsp chopped parsley

1 lemon, cut into wedges, to serve

1 Put the chickpeas, onion, garlic and stock in a saucepan and bring to the boil. Reduce the heat and simmer for 20 minutes or until the chickpeas are falling apart.

2 Ladle about one-third of the soup into a blender or food processor and purée it until smooth. Return the puréed soup to the pan and bring back to simmering point. Add the asparagus, cover and cook gently for 5–6 minutes or until the asparagus is just tender.

3 Meanwhile, cook the orzo in a large pan of boiling water according to the packet instructions. Drain the pasta and add it to the soup, with pepper to taste.

4 Mix together the lemon zest and parsley. Top each bowl of soup with a small spoonful of the lemon and parsley mixture and serve immediately, offering lemon wedges so that the juice can be added to the soup to taste.

Some more ideas

• Use small broccoli florets instead of asparagus. Broccoli is an excellent source of vitamin C, and the quantity in this soup will provide about one-quarter of the recommended daily intake of that vitamin.

• There are many tiny pasta shapes for soup (called *pastina* in Italy). Orzo is rice-shaped; other shapes are stelline (stars), ditalini (tubes), conchigliette (shells) and farfallini (bow ties). You can also use larger pasta shapes (penne or rigatoni, for example), if you prefer.

Health points

• Asparagus is a rich source of many of the B vitamins, especially folate. New research suggests that folate may have a role in helping to prevent Alzheimer's disease.

Each serving provides   Key nutrients 280kcals, 3.5g fat (of which 0.6g is saturated fat), 14g protein, 51g carbohydrate, 66mg sodium (0.16g salt), 6g fibre

Useful source of potassium (530mg)

Moroccan vegetable tagine

Even meat eaters will love this flavour-packed vegetable stew. Despite the long list of ingredients, the stew is simple to prepare for a hearty family meal. Serve it with couscous spiced with a little harissa sauce.

Preparation time **25 minutes**   Cooking time **30 minutes**   *Serves 4*

1 tbsp olive oil

1 large red onion, chopped

4 garlic cloves, sliced

1 tbsp shredded fresh root ginger

550g (1¼lb) butternut squash, peeled, seeded and cubed

1 tsp each ground cinnamon, cumin and coriander

6 green cardamom pods, split open and seeds lightly crushed

3 bay leaves

2 cans (400g each) no-salt-added chopped tomatoes

3 large carrots, thickly sliced

300ml (10fl oz) low-sodium chicken or vegetable stock

55g (2oz) raisins

25g (1oz) dried cherries

125g (4½oz) okra, each sliced lengthways into 3

1 large red pepper, chopped

1 can (about 400g) chickpeas, no-added-salt variety, drained and rinsed

25g (1oz) toasted flaked almonds

3 tbsp chopped parsley

1 Heat the oil in a very large pan, add the onion and sauté over high heat for 2–3 minutes or until beginning to soften and colour. Add the garlic and ginger, and cook for a few more seconds, then add the squash and sauté for about 1 minute.

2 Turn down the heat to medium. Add the spices, bay leaves, tomatoes and carrots. Pour in the stock and bring to the boil. Stir in the raisins and cherries, then cover and simmer for 10 minutes.

3 Stir the okra and red pepper into the stew. Cover again and leave to simmer for 5 minutes. Add the chickpeas and stir. Simmer, covered, for a further 5–10 minutes or until all the vegetables are tender, but still retain their shape.

4 Pile the vegetable stew on a platter, on top of hot couscous, and scatter over the toasted almonds and chopped parsley.

Some more ideas

Apricot and coriander tagine Replace the cherries and raisins with 85g (3oz) dried apricots, and substitute halved French beans for the okra. Instead of sprinkling the tagine with parsley, add 2 tbsp chopped fresh coriander to the stew at the end of the cooking time and scatter more over the finished dish.

• Whole new potatoes can replace the carrots, and red kidney beans can be used as an alternative to chickpeas.

Health points

• Beans and chickpeas are excellent sources of protein, even better when they are eaten with grains such as wheat (couscous) and rice. Canned versions are a convenient way of including them in the diet with the minimum of effort.

photo, page 235

Each serving provides   Key nutrients 352kcals, 9g fat (of which 1g is saturated fat), 14g protein, 57g carbohydrate, 142mg sodium (0.36g salt), 12g fibre

Excellent source of potassium (1778mg)

Speedy two-bean chilli

Here's a hearty and satisfying chilli – without the meat but with all the flavour. This version combines two varieties of beans with sweetcorn in a rich tomato sauce seasoned with herbs, fresh chilli and chilli sauce.

Preparation time **5 minutes**   Cooking time **25 minutes**   *Serves 4*

2 tbsp olive oil

1 large onion, halved and sliced

1 fresh red chilli, deseeded and chopped

1 can (about 400g) no-salt-added chopped tomatoes

1 tbsp chilli sauce

2 tbsp tomato ketchup

600ml (1 pint) low-sodium chicken or vegetable stock

1 tbsp chopped parsley

1 tbsp chopped fresh oregano

pepper to taste

1 can (about 400g) red kidney beans (no-salt-added variety), drained and rinsed

1 can (about 400g) cannellini beans, drained and rinsed

200g (7oz) frozen sweetcorn, thawed

150g (5½oz) fromage frais

2 tbsp snipped fresh chives

fresh oregano leaves to garnish *(optional)*

1 Heat the oil in a large frying pan. Add the onion and chilli, and cook over medium heat, stirring occasionally, for about 5 minutes or until the onion is lightly browned.

2 Stir in the tomatoes with their juice, the chilli sauce, ketchup, stock, parsley and oregano, with pepper to taste. Bring to the boil, then reduce the heat and simmer for 10 minutes, stirring occasionally.

3 Add the kidney and cannellini beans and the sweetcorn. Simmer for 10 minutes.

4 Meanwhile, mix the fromage frais with the snipped chives. Serve the chilli sprinkled with oregano leaves and offer the fromage frais mixture to be spooned on top.

Some more ideas

Vegetarian chilli burgers
Cook the onion and chilli as in the main recipe, then place in a food processor. Omit the tomatoes and stock, but add all the remaining ingredients to the processor. Add 200g (7oz) fresh breadcrumbs and 1 egg yolk. Process until smooth, then divide into 8 portions. Shape into burgers and chill for at least 1 hour. Coat the burgers with more fresh bread-crumbs, pressing them on neatly. Brush each burger with a little olive oil and cook in a nonstick frying pan for 10 minutes on each side.

Health points

• Beans have a lot going for them. They are a cheap source of protein, a good source of B-group vitamins and, when sprouted, are an excellent source of vitamin C. Kidney beans and cannellini beans provide more than three times the amount of fibre found in many vegetables.

photo, page 235

Each serving provides   Key nutrients 353kcals, 11g fat (of which 3g is saturated fat), 20g protein, 50g carbohydrate, 312mg sodium (0.79g salt), 13g fibre

Good source of potassium (1197mg)

Sweet things

Frozen pineapple and berry slush

A cross between a sorbet and a thick drink, this refreshing, virtually fat-free fruit slush takes just seconds to whiz up. The secret of preparing it quickly is to keep a selection of chopped fruit in the freezer.

Preparation time **5–15 minutes, plus about 1½ hours** *Serves 4*

8 ice cubes

225g (8oz) hulled strawberries, frozen

225g (8oz) fresh pineapple chunks, frozen

125ml (4fl oz) pineapple juice

2 tbsp skimmed milk powder

1 tbsp caster sugar, or to taste

sprigs of fresh mint to garnish

1 Put the ice cubes in a food processor or heavy-duty blender and process until they are finely crushed. Alternatively, crush the ice cubes in a freezerproof bag, using a rolling pin, and then put them in the processor or blender.

2 Add the strawberries, pineapple chunks, pineapple juice and milk powder, and process until blended but still with small pieces of fruit and ice visible.

3 Taste and sweeten with sugar, if necessary. (The amount of sugar required will depend on the sweetness of the fruit.) Process briefly, using the pulse button.

4 Spoon into tall glasses, decorate each with a sprig of mint and serve, with long spoons.

Some more ideas

• If the recipe makes more than you need, freeze it in ice cube trays. Then you can just whiz the cubes in a food processor or blender for an instant slush. Add fruit juice to dilute it, if necessary.

Summer fruit slush Use a 500g bag of frozen mixed summer fruit (blackberries, blueberries, cherries, red currants, raspberries, and strawberries). Add 4 tbsp orange juice and 2 tbsp skimmed milk powder, and process. Sweeten with a little sugar to taste, if necessary.

Tropical slush Use 2 mangoes, stoned, chopped and frozen, and 1 fresh banana. Add 4 tbsp reduced-fat coconut milk and 4 tbsp orange juice.

Health points

• Skimmed milk powder, used here to give the slush some body, provides calcium, which is essential for healthy bones and teeth. It also supplies protein, zinc, and vitamins B_2 and B_{12}.

Each serving provides Key nutrients 68kcals, 0.2g fat (of which 0g is saturated fat), 1g protein, 17g carbohydrate, 15mg sodium (0.01g salt), 1.5g fibre

Frozen pineapple and berry slush *p242*

Fruit boats with orange glaze *p246*

Far Eastern fruit salad *p247*

Mango, peach and apricot fizz *p244*

Mango, peach and apricot fizz

Fruit puréed with a little fizzy ginger ale makes a wonderfully refreshing drink that also offers a healthy serving of fruit. Choose perfectly ripe, fragrant fruit for the smoothest fizz.

Preparation time **5–10 minutes**   *Serves 4*

1 ripe mango

1 ripe peach

2 large ripe apricots

450ml (16fl oz) ginger ale

fresh mint leaves to garnish

1 Peel the mango and cut the flesh away from the stone. Roughly chop the flesh and put it into a blender or food processor.

2 Cover the peach and apricots with boiling water and leave for about 30 seconds, then drain and cool under cold running water. Slip off the skins. Roughly chop the flesh, discarding the stones, and add to the mango in the blender or food processor.

3 Pour in just enough ginger ale to cover the fruit, then process until completely smooth. Pour in the remaining ginger ale and process again.

4 Quickly pour into tall glasses, preferably over crushed ice. Decorate with fresh mint. Serve immediately, with wide straws or swizzle sticks.

Some more ideas

• Use low-calorie ginger ale to reduce the calorie content.

• So many different fruit and fizz combinations are possible. Using about 450g (1lb) fruit in total, try: raspberry, peach and melon with low-calorie bitter lemon; or strawberry, banana and orange segments with tonic water.

• When soft fruits are not in season, use fruit canned in juice as a substitute. A delicious combination is fresh melon, banana and canned apricots with sparkling mineral water.

Health points

• Peaches are full of vitamin C; apricots are a good source of the B vitamins (B_1, B_6 and niacin); and mangoes are an excellent source of vitamin A.

• A wide variety of fruit is now available frozen. This may be a better source of vitamins than some 'fresh' fruit that has been badly handled or has languished on the shelf. It is particularly useful for blended drinks.

photo, page 243

Each serving provides   Key nutrients 70kcals, 0.2g fat (of which 0g is saturated fat), 1g protein, 17g carbohydrate, 2mg sodium (0.05g salt), 2g fibre

Tomato and citrus blush

This sweet yet tangy drink makes an excellent alcohol-free alternative to a cocktail before lunch or dinner. It is best made with full-flavoured tomatoes, preferably vine-ripened, and a perfectly ripe mango.

Preparation time **10 minutes**   *Serves 4*

1 ripe mango

450g (1lb) tomatoes, peeled, halved and deseeded

600g (1lb 5oz) watermelon, peeled, deseeded and cut into chunks

grated zest and juice of 1 orange

grated zest and juice of 1 lime

To serve

ice

orange and lime slices

1 Peel the skin off the mango, then cut the flesh away from the stone. Coarsely chop the flesh.

2 Put the chopped mango, tomatoes, watermelon, and orange and lime zests and juices in a food processor or blender, and purée until smooth. (Depending on the capacity of your blender, you may have to do this in two batches.)

3 Half-fill four large tumblers with ice and pour over the tomato and citrus blush. Garnish with orange and lime slices. Serve immediately.

Some more ideas

• For a summer starter, serve as a cold soup. Omit the ice cubes and orange and lemon slices, and swirl in a little plain low-fat yoghurt.

Gazpacho quencher Skin, deseed and roughly chop 225g (8oz) tomatoes. Chop a 5cm (2in) piece of cucumber, 1 celery stick, 2 spring onions and 1 garlic clove. Purée the ingredients with 200g (7oz) passata. Stir in 2 tsp balsamic vinegar and 225ml (8fl oz) water. Half-fill four tall tumblers with ice and pour in the drink. Sprinkle with diced tomato and spring onions. Serve with long celery sticks for stirring.

Health points

• Tomatoes, mangoes and watermelon all provide vitamin C, an important nutrient for healthy blood pressure, maintaining immunity and promoting healthy skin.

• Mango also provides beta-carotene, which the body converts to vitamin A, essential for good vision, especially in dim light.

Each serving provides   Key nutrients 101kcals, 1g fat (of which 0.3g is saturated fat), 2g protein, 23g carbohydrate, 16mg sodium (0.04g salt), 1g fibre

Useful source of potassium (549mg)

Fruit boats with orange glaze

Fresh melon boats, carved in only minutes and overflowing with kiwi fruit, ripe berries and juicy melon balls, are the perfect refresher. A sweet-and-sour glaze gives the fruits unexpected zest for a summery lunch.

Preparation time **20 minutes**   Cooking time **5 minutes**   *Serves 4*

1 large cantaloupe or other sweet melon

350g (12oz) strawberries, hulled and quartered

150g (5½oz) blueberries

125g (4½oz) raspberries

2 kiwi fruits, peeled, halved and cut into thin wedges

For the orange glaze

4 tbsp balsamic vinegar

¼ tsp grated orange zest

2 tbsp fresh orange juice

2 tsp brown sugar

1 First make the glaze. Combine the balsamic vinegar, orange zest and juice, and brown sugar in a microwave-proof dish. Microwave on High for 2–3 minutes or until syrupy. Alternatively, cook in a small saucepan over medium-high heat for 4–5 minutes. Set the glaze aside.

2 Cut the melon in half and remove the seeds and fibres. Using a melon-ball scoop or a small spoon, scoop out as many melon balls as you can from the flesh. Put the melon balls, strawberries, blueberries, raspberries and kiwi fruit in a large bowl.

3 Scrape out the excess flesh from the melon halves, then cut each one in half to make four 'boats'.

4 Drizzle the fruit with the orange glaze and toss to coat evenly. Spoon the fruit into the melon boats and serve.

Some more ideas

• Top the fruit boats with a scoop of fruit sorbet.

• Use the orange glaze to drizzle on cooked salmon.

• Omit the melon and use fresh pineapple chunks instead. Serve in the pineapple shells or small glass serving bowls.

Health points

• Raspberries are one of the highest-fibre berries. It is the little drupelets, the individual sections of fruit that contain their own seed, that make raspberries such a good source of fibre.

• Balsamic vinegar has a subtly sweet taste, so it can give food sweetness without the need for much sugar.

photo, page 243

Each serving provides   Key nutrients 100kcals, 0.6g fat (of which 0.1g is saturated fat), 3g protein, 23g carbohydrate, 45mg sodium (0.01g salt), 4g fibre

Useful source of potassium (642mg)

Far Eastern fruit salad

A can of fruit can be transformed into a special-tasting salad with the minimum of effort. Here canned lychees are enhanced with ginger and lime for an Oriental flavour, then tossed with apple, oranges and grapes.

Preparation time **15–20 minutes**   *Serves 4*

1 can (about 425g) lychees in syrup

3 pieces crystallised ginger, cut into thin strips

grated zest and juice of 1 lime

2 oranges

200g (7oz) black grapes, halved and deseeded

1 red dessert apple, cored and chopped

fine shreds of lime zest to garnish

1 Drain the lychees in a sieve set over a bowl. Discard half of the syrup that has drained into the bowl, then add the lychees. Stir in the ginger and the lime zest and juice.

2 Cut the peel and pith away from the oranges with a sharp knife. Holding the oranges over the bowl so that all the juice will drip into the salad, carefully cut between the membrane to release the segments. Add the segments to the bowl. Squeeze the membrane and add the juice to the bowl.

3 Stir in the grapes and apple, and toss to mix. Pile the salad into small bowls and sprinkle with shreds of lime zest.

Some more ideas

• If you usually serve cream or ice cream with a fruit salad, you might instead try topping with a scoop of sorbet, which is deliciously fruity and fat-free. A sorbet such as lemon or mango would be particularly good with this fruit salad.

Health points

• Black grapes provide useful amounts of bioflavonoids and antioxidants, which help to protect the body against the damaging effect of free radicals.

• Oranges provide useful amounts of the B vitamin folate. They also provide pectin, which is a type of soluble fibre that may help stabilise blood sugar and lower cholesterol levels.

photo, page 243

Each serving provides   Key nutrients 145kcals, 0.2g fat (of which 0g is saturated fat), 1.5g protein, 42g carbohydrate, 7mg sodium (0.01g salt), 2.7g fibre

Raspberry frozen yoghurt

This frozen yoghurt, exotically flavoured with rose water, is much lower in sugar than shop-bought frozen yoghurt. Serve scoops on their own, or pile into sundae glasses with fresh fruit and mint.

Preparation time **15–20 minutes, plus freezing**   *Serves 8*

450g (1lb) raspberries

4 tbsp seedless raspberry jam

2 tbsp rosewater

500g (1lb 2oz) Greek yoghurt

3 tbsp icing sugar, or to taste

To serve (optional)

raspberries

fresh mint leaves

1 Put the raspberries into a saucepan and add the raspberry jam. Warm over a low heat for about 5 minutes or until the raspberries are pulpy, stirring occasionally.

2 Press the raspberries and their juice through a sieve into a bowl; discard the seeds in the sieve. Stir in the rosewater. Whisk in the yoghurt until smoothly blended. Taste the mixture and sweeten with the sugar.

3 Pour into an ice-cream machine and freeze according to the manufacturer's instructions. When you have a smooth and creamy frozen mixture, spoon it into a rigid freezerproof container. Freeze for at least 1 hour. If you do not have an ice-cream machine, pour the mixture straight into a large freezer-proof container and freeze for about 1 hour or until set around the edges. Beat until the mixture is smooth, then return to the freezer. Freeze for 30 minutes, then beat again. Repeat the freezing and beating several more times until the frozen yoghurt has a smooth consistency, then leave it to freeze for at least 1 hour.

4 If storing in the freezer for longer than 1 hour, transfer the frozen yoghurt to the fridge 20 minutes before serving, to soften slightly. Decorate with raspberries and mint, if desired.

Some more ideas

• Use frozen raspberries instead of fresh.

Mango frozen yogurt Replace the raspberries and jam with 2 cans (425g each) mangoes, drained and puréed, and the rosewater with orange-flower water. There should be no need to sweeten the mixture.

Health points

• Raspberries are an excellent source of vitamin C, whether fresh or frozen. If freshly picked, there may be more C, but it is not always easy to tell how long fruit has been sitting on the shelf, and vitamin C content will be going down steadily following picking. Frozen fruits are usually processed immediately after picking and may therefore be a richer source of this vitamin.

Each serving provides   Key nutrients 128kcals, 6.5g fat (of which 3.5g is saturated fat), 5g protein, 15g carbohydrate, 49mg sodium (0.1g salt), 1.5g fibre

Ambrosia *p250*

Raspberry frozen yoghurt *p248*

Apple crumble *p252*

Flamed pineapple *p251*

Ambrosia

This American fresh fruit dessert is so delectable that it's called ambrosia, which in Greek mythology was the food of the gods. It's a great alternative to the pudding after Christmas lunch.

Preparation time **30 minutes plus chilling**   *Serves 6*

3 navel oranges

1 small pineapple

2 large bananas

40g (1½oz) miniature marshmallows

25g (1oz) sweetened, flaked desiccated coconut

sprigs of fresh mint to garnish

1 Peel the oranges, removing all the white pith. Holding each orange in turn over a large bowl, cut between the membranes to release the segments, letting them fall into the bowl with the orange juice.

2 Using a long serrated knife, cut the top and bottom off the pineapple, then cut off the peel. Halve the pineapple lengthways. Place one half, cut-side down, on a cutting board and cut lengthways into 3 equal sections. Slice off the hard core from each section, then cut the sections crossways into chunks about 2.5cm (1in) thick. Add to the oranges in the bowl and toss. Repeat with the other half of the pineapple.

3 Slice the bananas 5mm (¼in) thick and add immediately to the other fruit and juice in the bowl. Toss to coat. Gently fold in the marshmallows and coconut. Cover with cling film and chill for at least 2 hours or overnight to blend the flavours. Garnish with mint sprigs before serving.

Some more ideas

• Use chopped dessert apples instead of the oranges.

• Add 1 tbsp dark rum.

• Add black grapes for more colour. Halve 150g (5½oz) seedless grapes and toss in with the oranges, pineapple and banana.

Health points

• The fruits in this dish are high in bioflavonoids, substances with antioxidant properties that prevent tumour growth and help keep arteries healthy. Plus, there's as much fibre per serving as in a bowl of whole-grain breakfast cereal.

photo, page 249

Each serving provides   **Key nutrients** 136kcals, 3g fat (of which 2g is saturated fat), 2g protein, 27g carbohydrate, 9mg sodium (0.02g salt), 3g fibre

Useful source of potassium (388mg)

Flamed pineapple

Here's an impressive dessert to try: fresh pineapple sautéed in butter with dark rum, orange liqueur and brown sugar, then flambéed. It's sure to be greeted with applause.

Preparation time **15 minutes**　　Cooking time **10 minutes**　　*Serves 4*

1 large ripe pineapple

15g (½oz) unsalted butter

3 tbsp light brown sugar

¼ tsp grated nutmeg

3 tbsp dark rum

2 tbsp Grand Marnier or other orange liqueur

4 small scoops low-fat vanilla frozen yoghurt

1 Cut the top and bottom off the pineapple. Remove the skin. Slice the pineapple into rings 2cm (¾in) thick. Cut each ring into thirds and remove the hard core.

2 Melt the butter in a large frying pan over moderate heat. When the butter begins to foam, add the brown sugar and nutmeg, and heat until the sugar dissolves. Stir in the rum and bring to a simmer. Add the pineapple and cook, turning often, for about 4 minutes or until the pineapple is warmed through.

3 Leaving the pan on the heat, drizzle the orange liqueur over the pineapple. Standing back, ignite the liqueur with a long match. Shake the pan gently until the flames die down. Spoon the pineapple slices and sauce over the frozen yoghurt.

Some more ideas

• Instead of pineapple, use 4 bananas, thickly sliced.

• This dessert is just as delicious served cold.

Health points

• Fresh pineapple contains a substance called bromelain, which aids digestion. It is also a good source of vitamin C.

photo, page 249

Each serving provides　**Key nutrients** 254kcals, 5g fat (of which 2g is saturated fat), 3g protein, 37g carbohydrate, 27mg sodium (0.06g salt), 2g fibre

Apple crumble

Why not enjoy your proverbial 'apple a day' in a satisfyingly sweet dessert? An abundance of apples, a crunchy oat topping and a spoonful of frozen yoghurt add up to a treat that's full of flavour and nutrients.

Preparation time **25 minutes**   Cooking time **40 minutes**   *Serves 12*

2 tbsp light brown sugar

2 tbsp plain flour

½ tsp ground cinnamon

3 tbsp fresh lemon juice

1.3kg (3lb) Bramley apples

1 tsp vanilla extract

1 litre (2 pints) low-fat vanilla frozen yoghurt

For the topping

40g (1½oz) rolled oats

50g (1¾oz) plain flour

115g (4oz) light brown sugar

½ tsp ground cinnamon

85g (3oz) cold butter, cut into pieces

1 Preheat the oven to 180°C (350°F, gas mark 4). Lightly coat a rectangular ovenproof dish with cooking spray. Put the brown sugar, flour and cinnamon in a food processor. Pulse to combine. Alternatively, put the ingredients in a medium bowl and mix together with your fingers.

2 Put the lemon juice in a large bowl. Peel the apples and cut into 5mm (¼in) slices. Add to the bowl, tossing with the juice. Sprinkle with the brown sugar mixture and add the vanilla extract. Toss until evenly coated. Turn into the prepared ovenproof dish.

3 To make the topping, combine the oats, flour, brown sugar and cinnamon in a medium bowl. Using your fingers, rub the butter into the flour mixture until it resembles coarse crumbs. Sprinkle over the apples. Bake for about 40 minutes or until the topping is golden and the apples are tender. Serve with scoops of frozen yoghurt.

Some more ideas

• Make a pear crumble by substituting firm dessert pears for the apples.

• Increase the fibre in this favourite dessert by using wholemeal flour.

Health points

• Both apples and oats are useful health-healthy foods. to The soluble fibre they contain can help to lower levels of harmful cholesterol.

photo, page 249

Each serving provides   **Key nutrients** 273kcals, 8g fat (of which 4g is saturated fat), 4g protein, 41g carbohydrate, 48mg sodium (0.1g salt), 2g fibre

Fruit with apricot-chocolate cream

Here's a luscious concoction to dip fresh apple and pear wedges into. It may seem rich and decadent, but as it's made with cottage cheese it is surprisingly light in calories and fat.

Preparation time **15 minutes**   *Serves 4*

225g (8oz) fromage frais

2 tbsp single cream

2 tbsp caster sugar

½ tsp vanilla extract

40g (1½oz) dried apricots, coarsely chopped

2 tbsp mini chocolate chips or finely chopped dark plain chocolate

To serve

2 dessert pears, cut into 1cm (½in) wedges

2 large dessert apples, cut into 1cm (½in) wedges

1 Combine the cottage cheese, cream, sugar and vanilla extract in a food processor and purée until smooth.

2 Transfer to a bowl and stir in the apricots and chocolate chips. (The creamy dip can be covered and kept in the refrigerator for up to a day.)

3 Arrange the pears and apples on a platter and serve the creamy dip in the centre.

Some more ideas

• Add fresh berries – diced strawberries or blueberries – to the creamy dip.

• Use dried mango instead of apricots.

Health point

• Ready-to-eat dried apricots are a great source of the mineral potassium. A higher intake of potassium combined with a low salt diet has been shown to lower high blood pressure. Apricots are also a good source of beta-carotene and provide useful amounts of fibre and iron.

Each serving provides   Key nutrients 212kcals, 8g fat (of which 5g is saturated fat), 5g protein, 31g carbohydrate, 29mg sodium (0.07g salt), 3g fibre

Useful source of potassium (451mg)

Fresh plum tartlets

These scrumptious tartlets, with their crisp, biscuit-like crust, are topped with both prune purée and sliced fresh plums to make a treat that is as delicious as it is heart-healthy.

Preparation time **25 minutes**   Cooking time **20 minutes**   *Serves 6*

100g (3½oz) rolled oats

125g (4½oz) walnut halves

25g (1oz) cornflakes

100g (3½oz) sugar

2 large egg whites

2 tbsp fresh lime juice

1 tsp grated lime zest, plus extra to garnish

125ml (4fl oz) prune purée

450g (1lb) fresh plums, halved, stoned and cut into thin wedges

1 Preheat the oven to 180°C (350°F, gas mark 4). Combine the oats and walnuts in a baking tray and bake for about 7 minutes or until the oats are toasted.

2 Transfer the oats and walnuts to a food processor and add the cornflakes and sugar. Process to fine crumbs. Add the egg whites and 1 tablespoon of the lime juice, and pulse until evenly moistened.

3 Line a large baking sheet with baking parchment. Divide the dough into 6 pieces. With moistened hands, pat each piece out to a 10cm (4in) round on the parchment. Give each round a raised edge. Bake for about 10 minutes or until crisp. Cool for 2 minutes on the baking sheet, then transfer to a wire rack to cool completely.

4 Combine the remaining 1 tablespoon lime juice with the lime zest and prune purée in a small bowl. Spread the mixture inside the cooled tartlet cases. Arrange the plums over the prune filling and garnish with lime zest. (The tartlets can be made the day before and kept in the fridge, loosely covered.)

Some more ideas

• Use pecan nuts or almonds in place of the walnuts.

• Instead of plums, use fresh peaches. Choose peaches that are ripe but firm. There is no need to peel them.

• If the tartlets are made the day before you serve them, they will soften enough to be eaten with a knife and fork.

Health points

• Plums and prunes are rich in potassium and soluble fibre, both key nutrients for battling high blood pressure. But they also contain phytochemicals, such as chlorogenic acid, which are thought to detoxify carcinogenic chemicals that enter your body from the environment, such as smoke.

Each serving provides   Key nutrients 332kcals, 16g fat (of which 1g is saturated fat), 8g protein, 42g carbohydrate, 50mg sodium (0.12g salt), 4g fibre

Useful source of potassium (493mg)

Daffodil cake *p258*

Fresh plum tartlets *p254*

Chequerboard cherry pie *p256*

Banana custard tart *p257*

Chequerboard cherry pie

Life is a bowl of cherries when you dig into a wedge of this juicy pie. And you can enjoy it without feeling guilty! The pastry is delectably flakey from a combination of fromage frais and butter.

Preparation time **25 minutes**   Cooking time **45 minutes**   *Serves 8*

280g (10oz) plain flour

4 tbsp sugar

25g (1oz) cold butter, cut up

125g (4½oz) fromage frais

3–4 tbsp iced water

2 cans (about 400g each) cherries in syrup, drained

2 tbsp cornflour

¼ tsp almond extract

1 small egg white beaten with 1 tsp water

1 Put the flour and 2 tablespoons of the sugar in a food processor and pulse to mix. Add the butter and mix until coarse crumbs form. Add the fromage frais, then with the motor running, add the water, 1 tablespoon at a time, processing until the pastry holds together. Shape into two 20cm (8in) discs, wrap in cling film and chill for 30 minutes.

2 Meanwhile, mix together the cherries, cornflour and almond extract in a large bowl. Set aside.

3 Coat a 23cm (9in) pie tin or dish with cooking spray or a teaspoon of olive oil. On a lightly floured surface roll out one of the pastry discs into a 38cm (15in) round. Gently roll the pastry on to the rolling pin and ease into the pie dish. Trim the edge, leaving a 2.5cm (1in) overhang. Brush the pastry with about 2 teaspoons of the egg white mixture, then spoon in the cherry filling.

4 Preheat the oven to 220°C (425°F, gas mark 7). Roll out the remaining disc of pastry into a 30cm (12in) round. Cut into strips 2cm (¾in) wide using a fluted pastry or pizza wheel. Weave the strips on top of the filling to make a lattice pattern. Trim the ends, leaving a 2.5cm (1in) overhang. Make a 2.5cm (1in) stand-up edge, folding in the ends of lattice strips as you go. Flute the edge.

5 Brush the top of the pie with the remaining egg white mixture, and sprinkle with the remaining 2 tablespoons of sugar. Place the pie dish on a foil-lined baking tray to catch any overflow. Bake for 10 minutes, then reduce the temperature to 180°C (350°F, gas mark 4). Bake for a further 35–40 minutes or until the pastry is lightly browned and the filling juices are bubbling in the centre.

Some more ideas

• In place of cherries, use other canned fruit packed in juice, such as apricots and peaches.

• You can also use frozen fruit for the pie filling.

Health points

• By using a little butter with fromage frais for the pastry, the fat content is quite modest when compared to the usual shortcrust.

• While the vitamin C in cherries is diminished by the canning process, cherries are still rich in phytochemicals that battle free radicals, inhibit inflammation and help keep arteries healthy. This combination makes them a particularly fine food for improving blood pressure.

photo, page 255

Each serving provides   Key nutrients 276kcals, 4g fat (of which 2.5g is saturated fat), 5g protein, 58g carbohydrate, 43mg sodium (0.01g salt), 2g fibre

Banana custard tart

A custard tart on a lower-blood-pressure diet? Absolutely! This one has all of the flavour of the traditional home-made custard tarts, but with less fat. And there is plenty of sweet nutritious banana in every bite!

Preparation time **30 minutes plus chilling**   Cooking time **15 minutes**   *Serves 8*

225g (8oz) sponge fingers

2 tbsp clear honey

2 tbsp water

100g (3½oz) caster sugar

50g (1¾oz) plain flour

600ml (1 pint) semi-skimmed milk

2 large eggs, beaten

2 tsp vanilla extract

6 bananas

4 tbsp orange juice

3 tbsp apricot jam, melted

1 Preheat the oven to 180°C (350°F, gas mark 4). Lightly coat a 23cm (9in) tin or pie dish with cooking spray or a teaspoon of olive oil. Put the sponge fingers, honey and water in a food processor and pulse until fine crumbs form. Press the mixture over the bottom and sides of the tin. Bake for about 10 minutes or until set. Cool on a wire rack.

2 Mix together the sugar and flour in a medium saucepan. Slowly whisk in the milk. Bring to the boil over medium heat and cook, whisking, until the mixture thickens. Remove from the heat and cool for a minute, then whisk in the eggs and vanilla extract. Leave to cool for 15 minutes.

3 Slice the bananas and toss with the orange juice. Line the biscuit crust with one-third of the bananas and top with half of the custard filling. Repeat the layers, then arrange the remaining banana slices on top in a spiral design, with the slices slightly overlapping. Brush the jam over the bananas. Cool for 30 minutes at room temperature, then chill for at least 4 hours.

Some more ideas

• Use strawberries instead of bananas and strawberry jam in place of apricot.

Health points

• When semi-skimmed is used instead of whole milk or cream for the custard filling, this tart is significantly reduced in fat. Skimmed milk will produce a filling that is too thin.

photo, page 255

Each serving provides **Key nutrients** 360kcals, 11g fat (of which 3g is saturated fat), 8g protein, 61g carbohydrate, 151mg sodium (0.38 salt), 1.5g fibre

Useful source of potassium (491mg)

Daffodil cake

Usher in spring by baking a daffodil cake – a fragrant, delicate sponge cake with swirls of yellow and white in every slice. This festive, healthy treat is lightly flavoured with orange.

Preparation time **20 minutes**   Cooking time **35 minutes**   *Serves 16*

4 large eggs, separated, plus 6 large egg whites

300g (10½oz) caster sugar

2 tsp grated orange zest

1 tbsp vanilla extract

½ tsp cream of tartar

150g (5½oz) plain flour

40g (1½oz) icing sugar, sifted

1 Preheat the oven to 190°C (375°F, gas mark 5). Put the egg yolks in the bowl of an electric mixer with 50g (1¾oz) of the caster sugar and the orange zest. Beat at high speed for about 10 minutes or until the mixture is thick and lemon-coloured, scraping down the bowl occasionally with a spatula. Beat in the vanilla extract.

2 Put all 10 egg whites into a separate large bowl. Beat with clean beaters at high speed until foamy. Add the cream of tartar and continue beating until soft peaks form. Add the remaining caster sugar, 2 tablespoons at a time, beating at high speed until the sugar has dissolved and stiff, glossy peaks form.

3 Sift the flour over the egg whites, in three batches, gently folding in each addition with a wire whisk just until the flour is no longer visible. Fold one-third of the egg white mixture into the yolk mixture.

4 Alternately spoon heaped tablespoons of the yellow and white cake mixtures into an ungreased nonstick 25cm (10in) angel cake tin. Swirl a palette knife through the mixtures to marble them. Lightly swirl the top. Bake for about 35 minutes or until the cake springs back when lightly touched. Invert the cake, in the tin, on to a wire rack and leave to cool completely.

5 Run a palette knife around the tin sides and centre to loosen the cake, then remove the cake from the tin and place on a serving plate. Sprinkle the cake with icing sugar before serving.

Some more ideas

• Make a lemon-flavoured daffodil cake. Use 2 tsp grated lemon zest instead of the orange zest.

• Present the daffodil cake whole and fill the centre with fresh berries or a fruit salad.

Health points

• The original recipe for daffodil cake dates back to the 1930s. This version increases the egg whites and reduces the yolks, contributing to a wonderfully low level of fat – just 2g per slice!

photo, page 255

Each serving provides   Key nutrients 143kcals, 2g fat (of which 0.5g is saturated fat), 4g protein, 30g carbohydrate, 46mg sodium (0.01g salt), 0.3g fibre

Cappuccino cake

This feather-light coffee-flavoured sponge is so easy to make. It's also delightfully low in calories, and – as it's made with oil instead of butter – in saturated fat.

Preparation time **15 minutes**   Cooking time **45 minutes**   *Serves 16*

280g (10oz) plain flour

300g (10½oz) caster sugar

1 tbsp baking powder

¾ tsp ground cinnamon

125ml (4fl oz) walnut oil or light olive oil

2 large eggs, separated, plus 4 large egg whites

175ml (6fl oz) brewed espresso or other dark roast coffee, at room temperature

2 tbsp cocoa powder

1 tsp vanilla extract

½ tsp cream of tartar

2 tbsp icing sugar, sifted

1 Preheat the oven to 160°F (325°F, gas mark 3). Stir together the flour, caster sugar, baking powder and cinnamon in a medium bowl. Whisk the walnut oil, egg yolks, espresso, cocoa powder and vanilla extract together in a large bowl until smooth. Fold the flour mixture into the yolk mixture.

2 In another large bowl, whisk the 6 egg whites until frothy. Add the cream of tartar and continue whisking until stiff peaks form. Gently fold the egg whites into the cake mixture.

3 Spoon into an ungreased 25cm (10in) angel cake tin. Bake for about 45 minutes or until a skewer inserted in the centre comes out clean. Invert the tin on a wire rack and cool.

4 Run a palette knife around the tin to loosen the cake, then remove the cake from the tin and place on a serving plate. Sprinkle the cake with icing sugar before serving.

Some more ideas

Vanilla chiffon cake Omit the espresso and cocoa, and increase the vanilla extract to 1 tbsp.

• Add 25g (1oz) very finely chopped walnuts to complement the flavour of walnut oil.

Health points

• Walnut oil is a rich source of heart-healthy monounsaturated fat. A little goes a long way, as walnut oil has such an intense flavour.

Each serving provides   **Key nutrients** 215kcals, 7g fat (of which 1.5g is saturated fat), 3g protein, 36g carbohydrate, 156mg sodium (0.39g salt), 0.8g fibre

Oaty chocolate chip cookies

Look what has happened to the traditional chocolate chip cookie! This one has only half the fat of the original, plus old-fashioned oats to give it a fibre boost. Yet all of the changes have not slimmed down the flavour.

Preparation time **15 minutes**   Cooking time **20 minutes**   *Makes 36*

140g (5oz) plain flour

½ tsp bicarbonate of soda

85g (3oz) rolled oats

55g (2oz) butter, softened

150g (5½oz) light brown sugar

100g (3½oz) caster sugar

1 large egg

1½ tsp vanilla extract

5 tbsp fromage frais

115g (4oz) chocolate chips or chopped plain dark chocolate

1 Preheat the oven to 190°C (375°F, gas mark 5). Line three large baking sheets with baking parchment. Stir together the flour and bicarbonate of soda in a medium bowl. Stir in the oats.

2 Cream the butter with the brown sugar and caster sugar in a large bowl using an electric mixer at high speed. Add the egg and vanilla extract, and beat for a further 3 minutes or until light yellow and creamy. Blend in the fromage frais with a wooden spoon, then add the flour mixture and stir just until combined (don't overmix or the cookies may be tough). Stir in the chocolate chips.

3 Drop heaped teaspoons of dough, 5cm (2in) apart, on to the baking sheets. Bake for about 10 minutes or until golden. Cool on the baking sheets for 2 minutes, then transfer to wire racks and cool completely. Store in an airtight tin for up to 2 weeks or freeze for up to 3 months.

Some more ideas

• Add 70g (2½oz) dried cherries to the dough. Cherries and chocolate are a great flavour combination.

• Make these cookies more fibre-rich by using wholemeal flour or a mixture of half plain and half wholemeal.

Health points

• Low-fat dairy products like fromage frais are good sources of calcium. This mineral is recognised mainly for its involvement with maintaining healthy bones, but it is also vital for the proper functioning of muscles and nerves and for blood clotting.

• Oats are a great source of vitamins B_1, B_2 and E, as well as a long list of phytochemicals that fight cancer, cardiovascular disease and diabetes.

Each serving (1 cookie) provides   Key nutrients 83kcals, 3g fat (of which 1.5g is saturated fat), 1g protein, 14g carbohydrate, 33mg sodium (0.08g salt), 0.5g fibre

aty chocolate chip cookies *p260*

Pecan biscuits *p262*

Lemon angel cake with strawberries *p264*

Ginger and pear upside-down cake *p265*

Pecan biscuits

These are the best standby biscuits. The dough is made ahead and kept in the refrigerator or freezer until it's time to bake them. So freshly baked biscuits are always only 10 minutes away.

Preparation time **15 minutes plus chilling**   Cooking time **10 minutes**   *Makes 72*

250g (9oz) plain flour

½ tsp ground cinnamon

¼ tsp bicarbonate of soda

55g (2oz) butter, softened

140g (5oz) caster sugar

70g (2½oz) light brown sugar

1 large egg

1 tsp vanilla extract

5 tbsp fromage frais

40g (1½oz) pecan nuts, chopped and toasted

1 Stir together the flour, cinnamon and bicarbonate of soda in a medium bowl. Cream the butter with the caster sugar and brown sugar in a large bowl using an electric mixer at high speed until well blended. Add the egg and vanilla extract, and beat until light and fluffy. Using a wooden spoon, stir in the flour mixture, followed by the fromage frais and pecans.

2 Spread out a 50cm (20in) sheet of cling film on the work surface and sprinkle lightly with flour. Transfer the dough to the cling film and shape into a 38cm (15in) log. Tightly roll in the cling film and chill for about 2 hours or until firm. (Or wrap the dough in freezer foil and freeze for up to 1 month.)

3 Preheat the oven to 190°C (375°F, gas mark 5). Cut the dough into rounds 6mm (¾in) thick. Place 1cm (½in) apart on ungreased baking sheets. Bake, in batches, for about 8 minutes or just until crisp and golden brown around the edges (do not overbake). If using frozen dough, bake for 10 minutes. Transfer the biscuits to wire racks to cool completely before storing in an airtight container.

Some more ideas

Chocolate biscuits At the beginning of step 1, mix 30g (1oz) cocoa powder into the flour mixture. Increase the butter to 70g (2½oz) and the fromage frais to 125g (4½oz).

• Toasting nuts doubles their flavour. To toast, put them in a dry frying pan and toss over medium heat for a few minutes or until lightly browned.

• Use almonds instead of pecan nuts.

Health points

• Cinnamon may have anti-bacterial and anti-microbial properties, and it may also reduce discomfort from heartburn. In addition, cinnamaldehyde, a phyto-chemical in the spice, may ward off bacteria such as *H. pylori,* the bacteria linked to ulcers.

photo, page 261

Each serving (1 biscuit) provides Key nutrients 35kcals, 1g fat (of which 0.5g is saturated fat), 0.6g protein, 6g carbohydrate, 11mg sodium (0.02g salt), 0.1g fibre

Chocolate snacking cakes

Craving some chocolate? Each one of these luscious little gems has only 81 calories and just over a gram of fat. So go ahead and indulge yourself!

Preparation time **15 minutes**   Cooking time **35 minutes plus cooling**   *Makes 25*

200g (7oz) self-raising flour

85g (3oz) plus 2 tsp cocoa powder

4 tbsp buttermilk

1 tbsp instant espresso powder

200g (7oz) caster sugar

115g (4oz) light brown sugar

280g jar Bramley apple sauce

2 tsp vanilla extract

2 large egg whites

85g (3oz) mini chocolate chips

1 tbsp icing sugar

1 Preheat the oven to 160°C (325°F, gas mark 3). Line a 20cm (8in) square cake tin with foil, leaving a 2.5cm (1in) overhang. Sift the flour and 85g (3oz) cocoa powder into a large bowl. Heat the buttermilk and espresso in a small saucepan over low heat until the espresso has dissolved.

2 Mix the caster and brown sugars, apple sauce, buttermilk mixture and vanilla extract in another bowl. Stir in the flour mixture just until blended. Whisk the egg whites until soft peaks form. Fold in together with the chocolate chips.

3 Turn into the tin. Bake for about 45 minutes or just until set (do not overbake). Cool in the tin on a wire rack for 15 minutes, then lift out on to the rack to cool completely. Sift the icing sugar and remaining cocoa powder over the cake. Cut into 4cm (1½in) squares to serve.

Some more ideas

• Add 1 tbsp coffee liqueur to the mixture for a more 'grown-up' taste.

• Substitute coarsely grated plain dark chocolate for the mini chocolate chips.

Health points

• By using apple sauce, this recipe needs no oil or butter. The slight apple flavour it imparts complements the coffee-chocolate taste combination.

Each serving (1 square) provides   Key nutrients 81kcals, 1.5g fat (of which 1g is saturated fat), 1.5g protein, 17g carbohydrate, 50mg sodium (0.01g salt), 0.6g fibre

Lemon angel cake with strawberries

Angel cake is a dream dessert for cholesterol-conscious eaters. Made from egg whites but no yolks, this lofty delight doesn't even require fat. The vividly colourful fruit sauce makes the cake worthy of a festive occasion.

Preparation time **20 minutes**   Cooking time **50 minutes**   *Serves 12*

For the fruit sauce

1 bag (about 500g) frozen strawberries, thawed

125ml (4fl oz) orange juice

For the cake

12 large egg whites, at room temperature

1¼ tsp cream of tartar

250g (9oz) caster sugar

grated zest of 3 lemons

1 tsp vanilla extract

140g (5oz) plain flour

1 Combine the strawberries and orange juice in a large bowl. Cover and chill.

2 Preheat the oven to 160°C (325°F, gas mark 3). Beat the egg whites with the cream of tartar in a large bowl using an electric mixer until foamy. Gradually beat in the sugar, 2 tablespoons at a time, and continue beating until thick, soft peaks form. Beat in the lemon zest and vanilla extract.

3 Gently fold the flour into the egg white mixture, adding it one-quarter at a time and folding just until incorporated. Spoon into an ungreased 25cm (10in) angel cake tin. Bake for about 50 minutes or until the top of the cake springs back when lightly pressed.

4 Invert cake, in the tin, on to a wire rack to cool. Then run a palette knife around the edges and centre of the tin and invert the cake on to a plate. Serve with the strawberry sauce.

Some more ideas

• Make the sauce with other berries. Both raspberries and blueberries are good choices.

• Add 5 tbsp mini chocolate chips or grated dark plain chocolate to the cake mixture. You'll get plenty of chocolate flavour, but with less fat than with a chocolate cake.

Health points

• When you just have to have a cake, an angel cake is a great choice. It's low in sodium and has no fat or cholesterol; its only vice is the sugar content. However, since it is served with a fruit sauce rather than being iced, you have a very healthy dessert.

photo, page 261

Each serving provides   **Key nutrients** 150kcals, 0.2g fat (of which 0g is saturated fat), 4.5g protein, 34g carbohydrate, 66mg sodium (0.16g salt), 0.8g fibre

Ginger and pear upside-down cake

Greet the first chilly days of autumn with a tender yellow cake topped with caramelised pears. Although very little fat goes into the cake mixture – just a little heart-smart olive oil – the cake has a warm, spicy richness.

Preparation time **15 minutes**   Cooking time **40 minutes**   *Serves 10*

2 tbsp dark brown sugar

3 firm ripe William's pears

150g (5½oz) plain flour

1 tbsp ground ginger

¾ tsp baking powder

¼ tsp bicarbonate of soda

3 tbsp light olive oil

150g (5½oz) caster sugar

1½ tsp grated lime zest

1 large egg plus 1 large egg white

175ml (6fl oz) buttermilk

1 Preheat the oven to 180°C (350°F, gas mark 4). Spray the bottom of a 23cm (9in) round nonstick cake tin with cooking spray or use a little olive oil. Sprinkle the brown sugar over the bottom, shaking the tin to coat it evenly.

2 Peel, core and halve the pears. Slice the pears crossways into slices 8mm (⅜in) thick. Evenly spread the pears in the tin, making sure the bottom of the tin is covered.

3 Mix together the flour, ginger, baking powder, bicarbonate of soda and a pinch of salt on a sheet of greaseproof paper. With an electric mixer, beat together the oil, caster sugar, lime zest and coconut extract in a large bowl. Beat in the whole egg and egg white until thick.

4 With a spatula, alternately fold the flour mixture and buttermilk into the egg mixture, beginning and ending with the flour mixture, until just blended.

5 Pour the mixture over the pears and smooth the top to cover the pears completely. Bake for about 40 minutes until golden brown and a skewer inserted in the centre comes out clean. Set the cake, in the tin, on a wire rack and cool for 10 minutes, then invert onto a platter. Let cool slightly before slicing.

Some more ideas

Apple upside-down cake
• Use 3 Granny Smith apples in place of the pears.

• For a stronger ginger taste, add 1 tsp grated fresh root ginger in step 3 with the oil and sugar.

• Make the cake more fibre-rich by substituting wholemeal flour for 55g (2oz) of the plain white flour.

Health points

• Pears contain ample amounts of potassium to help relieve high blood pressure.

• Pears also contain high amounts of pectin, a particular type of fibre that is very useful in preventing cholesterol from being absorbed in the body.

• Interestingly, pears are considered among the least allergenic of foods.

photo, page 261

Each serving provides   Key nutrients 180kcals, 4.5g fat (of which 1g is saturated fat), 3.5g protein, 34g carbohydrate, 96mg sodium (0.24g salt), 1g fibre

Lemon mousse with strawberries

Sampling this mousse, which sparkles with fresh lemon flavour, is like spooning up sunshine. It's been lightened up by substituting gelatine and yoghurt for the usual quantities of eggs and cream.

Preparation time **15 minutes**   Cooking time **5 minutes, plus chilling time**   *Serves 8*

350g (12oz) strawberries

1 packet (about 15g) powdered gelatine

125ml (4fl oz) cold water

150g (5½oz) caster sugar

2 tsp grated lemon zest

125ml (4fl oz) fresh lemon juice

1 tbsp light olive oil

1 large egg

300g (10½oz) plain low-fat yoghurt

1 Hull the strawberries and thickly slice. Set aside. Sprinkle the gelatine over half of the cold water in a small bowl. Leave to sponge for 5 minutes.

2 Whisk together the remaining water, the sugar, lemon zest, lemon juice, oil and egg in a medium saucepan until well combined. Cook over low heat, whisking constantly, for about 5 minutes or until the mixture is hot. Whisk in the softened gelatine and whisk until the gelatine has dissolved.

3 Remove from the heat and transfer to a medium bowl. Cool to room temperature, whisking occasionally. Then whisk in the yoghurt. Arrange alternate layers of strawberries and lemon mousse in eight dessert bowls. Cover and chill for about 3 hours or until set.

Some more ideas

Orange mousse Substitute grated orange zest and orange juice for the lemon zest and juice.

• Rather than strawberries, layer the mousse with other fruit. Blueberries, raspberries and sliced bananas are good choices.

Health points

• By using gelatine, you can create so many low-fat mousse-like desserts. The gelatine helps to stabilise dairy products that do not contain enough fat to set on their own.

• One serving of the mousse provides healthy portions of vitamin C and calcium.

Each serving provides   **Key nutrients** 132 kcals, 3g fat (of which 0.5g is saturated fat), 3g protein, 25g carbohydrate, 46mg sodium (0.11g salt), 0.5g fibre

Blueberry bavarian *p268*

Lemon mousse with strawberries *p266*

Old-fashioned glazed gingerbread *p270*

Chewy muesli bars *p269*

Blueberry Bavarian

Spoon up a tangy-sweet mouthful of this custardy berry blend and discover how sublime a heart-friendly dessert can be. Instead of double cream and whole eggs, it's made with low-fat milk, fromage frais and gelatine.

Preparation time **10 minutes**   Cooking time **15 minutes plus chilling**   *Serves 6*

225ml (8fl oz) semi-skimmed milk

4 tbsp skimmed milk powder

2 bags (about 350g each) frozen blueberries, thawed

100g (3½oz) plus 1 tbsp caster sugar

225g (8oz) fromage frais

1 packet (about 15g) powdered gelatine

4 tbsp cold water

75g (2½oz) fresh blueberries

1 Combine the semi-skimmed milk and milk powder in a small bowl and whisk until well blended. Place in the freezer to chill for 30 minutes.

2 Combine the frozen blueberries and 100g (3½oz) sugar in a medium saucepan over low heat. Bring to a simmer and cook for about 10 minutes or until the sugar has dissolved, the berries have broken up and the mixture has reduced to about 600ml (1 pint). Allow to cool to room temperature, then stir in two-thirds of the fromage frais.

3 Sprinkle the gelatine over the cold water in a heatproof cup or small bowl. Leave to sponge for 5 minute. Set the cup in a small saucepan of simmering water and heat until the gelatine has melted. Cool to room temperature.

4 Whisk the chilled milk mixture until thick, soft peaks form. Whisk in the remaining 1 tablespoon of sugar until stiff peaks form. Whisk in the gelatine mixture. Fold the milk mixture into the blueberry mixture.

5 Spoon into six dessert bowls or glasses. Cover and chill for about 2 hours or until set. Just before serving, top each dessert with a dollop of the remaining fromage frais and a few fresh blueberries.

Some more ideas

Strawberry-peach bavarian
Use 2 bags of either frozen strawberries or peaches for the filling and top with fresh blueberries and diced fresh peaches.

Health points

• By adding milk powder to semi-skimmed milk, you get a thick mixture that when chilled can be whipped like double cream. The mixture is then stabilised with gelatine to keep it firm.

• Blueberries are brimming with heart-protective nutrients, including potassium, folate, magnesium, fibre and vitamin C.

photo, page 267

Each serving provides   Key nutrients 200 kcals, 4g fat (of which 2g is saturated fat), 6g protein, 35g carbohydrate, 33mg sodium (0.08g salt), 3g fibre

Chewy muesli bars

Start with a double dose of oats and you're on your way to a heart-healthy snack. For a gift, wrap the bars in parchment or cling film, then in colourful wrapping paper, and tuck them into a pretty basket. They'll keep for about a week.

Preparation time **15 minutes**   Cooking time **40 minutes**   *Makes 12*

125g (4½oz) rolled oats or porridge oats

55g (2oz) oat bran

50g (1¾oz) plain flour

90g (3¼oz) dried apricots, coarsely chopped

40g (1½oz) walnuts, coarsely chopped

2 tbsp toasted wheatgerm

4 tbsp apple juice concentrate

2 tbsp light brown sugar

2 tbsp clear honey

1 tsp vanilla extract

1 Preheat the oven to 180°C (350°F, gas mark 4). Line a 28 x 18cm (11 x 7in) baking tin with foil, leaving a good overhang. Coat with cooking spray or a lteaspoon of olive oil. Set aside.

2 Place the oats and oat bran in a baking tray and toast in the oven for about 10 minutes or until the oats are lightly browned and fragrant. Transfer to a large mixing bowl and add the flour, apricots, walnuts and wheatgerm.

3 Combine the apple juice concentrate, brown sugar and honey in a small pan. Cook over medium heat until the brown sugar has dissolved. Remove from the heat and stir in the vanilla extract. Pour over the oat mixture, stirring to coat.

4 Spoon the oat mixture into the foil-lined baking tin. With moistened hands, press the mixture into an even layer. Bake for about 20 minutes or until firm. Using the foil overhang, carefully lift out the muesli cake and cool on wire rack. When cool, cut into 12 bars.

Some more ideas

• Substitute raisins, dried cherries or chopped dried apples for the apricots.

• Use peanuts, almonds or pecans instead of the walnuts.

• Experiment with different types of honey, for strong or delicate flavours.

Health points

• These bars are significantly lower in fat and total carbohydrate than commercially boxed muesli bars. They are also light in sodium, which is important for healthy blood pressure.

• Using fruit juice concentrate eliminates the need for oil in this recipe. The concentrate gives the bars moistness and provides extra flavour as well.

photo, page 267

Each serving (1 bar) provides   Key nutrients 140kcals, 4g fat (of which 0.2g is saturated fat), 4g protein, 24g carbohydrate, 8mg sodium (0.02g salt), 3g fibre

Old-fashioned glazed gingerbread

Here's a moist, rich cake that has the same memorable flavour as your granny's gingerbread did. But in this blood-pressure-friendly makeover, apple sauce stands in for some of the fat.

Preparation time **30 minutes**   Cooking time **45 minutes**   *Serves 12*

185g (6½oz) plain flour

1½ tsp mixed spice

¾ tsp bicarbonate of soda

150g (5½oz) Bramley apple sauce

4 tbsp molasses or treacle

1 large egg, lightly beaten

55g (2oz) butter

115g (4oz) dark brown sugar

2 tsp grated fresh root ginger

For the topping

35g (1¼oz) finely chopped crystallised ginger

85g (3oz) icing sugar, sifted

1½ tbsp water

1 Preheat the oven to 180°C (350°F, gas mark 4). Coat a 20cm (8in) square cake tin with cooking spray. Stir together the flour, mixed spice and bicarbonate of soda in a medium bowl. Mix together the apple sauce, molasses and egg in a separate bowl.

2 Put the butter and brown sugar in the bowl of an electric mixer and beat at high speed for 3–4 minutes or until light. Reduce the speed to low and beat in the apple sauce mixture. Stir in the flour mixture with a wooden spoon just until combined. Blend in the fresh ginger.

3 Pour the mixture into the cake tin. Bake for about 45 minutes or until a skewer inserted in the centre comes out with moist crumbs clinging to it. Cool in the tin on a wire rack for 10 minutes, then turn out and set, right side up, on the rack. Leave to cool completely.

4 Scatter the crystallised ginger on top of the gingerbread. Stir the icing sugar with enough of the water to make a glaze that coats the back of the spoon. Using a fork, drizzle the glaze over the crystallised ginger, letting some glaze drizzle down the sides of the gingerbread.

Some more ideas

• Add 2 peeled and finely diced pears or apples to the gingerbread mixture for extra flavour and fibre.

• If you want an even more distinctive flavour, substitute ¼ tsp each ground cinnamon, grated nutmeg and ground cloves for the mixed spice.

Health points

• Using three types of ginger – ground (in mixed spice), fresh and crystallised – gives a very punchy flavour to this cake. In addition to its extraordinary flavour, ginger is considered one of the most healthful spices available. Substances in ginger – including gingerol, shogaol and zingiberene – have antioxidant capabilities, which may help to prevent heart disease. Ginger also has anti-inflammatory properties, and its soothing effect for digestion is well known.

photo, page 267

Each serving provides   Key nutrients 181kcals, 4.5g fat (of which 2.5g is saturated fat), 2.5g protein, 35g carbohydrate, 130mg sodium (0.33g salt), 0.6g fibre

Chocolate-nut meringues

Here's an astounding achievement: a chocolately treat that is very low in fat! The secrets are using meringue, that versatile blend of whisked egg whites and sugar, and cocoa powder rather than chocolate.

Preparation time **10 minutes**   Cooking time **30 minutes plus cooling**   *Makes 36*

40g (1½oz) walnuts

55g (2oz) plus 2 tbsp icing sugar

4 tsp cocoa powder

¼ tsp ground cinnamon

2 large egg whites

1 Preheat the oven to 150°C (300°F, gas mark 2). Line two baking sheets with baking parchment. Toast the walnuts in a small frying pan, stirring frequently, for about 7 minutes or until crisp and fragrant. When cool enough to handle, coarsely chop the walnuts.

2 Sift 55g (2oz) of the icing sugar, the cocoa powder and cinnamon on to a sheet of greaseproof paper.

3 Whisk the egg whites with a pinch of salt in a large bowl until stiff peaks form. With a rubber spatula, gently fold in the cocoa mixture followed by the walnuts.

4 Drop generous teaspoons of the mixture, 2.5cm (1in) apart, on to the baking sheets. Bake for about 20 minutes or until set. Remove to a wire rack to cool. Dust with the remaining 2 tablespoons of icing sugar just before serving.

Some more ideas

• Omit the cocoa powder and add 1 tsp vanilla extract to the egg whites, to make vanilla-nut meringues.

• Use pecan nuts or almonds instead of walnuts.

Health points

• Using baking parchment eliminates the need for greasing baking sheets and trays. The small amount of fat in each meringue comes from the nuts, which contain healthy omega-3 fatty acids.

• It's the yolk of the egg that provides the nutrients to a chick embryo, so that's the part with the fat. Egg whites contain no fat, but do have lots of protein as well as vitamins and minerals.

Each serving (1 meringue) provides   Key nutrients 19kcals, 1g fat (of which 0.1g is saturated fat), 0.5g protein, 2.5g carbohydrate, 9mg sodium (0.02g salt), 0.1g fibre

The Beat High Blood Pressure Plan

B lood pressure is a measure of how easily blood flows through your body. More specifically, it is the pressure of blood in your arteries – the muscular tubes that carry blood away from the heart.

Uncontrolled high blood pressure is potentially dangerous, yet the condition often goes undetected. Many people are unaware of its import and do not understand how to control it or how – untreated – it can affect their future health.

Doctors recommend regular blood pressure checks. This means taking a reading that features a 'top number' (systolic pressure) and a 'bottom number'. (diastolic pressure). Confusingly, in the same individual, these numbers change all the time, based on activity, time of day,

and state of mind. Many things can affect blood pressure – for better and for worse. Add to that the different effects high blood pressure can have on your body, and the fact that this symptomless condition can have a potentially deadly outcome, and you start to understand how vital it is to learn more about blood pressure.

Here's an important question to start with and one this book addresses: What is perhaps the most important lifestyle factor that influences your blood pressure?

The answer is food. Both doctors and scientists have long known that food has an enormous influence on the health of your circulatory system. One of the plans in use today in the USA is called DASH – which stands for Dietary Approaches to

Stop Hypertension. It is a set of guidelines established in 1997 and based on an extensive study of how healthy food choices and reducing salt intake can best reduce blood pressure. Many experts consider it a 'gold standard' programme for eating for healthy blood pressure.

We have gone further, and added even more simple, natural ways to battle blood pressure to create what we believe is the best plan of attack possible for this escalating health problem. You'll learn more about our *Beat High Blood Pressure Plan* in the pages ahead.

To start, let's explore the facts and myths of high blood pressure. Armed with this knowledge, it is much easier to see why eating healthily is *so* important.

Defining blood pressure

It's 7 pm on a Friday in the height of summer. You're driving – along with what seems like 300,000 others – out of your town or city to escape for the weekend. Two miles from the centre, traffic slows to a crawl. There's no accident, no road works – simply too many cars trying to move on a motorway that just can't accommodate that much traffic. So the pressure builds as you sit in your steaming car, waiting and waiting and waiting.

Much the same thing happens when you have high blood pressure. With every beat of your heart, oxygen-rich blood is pumped throughout the 60,000 miles of blood vessels in your body. Blood pressure describes the force of that blood as it wends its way through your arteries. As long as the walls of your arteries are clean, smooth and flexible, the blood flows effectively and your pressure remains low.

Sometimes, though, artery walls become stiff or hardened, so they're unable to contract and expand easily. Or they get clogged with sticky plaque, clots and other debris, thus narrowing the space through which blood can flow. Or too much fluid enters them. When any one of these things happens, pressure builds inside your blood vessels and the next thing you know, you're listening to a doctor reading you the riot act about your diet, exercise, weight and health.

Like the unexpected traffic jam, there are no warning signs of high blood pressure (known medically as hypertension). If you don't have regular checkups with your doctor that include blood pressure monitoring, you could walk around for years with dangerously high levels without realising it. It's no wonder they call hypertension the silent killer.

What is high blood pressure (hypertension)?

Blood pressure is measured by taking two readings - expressed like a fraction. The top figure shows the pressure in your arteries when blood is being forced through. The lower figure shows the diastolic pressure in your arteries when your heart relaxes.

A reading of 120/80 or lower is judged optimal. A reading between 130/85 and 139/89 is on the high side of normal and should be addressed. If your blood pressure reading is above 140/90, you have hypertension and need ongoing monitoring and treatment.

In the UK, more than one woman in three and two men in five have high blood pressure, with larger numbers affected in older age groups.

Make no mistake: Blood pressure can kill. Just as the growing rush-hour tension on the motorway increases the likelihood of an accident, so the growing pressure of blood against arterial muscles increases the risk of serious damage. It could be a clot breaking loose from an artery wall and travelling to your brain, causing a stroke. It could be microscopic damage to the artery walls themselves that eventually leads to plaque build-up and a heart attack. Or it could be long-term damage to the heart itself as it's forced to pump harder and harder to get blood through narrowed arteries.

Overall, a diagnosis of hypertension means that your risk of heart attack, heart failure, stroke and kidney disease has just skyrocketed. Consider this: If you're aged between 40 and 70, each 20-point increase in systolic blood pressure (the top number) or 10-point rise in diastolic pressure (the bottom number) *doubles* your risk of *any* cardiovascular disease.

If you lower those readings to normal levels, you reduce your risk of stroke by 35 to 40 per cent, cut your risk of heart attack by 20 to 25 per cent, and lower your risk of heart failure by more than 50 per cent.

Obviously, then, the benefits of following a healthy diet and making use of the recipes in this book are enormous. And what is even better – it doesn't take long to make a difference, as you'll see.

What causes high blood pressure

There are two types of hypertension. 'Essential' hypertension is by far the most common, affecting an estimated 90 to 95 per cent of those with high blood pressure. This is also the type for which no specific cause is known.

The other form of high blood pressure, called secondary, is a by-product of having a specific medical condition, such as kidney disease, problems with the adrenal glands, Cushing's syndrome (which is a rare hormonal condition), pregnancy, an overactive thyroid gland and neurological disorders. And some medicines can cause secondary high blood pressure, such as high doses of oestrogen, corticosteroids and nonsteroidal anti-inflammatory drugs.

Hypertension is not a modern illness. A century ago, blood pressure was poorly understood and the mechanics for measuring it did not exist, but 'apoplexy', an outdated term for stroke, was one of the most common causes of death – no doubt as a consequence of high blood pressure. In Nelson's time, sailors died of strokes at the age of 30 – probably because their diet was so high in the salt that preserved the food consumed on long voyages.

You don't get high blood pressure from viruses or bacteria; it is usually a result of the way you live. Although researchers aren't sure of the precise physiological

mechanism that increases blood pressure, they certainly know the triggers. Stated simply, the way you live is the greatest contributor to your risk of developing high blood pressure. Among the things that increase your risk of hypertension:

- A high-salt diet
- Lack of potassium
- Being overweight
- A sedentary lifestyle
- Excess alcohol consumption

What's noteworthy is that all of these factors are within your control. While medicines can deal with the physiology of high blood pressure, what you eat and the amount of exercise you take can have an enormous impact on your ability to achieve healthy blood pressure levels.

Demystifying blood pressure

You probably know how blood pressure is measured. A doctor or nurse wraps the cuff of a sphyganometer around your arm and squeezes on a hand-held pump to inflate the cuff, cutting off the blood flow in your artery for a few seconds. Then, when your arm feels pumped to bursting, a valve is released to let some of the air out of the cuff, enabling your blood to flow again. Whoever is taking the reading then listens with a stethoscope placed on your

FYI. *You're not alone.*

In the UK, about 16 million people have high blood pressure.

arm to detect when blood flow has resumed. A numbered dial or column of mercury on the blood pressure apparatus shows the blood pressure reading, which is marked on your chart. Fancier digital versions work automatically, and if you've ever been in hospital, you may have found yourself hooked up to a device that automatically inflates and deflates every few minutes to monitor your pressure.

You may be told what your reading is – say, 160 over 90, or 120 over 80. But whoever was taking the reading may not have explained precisely what those numbers really mean.

First, the numbers you hear are not set in stone. They can change from one GP visit to the next, and even from one hour to the next. Your blood pressure is not static. It is generally highest in the morning and lowest at night when you're sleeping. Thus, one reading of 'high' blood pressure is not something to worry about. It's when you have several high readings over a relatively short period of time that you should begin to be concerned.

Blood pressure is measured in mmHg, or millimetres of mercury. The systolic reading indicates the pressure when the left ventricle of your heart contracts. That means it's a measurement of how high your pressure is when your heart has just pushed fresh blood into the arteries. The diastolic reading indicates the pressure when the ventricle relaxes, or when blood is flowing on its own. The higher either of those numbers, the harder your heart is working to pump blood through your arteries.

In cardiovascular disease, the systolic pressure is of primary concern: in people over 50, pressure higher than 140mmHg contributes more to cardiovascular disease than high diastolic pressure. Work closely with your doctor to bring your systolic pressure down, as studies find that this is most effective for reducing blood vessel damage from hypertension.

But you should not ignore the diastolic pressure. If it is significantly elevated (above 120mmHg), it's an emergency and you may need to be admitted to hospital to lower it and avoid organ damage.

Here's how the British Hypertension Society classifies the different levels:

Optimal blood pressure This is a systolic reading of less than 120mmHg and a diastolic pressure of less than 80mmHg. This is ideal but your lifetime risk of developing hypertension is still as high as 90 per cent. Follow the guidelines in this book to make sure that your blood pressure remains normal.

Normal blood pressure Systolic blood pressure of up to 130mmHg and diastolic pressure of up to 85mmHg. Do not let it rise and try to lower it a little if possible.

High-normal blood pressure Systolic pressure of 130 to 139 and diastolic of 85 to 89. Think of figures within this range as a warning sign: if you fall into this category, you have twice the risk of progressing to more serious hypertension.

Stage 1 (mild) hypertension Systolic blood pressure of 140 to 159mmHg or diastolic pressure of 90 to 99mmHg. In this stage, you may require medication,

Getting an accurate reading

No doubt you've heard of 'white-coat hypertension'. Basically, this occurs when your blood pressure is high in the doctor's surgery but normal otherwise, because the stress of seeing the doctor acts on its own to increase it. Some studies have found the 'white-coat' effect in 20 to 35 per cent of patients.

Other things can cause a high reading, include an over-tight blood pressure cuff, tight sleeves, or an artery that is too stiff to be compressed, a problem sometimes seen in the elderly. For your regular check-up, however, you can ensure a more accurate reading by:

• Not smoking or eating or drinking anything containing caffeine for at least 30 minutes before the visit.

• Sitting quietly in a chair for at least 5 minutes before the pressure is taken, with your arm at heart level.

• Asking the health professional to take a second reading 2 minutes after the first so that you can compare the two results. If the two measurements differ by more than 5 points, additional readings need to be taken to establish a more accurate average reading.

although making determined lifestyle changes (iimproving your diet and taking more exercise) may help you avoid having to take prescription drugs. 140/85 is the level you should be aiming for, once your condition has been diagnosed and you have started to change your lifestyle.

Stage 2 (moderate) hypertension

A systolic reading of 160 to 179mmHg and a diastolic reading of 100 to 109mmHg. You can expect to receive medication, and should make significant lifestyle changes.

Stage 3 (severe) hypertension

A systolic reading of 180 or more and a diastolic of 110 or more are serious, and need careful and immediate attention.

Naturally, there are other considerations when contemplating your blood pressure readings. Here are a few:

- **If you have diabetes or kidney disease** New guidelines say you should aim to keep your blood pressure below 130/80mmHg to avoid the risk of heart attack or stroke. In other words, the threshold for taking action against high blood pressure is lower for you than for people without diabetes or kidney disease.

- **If you are in your late 60s or older.** You may have what's called isolated systolic hypertension (ISH), in which your systolic blood pressure remains high while your diastolic pressure is normal. As recently as 20 years ago most doctors did not even treat this condition, believing that it was a normal part of ageing. Now the medical world knows differently. Treating ISH with

Contraception, pregnancy, and high blood pressure

Women of child-bearing age face some particular issues when it comes to high blood pressure.

Contraception The combined oral contraceptive pill (COC) can cause blood pressure to rise – especially in obese and older women – by about 5/3mmHg. In a small minority the COC induces severe hypertension. That's why your doctor will question you about your blood pressure history before prescribing the COC and will want to keep a close watch on your blood pressure when you're taking it. The progestogen-only pill does not appear to cause these problems.

Interestingly, there is no evidence that hormone replacement therapy, which contains significantly less oestrogen than oral contraceptives, increases blood pressure.

low-dose (and inexpensive) diuretic drugs has been shown to reduce the incidence of stroke by 36 per cent and non-fatal heart attack by 27 per cent in those over 60.

Pregnancy A visit to the obstetrician or from your midwife usually includes a blood pressure check. This is to check for the start of gestational hypertension, in which your blood pressure rises during pregnancy.

One in every 20 women will develop high blood pressure during pregnancy, but as long as no protein is found in the urine, there is no danger of pre-eclampsia. If pre-eclampsia occurs, you and the baby will be monitored carefully.

Several blood pressure treatments are considered safe to use during pregnancy, but medication will be avoided unless there is no alternative. Of course, a healthy diet and regular exercise can also help you to maintain acceptable blood pressure during pregnancy.

- **If your systolic and diastolic readings fall into different categories.** Your doctor will look at the two levels and rate your blood pressure by the highest category.

- **If your systolic and diastolic numbers are unusually far apart** Pulse pressure is the difference between the systolic and diastolic figures. Some experts have suggested that it is a better predictor of overall heart disease risk than either blood pressure reading. A normal pulse pressure is 40mmHg. Much more or much less is considered a problem.

- **If your blood pressure readings vary from time to time** As mentioned earlier, a single blood pressure reading is may reflect as much on the previous few days' diet and stresses as on your

broader health. Some people's pressure increases merely because they become agitated when they visit their GP's surgery to have their blood pressure measured (see Getting an accurate reading on page 276). If you and your doctor have reason to believe that your blood pressure needs to be more accurately monitored, you may be advised to consider ambulatory blood pressure monitoring, in which you wear a monitor for 24 hours. During that time, the monitor takes periodic readings, collecting them for your doctor to evaluate.

Buying your own blood pressure monitor

With the plethora of easy-to-use home blood pressure monitors on the market, people with high blood pressure may wish to buy one and use it frequently to monitor their blood pressure. These machines automatically detect your systolic and diastolic pressure, unlike the mercury sphygmomanometers, that a health professional would use.

Some new models measure blood pressure from the wrist or finger but the UK's Blood Pressure Association does not recommend these at the moment as they are not thought to give as accurate a reading as upper arm models. If you do use a wrist monitor, it is essential to keep your wrist at the same height as your heart to ensure an accurate reading.

Most models carry a 'CE' marking to indicate some testing but this does not necessarily reflect their accuracy. The Blood Pressure Association is currently working with the Department of Health and the British Standards Institute to try and ensure that all blood pressure monitors are tested for their accuracy.

The British Hypertension Society has compiled a list of upper arm monitors – ranging in price from around £55-£115 – that have been independently tested and shown in research to be accurate. The list and information on monitors appears on the Blood Pressure Association's web site at: www.bpassoc.org.uk/information/information.htm

How well do you sleep?

Your answer may provide a clue to the state of your blood pressure. If you often wake up still tired and with a headache, if you've been told you snore heavily, and/or you find that you nod off during the day, you may suffer from obstructive sleep apnoea.

With this condition, your breathing is frequently interrupted in the night as your throat keeps closing. Studies have found that half of those with obstructive sleep apnoea also have hypertension.

Apnoea can be treated with surgery or continuous positive airway pressure, in which you wear a device at night that keeps your airway open and allows you to breathe freely.

If you suspect sleep apnoea is your problem, it is advisable to talk to your doctor about it. Apnoea can be indicative of a number of health conditions. Treating apnoea will also reduce hypertension and could save your life.

The dangers of high blood pressure

The threat to your health isn't just from the high pressure itself but from the damage such pressure eventually causes to arteries and smaller blood vessels. This damage is particularly devastating to the small blood vessels in organs such as your eyes, kidneys, brain and heart. These vessels are simply not designed to consistently withstand high levels of pressure. They cope with it by becoming more muscular, a process called hypertrophy, or enlargement of tissue. This harms the organ that contains the vessels because even though the vessels get bigger overall to handle the increased pressure, the space (or lumen) within them narrows. This narrowing makes it harder for blood to flow through the vessels, prompting the heart to work harder to push blood through.

All of this further increases blood pressure, creating a dangerous cycle that continues until blood flow to the organ is compromised or the blood vessels are damaged, leading, most commonly, to kidney failure, heart attack or stroke. Here's an overview of the conditions strongly linked to hypertension.

Atherosclerosis This is hardening and narrowing of the arteries caused by the slow build-up of plaque on the inside of artery walls. It can lead to several serious medical conditions, including coronary artery disease, angina, heart attack, sudden death, stroke and transient ischaemic attacks (TIA), or mini-strokes.

Cardiovascular disease (CVD) This is a catch-all term for all diseases affecting the heart and blood vessels.

Coronary artery disease (CAD) or coronary heart disease (CHD)
Coronary artery disease occurs when the arteries that supply blood to the heart muscle (coronary arteries) become hardened and narrowed by the build up of plaque on their inner walls or lining (atherosclerosis). This, in turn, reduces blood flow to the heart, decreasing oxygen supply to the heart muscle. Over time, this lack of oxygen decreases the ability of the heart muscle to pump at full capacity when you're doing more than basic activities.

Symptoms of CAD can include chest pain (angina) and shortness of breath with exertion.

Heart attack Also referred to as a coronary occlusion, a heart attack occurs when the supply of blood and oxygen to an area of heart muscle is blocked, usually by a clot in a coronary artery. Unless the blockage is treated within a few hours, the affected heart muscle dies and is replaced by scar tissue.

Heart failure This condition develops over time as the heart has increasing trouble pumping blood throughout the body. It's also known as congestive heart failure (CHF).

Stroke There are two main types of stroke. The most common is ischaemic stroke, which occurs when something suddenly blocks the blood supply to an

Emergency signs

Call 999 immediately if you have high blood pressure and begin experiencing any of the following symptoms.

- Numbness
  and tingling in your hands and feet

- Coughing up blood
  or severe nosebleeds

- Shortness of breath

- Chest pain

- Sudden, severe headache
  with no known cause

- Sudden weakness or numbness
  in your face, arm, and/or leg on one side of the body

- Sudden dimming
  or loss of vision

- Trouble speaking
  or understanding speech

- Shakiness
  or a sudden fall

area of the brain. The other form is haemorrhagic stroke, which occurs when a blood vessel in the brain bursts, spilling blood into the spaces surrounding the brain cells. Both lead to the death of brain cells as oxygen is cut off and result in temporary or permanent neurological damage or death.

A transient ischaemic attack (TIA), or mini-stroke, is technically not a stroke but rather a neurological deficit with symptoms lasting less than 24 hours. It's caused by a temporary interruption of the blood supply to an area of the brain and should serve as a warning sign, since about one-third of those who have a TIA will have an acute stroke some time in the future.

Dementia People with hypertension are more likely than those with normal blood pressure to experience dementia and other cognitive problems as they age. There is also some evidence that uncontrolled hypertension may increase the risk of Alzheimer's disease. Although scientists do not know all the reasons for the connection, one theory is that over

years, hypertension decreases the elasticity of blood vessels in the brain, increasing resistance and reducing their responsiveness.

Kidney disease Uncontrolled hypertension is the second leading cause of chronic kidney disease (diabetes is the first). It speeds the deterioration of kidney function to the point where life-saving measures, such as dialysis or kidney transplant, are needed.

Blood vessel damage Constant high blood pressure can damage the lining of the blood vessels. This can increase the rate at which plaque accumulates on blood vessel walls (atherosclerosis), narrowing the blood vessels and reducing the amount of blood flowing to the body's organs.

Retinopathy (eye damage) High blood pressure affects the blood vessels on the inner surface of the eye in much the same way that it affects blood vessels in the heart or kidneys. Over time, uncontrolled high blood pressure can cause a blood vessel in the eye to burst, bleed, or occlude, leading to blurred vision or even blindness.

FYI. *Blood pressure rises with age: About 50% of all people over 65 have high blood pressure. About 25% of all middle-aged people have high blood pressure*

A growing number of clinical studies attest to the role of lifestyle changes in controlling and reducing blood pressure. Modifying, for instance, what you eat and how much, how you cope in a traffic jam and how much exercise you take, can do as much as, if not more than, medication to lower blood pressure.

Here are seven major studies that provide proof that a healthy lifestyle lowers blood pressure:

Framingham Heart Study The world's longest-running population-based study, began in 1948 when scientists from the US Public Health Service chose residents of the town of Framingham, Massachusetts, to help them to learn more about the growing epidemic of heart disease. Results have proved the connection between hypertension and heart disease, exercise and hypertension, diet and heart disease and diabetes and heart disease.

Dietary Approaches to Stop Hypertension (DASH) This study was published in the *New England Journal of Medicine* in 1997, and evaluated 459 middle-aged Americans with and without high blood pressure as they followed one of three diets: the typical American diet; one that included more fruits and vegetables than the typical American diet; or the DASH diet, an eating programme specifically designed to be high in those nutrients found to positively affect blood pressure and low in those found to negatively affect it.

Leading studies on reducing blood pressure without drugs

A later study, the DASH-sodium study, coupled the DASH diet with reduced sodium intake and found an even greater drop in blood pressure.

Nurses' Health Study This long-term, ongoing study evaluates the health and lifestyle habits of 82,473 nurses in the USA. One major finding was that each kilo (2.2lb) of weight gain after the age of 18 increased a woman's risk of hypertension by 5 per cent. This risk increase occurred even if a woman's weight remained in the so-called normal range, generally defined as a body mass index (BMI) of less than 25. Conversely, a group of studies finds that losing 4 to 8 per cent of body weight results in at least a 3/3mmHg drop in blood pressure and less need for medication.

TOMHS The best currently available data on combined dietary intervention comes from the Treatment of Mild Hypertension Study (TOMHS), in which 902 patients with mild diastolic hyper-tension (90 to 99mmHg) followed a programme to lose weight, restrict sodium and alcohol and increase physical activity. All were then given placebos (dummy pills) or one of five different kinds of antihypertensive drug.

After four years, all subjects showed blood pressure reductions of, on average, 15.9/12.3mmHg for those on drugs and 9.1/8.6mmHG for those on placebos. Plus, their levels of 'bad' cholesterol dropped while their levels of 'good' cholesterol rose, reducing overall cardiovascular risk.

Trials of Hypertension Prevention, Phase II This study focused on 2,382 men and women, aged 30 to 54, who had blood pressures of less than 140/83-89mmHg and were between 10 per cent and 65 per cent above their ideal body weight. All were given the same medical treatment,then split into four groups. The first received no extra guidance, the second reduced their salt intake, the third began a weight-loss programme, and the fourth reduced salt intake and lost weight. Compared with those who received no extra guidance, those who cut back on salt saw their blood pressure fall by an average of 2.9/1.6mmHg and those on the weight-loss programme saw average reductions of 3.7/2.7mmHg. But those on the combined therapy had the greatest reduction: 4.0/2.0mmHg. Four years after the study ended, those who had received the interventions were less likely to have developed hypertension than those who received only medication.

TONE The Trial of Nonpharmacologic Interventions in the Elderly (TONE), was the first multi-centre clinical trial of sufficient size and duration (30 months) to show that lifestyle modifications can be used to control high blood pressure in older people. The first results from this trial, published in the *Journal of the American Medical Association* in March 1998, found that losing weight and cutting down on salt could lessen and even eliminate the need for blood pressure-lowering medications in the elderly.

PREMIER Clinical Trial This clinical trial to put together what is known about lifestyle changes and blood pressure to see how different changes interact with one another to reduce blood pressure. Supported by the National Heart, Lung, and Blood Institute in the USA, the study compared the effects of two behavioural interventions on blood pressure in 810 adults who had high blood pressure but were not taking antihypertensive medications.

At the start of the trial, 38 per cent of participants were diagnosed as hypertensive and most were over-weight and got little physical activity. Participants either received advice only (typically from a dietitian), or were encouraged to implement established recommendations for lowering blood pressure (giving up smoking, losing weight, increasing exercise), or combined established recommenda-tions with the DASH diet. After six months, participants in both interven-tional groups lost weight, improved their fitness, lowered their sodium intake and reduced their blood pres-sure. The group following established guidelines reduced their systolic blood pressure by an average of 3.7mmHg, while those who also followed the DASH diet had reductions of 4.3mmHg.

By the end of the study, 26 per cent of those in the advice-only group still had hypertension, compared with just 17 per cent who followed the estab-lished guidelines and 12 per cent who also used the DASH diet.

Eat to beat high blood pressure

Wouldn't it be reassuring to know that while eating delicious, interesting, healthy foods, you could almost certainly prevent a deadly major disease such as hypertension? Well, there is compelling evidence that this is indeed the case.

First, consider the general trends. Hypertension rates are highest in populations who are overweight, lead a sedentary life and eat a high-salt diet. Contrary to popular belief, these are not always people living in the highly developed Western world. According to the World Health Organisation (WHO), high blood pressure now affects between 10 and 30 per cent of adults in almost every country. WHO says that high blood pressure is a significant cause of about 50 per cent of the cardiovascular disease which kills around 12 million people worldwide each year. Other significant factors include an inactive lifestyle, tobacco use and low fruit and vegetable intake.

In the UK, our diet contains too much salt, fat and sugar, too many processed foods which are packed with all three, and not enough fruit, vegetables and wholegrain cereals. As a result we are one of the countries with the greatest number of deaths from strokes and heart attacks. So how can this be addressed?

There is strong evidence that increasing your intake of one key nutrient – potassium (found in fruit and vegetables) – while limiting salt in your diet is of key importance. According to top British blood pressure specialists, these two dietary strategies, coupled with a healthy lifestyle, are the best possible ways to reduce your blood pressure.

Research has shown, too, that people who maintain a healthy weight are less likely to have hypertension than people who are overweight or obese. Also, vegetarians and those who follow the so-called Mediterranean diet (high in vegetables, fruits, whole grains and unsaturated fats) tend to have lower than average blood pressure – although this is not necessarily true for people who consume a lot of salt and are overweight and unfit.

So before you turn to medication, take a good, hard look at what you're eating. The following pages outline the most proven eating plan for healthy blood pressure and look at the foods and nutrients that are useful in the battle against high blood pressure, as well as the foods that cause the most damage. Finally, the book looks at the role of weight loss in managing high blood pressure and presents a top 10 of essential steps for launching a successful weight-loss effort.

The sodium/salt connection

This is necessarily the starting point when considering blood pressure and diet. All the evidence suggests that reducing salt intake is the single most effective way to reduce high blood pressure.

Salt (sodium and chloride) is one of the most studied nutrients when it comes to blood pressure. We know that excess sodium in the body causes arterioles – thin-walled arteries that end in capillaries – to contract, which raises blood pressure. Sodium also draws more fluid into the bloodstream and holds it there. The more fluid, the more pressure. Think of a garden hose. If you turn the water on as a trickle, there's little pressure. Turn it on full blast, and it gushes out with such force that the hose may jump out of your hands.

In their paper 'How Far Should Salt Intake Be Reduced', published in the journal *Hypertension* in 2003, researchers from the Blood Pressure Unit at St George's Hospital Medical School in London showed that reducing our current salt intake – 9g-12g a day – by just 3g a day would reduce strokes by 13 per cent and ischaemic heart disease (IHD) by 10 per cent.

The researchers, who had evaluated all major trials in this area in the past 20 years went on to conclude that reducing our daily salt intake by 6g would double the effect and reducing it by 9g would triple it – preventing as many as 20,500 stroke deaths and 31,400 deaths from IHD every year in the UK.

Being overweight is also a major risk factor. A major study in the *Journal of the American Medical Association* in December 1999, found that for people who consumed the most salt and were overweight, the risk of a stroke increased by 32 per cent. They were also 89 per cent more likely to die from a stroke, 44 per cent more likely to die from coronary heart disease, 61 per cent more likely to die from all cardiovascular diseases and 39 per cent more likely to die from all causes than those who ate 2,300mg of sodium (5.75g salt) or less a day.

The DASH-sodium study, linked to the US guidelines – Dietary Approaches to Stop Hypertension (DASH) – mentioned earlier, is hugely significant in the diet debate. This study compared the effects of three levels of salt intake and two dietary patterns on people with both normal and high blood pressure. Full details of this study appear on page 285.

In brief, the study discovered that those on the DASH diet who had the lowest salt intake (4g a day) achieved the greatest reduction in blood pressure. In addition, a fall in cholesterol levels was reported in participants who combined the diet with a low salt intake.

The UK's Blood Pressure Association strongly believes that almost everyone would benefit from a reduction in salt intake to around 6g a day. Most people would agree that the typical UK diet, which currently includes 9g to 12g salt (3,600 to 4,800mg of sodium) a day, is simply too high in the mineral.

The recipes in this book are designed to complement medical advice on controlling your blood pressure. They feature delicious natural foods – many rich in potassium, the most important blood pressure nutrient. The recommended daily intake for potassium in the UK is 3500mg; for each dish we tell you if a serving is a 'useful' source (providing 10-25 per cent of the recommended daily intake), a 'good' source (25-50 per cent) or an 'excellent' source (providing more than 50 per cent).

In addition, the recipes have no added salt and, instead, use fresh herbs, garlic and onions to provide flavour and are perfectly in keeping with DASH recommendations.

Painless ways to cut down salt

You don't *have* to count grams of salt or milligrams of sodium as if they were diamonds. But you should stay away from the salt cellar on your table – and stick to 'real' foods.

By 'real', we mean foods that are close to their natural state, such as fresh vegetables and fruits; unadorned meats, poultry and fish; and unaltered grains and cereals.

It's when foods are processed that salt gets poured in – a cheap way to boost taste. It is estimated that 75 per cent or more of our salt intake comes from processed foods. Just see below:

Natural food	sodium (mg)	salt (g)		Processed food	sodium (mg)	salt (g)
1 bowl of muesli	24	0.06	vs	1 bowl cornflakes	300	0.76
100g boiled red kidney beans	2	0.005	vs	100g canned red kidney beans	390	0.99
100g fresh tomato	9	0.02	vs	100g tomato-based pasta sauce	410	1.0
50g unsalted peanuts	1	0.002	vs	50g roasted, salted peanuts	200	0.5
100g boiled new potatoes	0–5	0.02	vs	100g potato waffles	430	1.0
100g roast pork	67	0.17	vs	100g ham	1200	3.0

Source: National Heart, Lung, and Blood Institute

Learning the language of salt

One way to help reduce your salt intake is to read labels and know what they mean. Confusingly sodium or salt may be listed and the sodium content may appear in grams or milligrams. To convert from sodium to salt, remember 1g (1,000mg) sodium = 2.5g salt, so you simply multiply by 2.5 or (if in mg) divide the sodium by 1,000 first. And be aware that the 'serving' listed on labels is usually quite small so your *actual* serving may supply much more salt.

Phrase	What it means
Sodium free or salt free	No more than 5mg sodium per 100g or 100ml
No added salt	No salt or sodium should have been added to the food or any of its ingredients
Reduced sodium	Contains at least 25 per cent less sodium than the standard version
Low salt	No more than 40mg sodium per 100g or 100ml
Low sodium/salt food	Food is naturally low in sodium/salt

The DASH trials

It might be easier to eat healthily and lose weight if someone else shopped for and prepared every morsel of food that entered your mouth. Well, that's the advantage the participants in the Dietary Approaches to Stop Hypertension (DASH) study had when they joined the trial in the early 1990s.

The diet isn't a weight-loss diet as such, as it is based on 2,000 calories a day. If you're overweight, though, you'll probably find yourself losing weight anyway, with the bonus of watching your blood pressure drop along with your weight. Another advantage is that the diet helps to lower levels of cholesterol and homocysteine, both major risk factors for heart disease.

Before we get into the specifics of what our *Beat High Blood Pressure* diet offers, here's more about the DASH trials on which the recommendations are based.

Even before it began, researchers knew that certain diets, primarily vegetarian diets and those with moderate amounts of lean protein, lowered blood pressure. They also knew that meatless meals had limited appeal, so they were anxious to find a programme that would satisfy the largest number of participants.

The 459 people who joined the study were 44.6 years old on average and had blood pressures that were lower than 160/95 mmHg. Nearly half were women, and 6 out of 10 were African-American, which was important because high blood pressure is particularly prevalent among black people. Also important was the fact that 62 per cent of the women and half of the men were obese, with a body mass index (BMI) of 30 or higher.

The volunteers spent three weeks eating their normal diets before their blood pressure was measured. Then they were assigned to one of three groups. The first group continued eating the average US diet, high in fat and limited in fruits, vegetables and fibre. The second group increased the amount of fruit and vegetables they ate but made no other changes to their lifestyles. The third group followed what eventually became known as the DASH diet.

The groups consumed the same amount of sodium (about 3,000mg a day, or 7.5g salt, a little less than the typical UK intake), limited the amount of alcohol they drank to one or two drinks a day and had no more than three servings a day of caffeinated drinks (cola, coffee or tea).

In addition, the participants' calorie intakes were closely monitored to prevent any changes in their weight for the duration of the study.

After eight weeks, all of those on the DASH diet saw their blood pressures drop an average of 5.5/3.0mmHg, or about as much as might be expected if they were taking antihypertensive medications. Those who were already hypertensive, however, had the greatest reductions: an average of 11.4mmHg in systolic pressure and 5.5 mmHg in diastolic pressure. The news was even better for the African-Americans, whose blood pressure dropped an average of 13.2/6.1mmHg. Researchers estimated that even the smaller reductions could reduce the overall incidence of coronary artery disease by 15 per cent and of stroke by 27 per cent.

Then, to see if reducing salt would improve the results, researchers launched a second trial, this time putting DASH diet participants on either a high-sodium (3,300mg sodium/ 8.25g salt), intermediate-sodium (2,400 mg sodium/ 6g salt) or low-sodium (1,500mg sodium/3.75g salt) diet for one month. Those on the low-sodium DASH plan saw their blood pressure drop by the

FYI. *Beware. Foods such as olives, bacon, pickles, tomato sauce, barbecue sauce, smoked salmon and seasoning blends can be high in salt.*

greatest amount, an average of 9.0/4.5mmHg. They even had fewer headaches. The best news, however, was that the results happened fast – in only a few weeks.

So what does this diet look like? Well, if you put all the basic nutritional advice we've received over the past 20 years and put it into one programme, you'd get the DASH-sodium diet. In fact, this is a programme your entire family should follow, regardless of their blood pressure. It might help them to avoid the almost inevitable rise in blood pressure that comes with age (although there are no studies as yet that prove this), and it will certainly reduce their risk of various cancers, heart disease, diabetes and other chronic health conditions.

In a nutshell, the diet reduces the overall amount of fat, saturated fat and cholesterol in the typical diet; increases the number of fruits, vegetables, and low-fat dairy foods; increases fibre with whole grain products; and reduces the number of sweets and sugary drinks.

This version will also help you to cut your salt intake dramatically. About 27 per cent of calories are derived from fats (principally from healthier unsaturated fats) and 18 per cent from protein with the remainder (55 per cent) from carbohydrates. Compare that with the typical UK diet, in which 36 per cent of calories come from fat, 47 per cent from carbohydrates, and 17 per cent from protein. It's not rocket science – just good, commonsense eating.

More specifically, the diet calls for:

 Seven to eight servings a day of whole grains or grain products, including bread, cereal and pasta. We're not talking Coco Pops here, but high-fibre, sugar free cereals such as muesli or porridge. And when you are buying bread, reach for the one on which 'whole grain' tops the ingredients list.

 Four to five servings of vegetables each day Don't be afraid of this; one bowl of salad is one serving. So is a tomato or three tablespoons of peas. Ensure that vegetables are the first things you put on your plate, and pile them high. Rethink dishes and menus so that everything you cook is vegetable-based, or at least has vegetables in it. Add sweetcorn to lasagne and broccoli to your curries. Be inventive – and healthy!

 Four to five servings of fruit daily You can eat them fresh, canned, cooked, juiced and even dried.

 Two to three daily servings of low-fat or fat-free dairy products That includes cheese, milk, yoghurt – even ice cream!

 No more than two servings a day of meat, poultry or fish This includes non-meat protein, such as eggs and tofu, and all types of seafood.

 Four to five servings a week of nuts, seeds and legumes Think of it as a handful of peanuts (strictly unsalted) every weekday. Nuts are great sources of magnesium, potassium, protein and fibre.

 No more than three servings a day of fats This includes all oils, butter, salad dressings and mayonnaise.

 No more than five servings a week of sweets That's basically anything with added sugar.

Put it all together, and here's what it looks like. We've provided portion sizes for three different daily calorie targets:

• 1,600 calories for healthy men or women seeking to lose weight, or small-framed women with sedentary lifestyles.

• 2,000 calories for average-framed women seeking a stable weight, or men with sedentary lifestyles.

• 2,400 calories for moderately active men, or highly active women.

YOUR EATING PLAN

Food group	Daily servings			Serving sizes	Examples
	1,600 calories per day	**2,000** calories per day	**2,400** calories per day		
Grains, potatoes and cereals	6	7–8	9–10	• 1 slice bread or 1 mini pitta bread • 2 tbsp muesli 3 tbsp porridge or cereal • 3 heaped tbsp cooked rice or pasta • 1 medium-sized potato	Wholemeal bread, English muffin, pitta, bagel, cereals, muesli, porridge, crackers, unsalted snacks and popcorn.
Vegetables Rich source of potassium	3–4	4–5	5	• 3 tbsp vegetables such as peas or carrots • 1 tomato or 7 cherry tomatoes • A cereal bowl full of salad • 150ml (¼ pint) vegetable juice	Fresh, canned (without salt) or frozen all count. Eat a variety and try new ones for a change.
Fruits Rich source of potassium	4	4–5	5	• 150ml (¼ pint) fruit juice • 2-3 small fruits • 1 medium-sized fruit • 3 heaped tbsp canned fruit	Dried fruit counts, too. Plums, apricots, satsumas. Apples, oranges, pears. Choose canned fruit in natural juice.
Low-fat or fat-free dairy foods	2–3	2–3	3	• 200ml (⅓ pint) milk • 150ml (¼ pint) yoghurt • 40g (1½oz) cheese	Skimmed or semi-skimmed milk, low-fat yoghurt, reduced fat or lower fat cheeses.
Meat, poultry and fish Rich source of potassium	2 or fewer	2 or fewer	2	• 60-90g (2-3oz) lean meat, • 75–125g (3-4oz) poultry or - oil-rich fish • 150g (5½oz) white fish or tuna (canned in water)	Select only lean cuts. Trim away visible fat. Grill, roast or stir-fry instead of frying. Remove skin from poultry.
Nuts, seeds, and dried beans Rich source of potassium	3 a week	4–5 a week	1 a day	• 2 tbsp unsalted nuts or seeds • 4 heaped tbsp cooked pulses or beans	Mixed nuts of all sorts, sunflower seeds, kidney beans (canned without salt or sugar), lentils.
Fats and oils	2	2–3	3	• 1 tsp soft margarine • 1 tbsp low-fat mayonnaise • 2 tablespoons low-fat salad dressing • 1 tsp vegetable oil	Soft margarine, low-fat mayonnaise, light salad dressing, vegetable oil (olive, corn, rapeseed, or safflower).
Sweets	0	5 a week	1 a day	• 1 tbsp sugar • 25g (1oz) chocolate • 3-5 sweets • 1 tbsp jam	Maple syrup, sugar, jelly, jam, chocolate, health bars, jelly beans, boiled sweets, sorbet, ice creams.

Some helpful nutrients

Whether or not you follow this diet to the letter, there are certain foods and nutrients you really should include in – or take out of – your diet. The recipes in the *Beat High Blood Pressure Cookbook* are full of healthy nutrients, such as potassium which is particularly helpful, and contain very few of the bad, such as salt and saturated fats. Therefore, simply by choosing dishes from this book, you are likely to benefit your blood pressure, even if you don't follow the diet strictly.

Potassium Potassium is a particularly significant mineral. The Blood Pressure Association strongly advises increasing potassium intake as it has the opposite effect to salt and actually helps to lower blood pressure.

Medical experts believe that potassium acts by increasing sodium excretion in the urine, which helps blood vessels to dilate, and by changing the interactions of hormones that affect blood pressure. In one analysis of several studies that looked at the ability of supplemental potassium to lower blood pressure, participants who were taking 2.3 to 4.7g a day of supplemental potassium had an average blood pressure reduction of 4.4/2.5mmHg. (However, doctors recommend eating potassium-rich foods rather than taking the mineral as a supplement.)

In one major international study, the INTERSALT study, all populations that consumed more salt than potassium saw their blood pressures rise, while those consuming more potassium than salt had no increase. And when Harvard researchers followed 43,738 men for eight years, they found a 38 per cent reduced risk of stroke in those who got the most potassium.

In the UK the recommended daily intake for potassium is 3500mg and in this cookbook we have indicated when a serving of a particular dish is a 'useful', 'good' or 'excellent' source, supplying a quarter, half or more of that intake.

• **BEST FOOD SOURCES: Fruit and fruit juices (especially dried fruit, bananas, melon, orange and tomato juice), vegetables, pulses, potatoes, seeds and nuts.**

Vitamins Fruit and vegetables are also an excellent source of the antioxidant vitamins C and E, which play an important role in preventing heart disease.

• **BEST FOOD SOURCES Fresh fruit, fruit juices, vegetables, potatoes for vitamin C. Vegetable oils, nuts, seeds and wheatgerm for vitamin E.**

Fibre Fibre – the indigestible part of plants – is extremely important in a healthy diet. There are two main types of dietary fibre – soluble and insoluble. Both types help to prevent constipation and may protect against large bowel disease too.

Souble fibre is also thought to help reduce cholesterol (like high blood pressure, high cholesterol is another risk factor for heart disease). The fibre is thought to do this by binding to cholesterol in bile and taking some of the cholesterol with it when it is excreted as waste. The recommended daily intake for fibre is 18g in the UK, but the average adult eats only about 12g.

• **BEST FOOD SOURCES: Whole grains, fruits and vegetables.**

Omega-3 fatty acids Found primarily in cold-water fish, this form of fat may help to reduce the risk of heart disease. There is also some evidence that increasing your consumption of omega-3 fatty acids may also help to lower blood pressure. Studies have demonstrated some modest improvements in blood flow in patients with atherosclerosis after taking fish oil supplements, which also appear to make the fatty deposits (plaques) on artery walls less likely to rupture.

• **BEST FOOD SOURCES: Mackerel, salmon, herring, fresh tuna.**

Garlic If you're looking for a savoury substitute for salt, try some crushed garlic mixed into your food. Not only does it pack a seasoning punch with no sodium, but several clinical trials attest to its blood pressure-lowering properties (although there are no large, well-controlled research studies that prove its efficacy).

FYI. *Less than 10 per cent of Britons with hypertension are diagnosed and receiving treatment to control their blood pressure.*

Blood pressure danger foods

Just as there are certain foods shown to improve blood pressure and reduce your risk of hypertension, there are also some that are known to make things worse. Salt is by far the most significant but there are others that it is wise to avoid or, at the very least, enjoy in moderation.

Alcohol More than 50 studies attest to the blood pressure-raising effects of consuming large amounts of alcohol, suggesting that the more you drink, the greater the effect. Precisely how alcohol affects blood pressure is not yet known. However, it is known that binge drinking is particularly harmful as blood pressure can soar when the alcohol level in the body falls after an excessive intake. But it seems that drinking small amounts of alcohol does not have any ill-effects. In fact, drinking a little can actually protect you against heart disease and stroke.

If you regularly drink much more than the recommended limits (see below) and you reduce your consumption, your blood pressure is likely to come down as well.

One unit is:
• A half-pint of ordinary strength beer or lager
• A small glass of wine
• A measure of spirits

For a man, the recommended healthy limit is no more than three or four units a day. For a woman it is no more than two or three units a day. Regularly drinking more is likely to affect your blood pressure. You should also have alcohol-free days in your week. And be aware that bars often serve larger than normal glasses of wine and strong beers.

Caffeine The data on caffeine and blood pressure is quite mixed. Researchers do not know with any certainty which chemicals in coffee affect blood pressure. It could be caffeine but recent studies suggest that some unknown ingredient or ingredients may actually be to blame. And while it is well-known that a cup of coffee temporarily raises your blood pressure, the long-term effects of coffee drinking are less clear. For instance, studies on young people with normal blood pressure find little effect, but studies on older people with high blood pressure find that coffee drinkers have even higher blood pressure – about 5/3mmHg higher than those who abstain. If you have high blood pressure it is probably best not to drink more than two cups of coffee a day.

Saturated fats Until the DASH study, there was no real awareness in the USA that changing levels of dietary fat affected blood pressure. Given the significant results of DASH, which calls for reduced levels of overall fat and saturated fat in particular, the significance of different kinds of fat has been recognised. Regardless of blood pressure research, there is clear evidence of the heart-damaging effects of a high intake of saturated fat, the kind found primarily in full-fat animal products such as dairy foods and meats.

The recipes in the *Beat High Blood Pressure Cookbook* have been developed to contain only small amounts of saturated fat (as well as healthy unsaturated fats),

Caution: painkillers and cold remedies

Be careful when using non-steroidal anti-inflammatory drugs – a class of painkillers that includes ibuprofen – as taking them may make your blood pressure tablets less effective. You should also be aware that many decongestants and cold and flu remedies contain compounds such as pseudoephedrine, phenylephrine, or phenylpropanolamine (also known as PPA). They ease a stuffy nose by constricting blood vessels, reducing swelling in nasal passages but this action also causes blood pressure to rise. Cocaine and other illegal drugs can also increase blood pressure.

to provide the heart health benefits and to assist you in your efforts to lose weight or maintain a healthy weight.

Liquorice If you love the strongly flavoured sweet and have high blood pressure, there could be a connection. A study by researchers in Iceland found that eating even small amounts of liquorice (comparable to a handful of jelly beans) raised systolic blood pressure an average of 3.5mmHg. Liquorice is full of salt and if you eat a lot of it, it actually encourages sodium retention, which is not helpful if you are trying to control your blood pressure. If you want a sweet snack it is much better to eat potassium-rich dried fruits instead.

Lose weight, lower blood pressure

Just as research associates lung cancer and emphysema with smoking, it shows a similarly strong correlation between hypertension and obesity. A body mass index (BMI) of 27 or more and significant fat deposits around the abdomen are directly linked to high blood pressure.

Body weight affects blood pressure in three ways. With increased weight, you have increased blood volume, which can lead to higher blood pressure. Also, people who are overweight are more likely to be salt sensitive. Finally, overweight people are more insulin resistant, meaning that their cells bar access to insulin so they

can't accept energy-providing glucose. The resulting excess of glucose and insulin contributes to high blood pressure.

The good news is that losing as little as 5kg (about 10lb) of body weight can significantly improve your blood pressure readings. Although the DASH diet was not designed for weight loss, that doesn't mean you can't lose weight while following it. In fact, one complaint of participants in the DASH study was that they had to eat *too much* food. For instance, a sample dinner might include 75g (3oz) of baked cod, 200g (7oz) boiled rice, 150g (5½oz) of broccoli, 125g (4½oz) of stewed tomatoes, a small spinach salad, one whole wheat bread roll with a teaspoon of margarine, and 125g (4½oz) of melon balls.

So it's quite likely you'll lose a few pounds on this DASH-based plan without even trying. If you are trying, some simple substitutions can make a big difference in your overall calorie intake. Couple that with an increase in your physical activity, and you should see the pounds drop off.

10 essential steps to losing weight

Follow the steps below – all proven to help you to lose weight and keep it off – and watch your weight, along with your blood pressure, drop.

1 Stick to real foods If you make fruits, vegetables, fish, poultry and even meat the mainstays of your diet and avoid processed foods, including cakes, crisps, sweets and stripped-of-nutrients grains, you'll find the weight dropping off with little or no effort.

2 Choose your fats Saturated fats – in dairy products and fatty meats – pile on the calories and are a heart risk too. But some fats, particularly omega-3 fatty acids and the mono-unsaturated fats found in olive oil and many nuts, appear to provide significant health benefits. But if you want to lose weight, it is sensible to keep an eye on the calorie content of what you are eating. Ultimately, as you know, losing weight is all about calories.

3 Pay attention to portions Food portions have grown from normal to super-size in the past 20 years, yet many people continue to clean their plates as if their parents were still standing over them. If you train yourself to eat half or even three-quarters of what's put in front of you, focus on your food, chew thoroughly and eat slowly, so that your brain gets the message that you're full, you'll find the pounds slipping off effortlessly. Sitting at the dining table and eating with friends or family helps to slow down the rate at which you eat, too.

4 Eat breakfast every day Studies suggest it's a good strategy for weight loss and it will help you to avoid mid-morning snacking. The best breakfast includes some kind of high-fibre food, such as wholemeal toast or cereal; a protein food, such as peanut butter or low-fat cheese; and a piece of fruit or glass of unsweetened fruit juice.

5 Eat healthy snacks If you do get hungry, make sure you will be able to reach for healthy snacks. Keep ready-to-eat dried fruits such as apricots, figs or prunes, packets of unsalted peanuts and small cartons of yoghurt at home or in the office (or even in the car). These will take the edge off your hunger and you'll be able to wait for a healthy meal without wolfing down a packet of crisps.

6 Go for 'low energy density' One of the newest terms in US weight-loss circles is energy density, or how much water a food contains. The higher the water content, the lower the energy density. The lower the energy density, the more you can eat and the fuller you'll feel, while consuming far fewer calories than if you choose a food with higher energy density. What this means is that you can probably have a whole bowl of chicken soup or several pieces of fresh fruit for the same number of calories found in a small packet of crisps because the soup and fruit have more volume per calorie.

7 Monitor your liquids Choosing a tall skinny latte (167 calories) rather than a tall regular latte (212 calories) can

save 45 calories – which may not seem much but every little helps. Studies show that liquids don't 'fill you up' in the same way as food. And calories from drinks can add up fast if you're not aware of what you're drinking.

8 Think about why you're eating Too often, we reach for food as a way to assuage a hunger that has nothing to do with our stomachs. Food soothes and comforts us when we're sad and releases frustration when we're having a bad day at work. But this emotional eating, or unconscious eating, packs on the weight with almost hideous efficiency. The next time you find yourself reaching for the ice cream, stop and think about why you want to eat it. Maybe taking a bath, writing in your diary or even going for a walk would help you to cope with those feelings better than eating will.

9 Write it down That means every bite you put into your mouth. People who are successful at weight loss keep an accurate food diary even after they've reached their goals. They write down every morsel that enters their mouths, from a fizzy drink to a bag of crisps.

10 Do more exercise The formula for weight loss is simple: calories in must be fewer than calories out. Other than starving yourself (proved time and time again to fail as a weight-loss approach), your best bet is to be more active. Look for hidden opportunities for exercise, such as going to the bathroom upstairs instead of to the one down the hall, walking to the shops, rather than driving, and using the stairs rather than the lift or the escalator.

Easy food substitutions

if you usually have	try instead
crackers and cream cheese	oatcake and reduced-fat cream cheese
sugar-coated breakfast cereal	muesli with sliced banana
mayonnaise on salad	mixture of balsamic vinegar and olive oil
vegetables with butter	vegetables with a squeeze of lemon juice
fruit canned in syrup	fresh fruit
pasta with cream-based sauce	pasta with tomato-based sauce
jacket potato with cheese and coleslaw	jacket potato with baked beans
tortilla chips with cream cheese dip	breadsticks with quark

Beyond food

What you eat – and how much you eat of it – are not the only contributors to high blood pressure, nor is changing them the only way to control it. How you live your life, more specifically whether you lead an active or sedentary life, is also a key factor. Additionally, for most people with hypertension, medication is a factor.

In the next few pages, we will show you how your day-to-day routines and even your reactions can affect your blood pressure, as well as easy ways to adjust them for better health. These will play a role in your new, healthier lifestyle so read on!

1 Lifestyle and habits

In a moment, we'll get to one of the most important lifestyle issues affecting blood pressure – exercise – and discuss another that is commonly thought to affect it, but may not – stress. But first, let's consider the even more basic topics of sleep, emotions and habits; the roles they play in your personal health.

It should come as no surprise that the worst of bad habits – smoking – damages your arteries and is the biggest risk factor for having a heart attack. While it does not actually *cause* high blood pressure, it will cause your arteries to narrow, just as hypertension does. If you have high blood pressure and smoke as well, your arteries will narrow much more quickly, rapidly increasing your risk of stroke or heart disease. Nicotine is highly addictive but

there are now very effective means of giving up. If you find quitting difficult, consult your GP who will help you to find an effective aid or suitable therapy.

Other eating and drinking habits – including drinking alcohol and overindulging in sweets or salty snacks – are also uniformly bad for blood pressure health. As we noted in the last chapter, too much alcohol – particularly binge drinking – is particularly troublesome for blood pressure, as are being overweight and binging on high-salt or high-sugar foods.

Your emotions also affect your blood pressure – albeit temporarily. For instance, some studies have found that depressed people with high blood pressure have more difficulty controlling it than those who are not depressed. However, there are

FYI *Many people are surprised when told they have high blood pressure. They discover it almost by accident.*

many possible reasons, including the fact that people who are depressed may lose interest in taking their medication and may be less likely to follow the kind of healthy lifestyle necessary to control blood pressure. In such cases, it is probably most important to treat the depression.

How well you sleep may also affect your ability to control your blood pressure. When researchers deprived 36 people with mild to moderate hypertension of sleep for one night, then compared blood pressure levels after the sleepless night with those following a good night's sleep, they found that both blood pressure and heart rate levels were higher after the sleepless night than after a good snooze. The results suggest that sleepless nights may represent increased risk for both organ damage and acute cardiovascular disease. It is certainly true that our blood pressure falls dramatically during sleep but most of us would probably not want to spend our lives in bed.

The point is simple: a healthy, active lifestyle contributes to healthy blood pressure. Unlike viral infections or allergies, which have clear external triggers and causes that are out of your control, high blood pressure is almost entirely linked to the daily choices you make for yourself and your family.

2 Exercise

Being regularly active can lower systolic blood pressure (the upper figure) by an average of 4-9mmHg, according to the Blood Pressure Association. And it is well established that regular physical activity reduces your risk of all forms of cardio-vascular disease. Being physically active will also help you to lose weight if you need to and maintain a healthy weight, and it will help you to reduce the amount of fat in your blood and to lower your cholesterol levels. So it is an important part of this plan.

If you are not currently active you should build up your levels of activity gradually. If you have very high blood pressure, you should also check with your doctor before you increase your physical activity and you should avoid very vigorous sports such as squash. But being active doesn't have to mean running miles. It could just be taking a regular stroll.

Studies have found that moderate-intensity activity is just as beneficial as high-intensity activity when it comes to blood pressure control, a plus for those of us who don't like jogging. In fact, one review of 16 studies on walking concluded that walking for about 30 minutes three to five times a week reduced systolic and diastolic blood pressure by 2 per cent. It doesn't take a huge amount of time and effort to become physically active. If you need ideas, look at the chart (right). All you need is about 30 minutes of moderate activity on most days of the week. And you can achieve this just by increasing the amount of physical activity in everyday life – parking at the far end of a car park, for example, taking the stairs instead of the lift, or walking to the shops instead of driving – can be as effective for reducing blood pressure as a structured aerobic exercise programme. For best

Easy exercise ideas

Common chores

Washing and waxing a car for 45–60 minutes

Washing windows or floors for 45–60 minutes

Gardening for 30–45 minutes

Pushing a pram or pushchair for 1½ miles in 30 minutes

Raking leaves for 30 minutes

Shovelling snow for 15 minutes

Climbing stairs for 15 minutes

Walking 2 miles in 30 minutes (1 mile in 15 minutes)

Sporting activities

Playing tennis for 45–60 minutes

Playing a round of golf

Dancing for 30 minutes

Taking part in an aerobics class for 30 minutes

Performing water aerobics for 30 minutes

Swimming laps for 20 minutes

Cycling for 30 minutes

Running 1½ miles in 15 minutes (1 mile in 10 minutes)

Caution If you have high blood pressure, consult your doctor before taking up a strenuous new sport.

results, try to be active enough to leave yourself just slightly out of breath – feeling warm and even sweating a little, but still able to talk.

You might also like to try some popular activities such as yoga and tai chi. There is some evidence to suggest that low-intensity exercises may be just as effective as high-intensity workouts for lowering blood pressure. For instance, one study comparing the blood pressure–lowering effects of tai chi with moderate aerobic activity found that both significantly decreased overall blood pressure. Tai chi, of course, is better suited for older, sedentary people, since it does not require the same heart rate elevation as aerobic exercises. Several studies have found similar benefits from yoga.

And don't forget resistance training, whether with weights and special equipment or simply with certain floor exercises that work against your body

weight. While studies to date don't show any significant improvement in blood pressure from resistance training alone, these muscle-building exercises play an important role in any programme to lose weight or maintain a healthy weight. But, take care. If you have high blood pressure, you should avoid lifting weights.

3 Stress

Who are the most likely candidates for high blood pressure? People who are very nervous or highly strung? Not according to the Blood Pressure Association. Contrary to popular belief, chairman Professor Graham MacGregor says that stress has not been shown to raise blood pressure. Even long-term stress alone is not thought to cause high blood pressure. Stress can lead to blood presssure rising temporarily but 'one hour later it is back to normal.'

Professor MacGregor likes to quote the example of the Yanomamo Indians who live in the Venezuelan jungle existing on a natural low fat and low salt diet, containing fruit, vegetables and roots with very little meat. 'They are very aggressive, fit and have most stressful lives as they spend a lot of their time fighting each other,' he says. But their average blood pressure as adults is less than 100/70mmHg and they have little or no vascular disease. Their total cholesterol is also less than 3.2mmols/l, whereas average cholesterol in the UK is around 5.5mmols/l.

However, the British Heart Foundation believes that stress does increase risk of

heart disease, even if its effect on blood pressure is less certain. Curiously, it does not appear to be the most high-powered individuals who suffer stress and conse-quent heart disease, but those who are in demanding jobs and have little control over their work. A long-running study of Whitehall civil servants shows that women in high demand/low control jobs are more than 70 per cent more likely to develop coronary heart disease than their counter-parts in jobs with high levels of control. Men in low control jobs are more than 50 per cent more likely to develop heart problems than men in high control jobs. And for those who already have heart disease, stress can bring on angina

Many specialists and counsellors today offer stress-management programmes, sometimes as part of a group or with individual counselling. And this is probably no bad thing. In the USA, one analysis of 37 studies that examined the effects of health education and stress management found a 34 per cent reduction in deaths from cardiovascular events, a 29 per cent reduction in heart attacks and significant positive effects on lifestyle, including dietary and exercise habits, weight, smoking, cholesterol levels and blood pressure.

4 Medicines

One of the greatest success stories in the history of health care has been the decline in deaths from heart disease in this country over the past 30 years. Some of that is due to healthier living – the number of people who smoke, for instance, has dropped – but much of it is a result of discovering better treatments for heart disease and stroke and the precursor conditions that contribute to it, such as high cholesterol and high blood pressure.

Nowhere has this been more successful than in the treatment for hypertension. Today, more Britons take prescription medications for hypertension than for any other medical condition.

If you fall into the category of Stage 1 (mild) hypertension – with systolic blood pressure of 140 to 159mmHg or diastolic pressure of 90 to 99mmHg – your doctor may not prescribe medicines at first but suggest that you lose weight or take more exercise. It is certainly worth following the advice in this book and looking at the Blood Pressure Association's web site: www.bpassoc.org/ where you will find similar guidelines and the answers to many questions you may have about your condition.

If, after six months, you still exhibit consistently high blood pressure, or if you have Stage 2 hypertension (a systolic reading of 160 to 179mmHg) or a diastolic reading of 100 to 109), you're likely to need a bit more help. In fact, most patients with hypertension eventually require two or more drugs to control it.

This doesn't mean that you or the healthy eating plan have failed. But you may find that in your particular case, altering your lifestyle and diet alone isn't enough to get you into the safe zone. In the UK, you will usually be advised to take medicines if your blood pressure

Reducing stress with Fido

For animal-lovers there's one excellent way to stay calm. Get a pet. In one study, 48 people with hypertension were given either lisinopril, a medicine prescribed for hypertension, or a dog. After six months, their responses to mental stress were measured.

The group who had been given pets had significantly lower blood pressure changes in reaction to stress than those who received only the drug. But this strategy might not work so well with goldfish; the researchers speculate that the increased social

support that pet ownership provides was responsible for the reaction, which is something you probably won't get with a fish. No doubt the extra dog-walking exercise helped the study participants as well.

The same social support theory comes into play with studies linking active religious faith with healthy blood pressure levels – but you have to go to church, mosque or synagogue. Just listening to religious services on the radio or watching them on television has no apparent effect.

readings are consistently above a level such as 160/100mmHg and if, despite making lifestyle changes, your blood pressure levels have not fallen. A doctor will also take into account your age (as the risk of cardiovascular problems rises with age), any other medical conditions you have such as diabetes, and any other risk factors such as high cholesterol or whether you smoke.

An important note: this doesn't mean you should stop following this action plan. Every study ever conducted shows extra benefits from the kind of lifestyle changes included in the plan compared with simply taking medication alone. Taking blood pressure medication without implementing a healthier lifestyle is like being treated for lung cancer without quitting smoking. It just makes no sense.

Understanding your medicines

With hypertension, the idea is to achieve a fairly stable blood pressure of less than 140/90mmHg, or less than 130/80mmHg if you have diabetes or kidney disease. Because most people will almost automatically reach the diastolic goal if they can meet the systolic goal, the focus is usually on the top number.

Today, doctors have a plethora of medicines to treat high blood pressure, most divided among five main categories.

Diuretics Commonly called water pills, diuretics are often the drugs of first choice for Stage 1 hypertension. They work by increasing the amount of salt that the kidneys excrete in urine. By flushing out salt which takes water with it, the amount of fluid around cells is decreased which lowers blood pressure.

There are three main types of diuretic. Thiazide diuretics, such as bendrofluazide, are the most commonly used in the UK for high blood pressure. Loop diuretics, such as frusemide and bumetanide, have a more immediate effect and are shorter acting (so you may need to take them

twice a day). But they are usually only used when the body is retaining fluid, in heart failure, for instance. Potassium-sparing diuretics, such as amiloride, are not usually taken alone but with a thiazide diuretic or a loop diuretic, and are designed to reduce the fall in potassium that the other drugs might cause. In people over 60 and in black people, thiazide diuretics are one of the first choices for treatment.

Beta-blockers This class of drugs, which includes acebutolol, atenolol, metoprolol, pindolol and timolol, work by reducing a particular hormone in the body – angiotensin 11 – which increases blood pressure. Beta blockers also slow the heart rate by about five to ten beats each minute. They were in the past the favoured treatment for high blood pressure but newer drugs are now taking their place.

ACE inhibitors Often a first treatment for younger, non-black people, ACE (angiotensin-converting enzyme) inhibitors, such as captopril, enalapril, lisinopril and ramipril, work by reducing the amount of angiotensin II made by the kidneys, as this has a role in raising blood pressure.

Angiotensin-II receptor blockers (ARBs). The drugs in this newer class of antihypertensives, such as candesartan, eprosartan, irbesartan and losartan work by blocking the effect of angiotension II on individual cells. Studies have shown that these tablets have few side effects. They are expensive but your doctor may consider an ARB if you are unable to tolerate an ACE inhibitor, or suffer a side effect such as a cough. Recent clinical trials have also shown that ARBs also reduce strokes and heart attacks.

Calcium channel blockers. The three types of calcium channel blockers, dihydropyridines, such as amlodipine, felodipine and isradipine; diltiazem; and verapamil work by relaxing arteries which are stiff or 'hardened', thereby lowering blood pressure. UK experts consider these the most effective treatment for people who have severely raised blood pressure.

Alpha-blockers These drugs with names such as doxazosin and indoramin, cause blood vessels to relax. They are rarely used as a first treatment but might be added if blood pressure is difficult to control. They also help to reduce symptoms in men with an enlarged prostate.

Direct vasodilators In the past, these tablets, such as hydralazine and minoxidil, were prescribed quite frequently but have now largely been superseded as they can cause an increase in heart rate and cause salt retention.

Centrally-acting drugs Moxonidine, is the only medicine of this type now used in the UK. It acts directly on the brain to lower blood pressure. It can cause drowsiness, nasal stuffiness and also depression, and is only added to treatment if blood pressure is hard to control.

Combination therapy for high blood pressure There are now some combination medicines which mean that you only have to take one rather than two medicines a day to control your blood pressure. These include beta-blockers with a diuretic, beta-blockers with a calcium-channel blocker, ACE inhibitors with a diuretic and ARBs with a diuretic.

Follow the Beat High Blood Pressure Plan

Over the next few pages, we'll show you exactly how to use the recipes in this book, as well as the knowledge you have gained in the previous chapters, to lower your blood pressure safely, substantially and permanently – if possible, without drugs. We are sure that you will find it all makes deliciously good sense.

Getting ready

Our plan goes several steps beyond the clinically proven DASH diet to incorporate a healthy life-style, physical activity and weight loss into one comprehensive programme that should enable you to lower your blood pressure dramatically, if you implement the entire plan at once.

However, we recommend that you take a more measured approach to this healthy-eating plan. Your first goal might be to lower your blood pressure quickly, but your real aim should be to keep it down for the rest of your life. By slowly and incrementally introducing the skills and practices of the plan, you make it that much more likely that it will be the last health programme you'll ever have to use.

In fact, to help make your efforts even more successful, we offer the following suggestions for preparing to start.

- **Most important: if you smoke, don't start the plan until you've stopped**. Smoking does not directly affect your blood pressure but if you smoke and have high blood pressure, you are much more at risk of a heart attack or stroke than if you have high blood pressure alone. Smoking causes your arteries to narrow just as high blood pressure does. So you are doubling your risk factors for cardio-vascular disease.

  Use whatever works for you – cold turkey; patches, lozenges, nasal sprays, inhalers, microtabs or gum; medication such as Zyban; support groups or talk therapy. There are helplines too, such as the NHS helpline (0800 169 0 169) and Quitline (0800 00 22 00); or you could go to www.ash.org.uk for help and advice on how to give up smoking.

  If you need motivation, just work out how much you have been spending each week on cigarettes and imagine saving that to spend on a real treat.
- **Consult your doctor** If your GP or specialist has diagnosed raised blood pressure and advised you to take steps to reduce it, let the doctor know that you are launching a serious effort to get your blood pressure into a healthy range, now and for ever. The surgery

can probably arrange for you to have regular check-ups so that you can monitor your progress and make sure you are keeping your blood pressure under control.

If your regular blood pressure readings appear to vary quite widely, you may want to discuss with your doctor whether you should have an ambulatory blood pressure test, which tracks your blood pressure over a 24-hour period. Depending on your age, you may also need an electro-cardiogram to test your heart health.

You may also be offered tests to examine your urine, monitor your blood glucose levels and test your potassium levels. You will probably also need to undergo a lipid test after a 9 to 12-hour fast to measure your cholesterol and triglyceride levels. These and other tests will provide a good overview of your health, including your heart and kidney health and your risk of diabetes.

Tell your doctor what you're planning to do to control your blood pressure; you may even want to discuss the guidelines with him. Ask if you should try to lower your blood pressure with lifestyle changes first, without medication. If you're already taking medicines, let your doctor know your plans so he or she can track your progress and reduce your dosages as necessary.

- As advised earlier, take advice from the Blood Pressure Association's web site (www.bpassoc.org,uk/) and **buy a home blood pressure monitoring device**. Just as scales can help you to keep tabs on your weight and make minor adjustments, regular blood pressure monitoring can send you a signal that it's time to exercise more or cut down on salt or stress.

- Next, it's time to **clean out the kitchen**. Pack a box with all the high-salt, prepared and canned foods in your pantry and donate them to a charity for the homeless. The same with bags of chips and packets of biscuits, cakes, snack foods and other nutritionally empty – yet calorie dense – foods. Rid your freezer of the same types of food, but throw them away.

This may seem wasteful at first, but if the food's not in your house, it won't tempt you.

- Then **make your shopping list**. The four-week daily food plan will give you a good start with your new eating pattern and help you to stock the essentials of a healthy kitchen. Fill your list with lots of fruits and vegetables (pick up at least two of each that you've never tried before), and be sure that any starches you buy – bread, pasta or rice – are whole grain. While you're at the supermarket, visit the spice aisle. Buy five kinds that aren't already in your spice rack. How about paprika? Or turmeric? Or cumin? What about coriander, star anise or lemongrass? Also pick up three different kinds of onion and two types of garlic for seasoning. Keep a jar of minced garlic for quick meals when you don't feel like crushing the cloves.

- The only equipment you'll need is a pair of **well-fitting walking shoes**, some **comfortable workout clothes** and a few sharp pencils, a notebook, and lots of copies of the logs that appear on page 310, so you can track your progress and remember the different components of the plan.

FYI The Food Standards Agency says we should all cut our salt intake from the current 10g-12g a day (2 teaspoons) to 5g-6g a day (1 teaspoon)

THE PLAN

Here are the actions you should take to maximise your fight against high blood pressure, now and for ever:

1 Follow the diet programme Specifically, make sure your daily diet is made up of the following:

- Seven to eight servings of wholegrains or grain products
- Four to five servings of vegetables
- Four to five servings of fruit
- Two to three servings of low-fat or fat-free dairy products
- No more than two servings of meat, poultry or fish
- No more than three servings of fat (butter, oil or mayonnaise)
- Eight or more glasses of water

In addition, your weekly diet can include:

- Four to five servings of nuts, seeds and pulses
- No more than five small servings of sweets (biscuits, cakes, chocolates and fizzy drinks)

2 Make 90 per cent of your diet fresh foods that have no added sodium or salt That means foods that are as close as possible to their natural state. Packaged foods, such as potato crisps, ready meals, breaded chicken nuggets and processed breakfast cereals should make up 10 per cent of your diet at most.

Remember, if you use good quality, fresh ingredients in cooking, you will be able to enjoy the natural flavour of the food, rather than having it masked by salt.

3 Reduce your reliance on the saltcellar Use lemon juice, salt substitutes, dried garlic or other savoury seasonings in place of salt.

4 Limit alcohol Women should have no more than 2-3 drinks a day and men 3-4 a day. See the guide on page 289.

5 Get 30 minutes or more of aerobic activity at least five days a week That means exercising hard enough to increase your heart rate but not so hard that it affects your ability to talk. Ideally, taking a 30-minute walk or two 15-minute walks daily is the easiest, simplest way to reach this goal.

6 Try strength training, or practise yoga or tai chi If you don't belong to a gym, buy an exercise video that includes resistance exercises or buy a set of hand weights and spent 15 minutes every other day using them. However, if your blood pressure is very high, you should consult your doctor before starting weight training. In that case, it may be better to try a different type of exercise – join a yoga or tai chi class, for instance, as both will help you to stay active and beat stress.

7 Each morning and evening, try to spend 5 minutes in a quiet room alone, with no distractions The goal is to relax, purge any anxiety about the day ahead or day behind, recharge your energy and clear your mind. You'll find it much easier to follow a diet and exercise plan for your own good health if you feel calm and in control.

8 Do a daily breathing exercise Again focused breathing could help you to relax and clear away any stress that may have temporarily raised your blood pressure. Try 15 minutes of focused breathing each day, concentrating on lengthening the exhale, not the inhale. Exhale slowly until you are at the point of tensing up to force out the last bit of air. Let your lungs reinflate naturally, then repeat the lengthy exhale. Do this any-where, anytime. Over the coming weeks, see if you detect a slowing in your breath-ing as a result of these exercises.

9 Each day, do three things to reduce stress and make you feel better These could include:

- Taking a short walk
- Doing a calming exercise, be it yoga or golf
- Stepping outside for a few minutes and stretching
- Putting on soothing music rather than watching TV

- Driving calmly in the left lane rather than overtaking on your way to work
- Giving extra hugs and kisses to your spouse or children
- Phoning a friend for a short chat
- Responding to hostility, anger or provocation with calm and humour
- Making yourself a cup of tea and taking 15 slow minutes to drink it to reward yourself for completing a tough task
- Turning off the car radio and driving in silence

Small steps like these add up to a healthier, calmer attitude far more quickly than you would expect. By consciously saying a few times a day, 'I'll take the calm choice here', you can feel better and improve your overall health.

10 **Track your efforts every day for the next six weeks** Make copies of the Daily Tracker on page 310 and check off your daily food portions, as well as your exercise and lifestyle efforts. At the end of each week, take your blood pressure, then pour yourself a glass of wine (if you drink) or fruit juice and go over your week. Where did you succeed? Where do you need to put more effort? How did your blood pressure change? Use the information you gather to plan the coming week.

Tips for the plan

Now that you've seen the plan, it seems easy, doesn't it? You can do it all, starting immediately, right? Wrong. Changing your diet takes time and commitment. So does exercising. So does relaxing. Here is advice for making the plan work its very best for you.

• Introduce the steps into your life one at a time Unlike many other health programmes, this isn't a '12 weeks and you're done' plan. Each of the 10 steps in the plan presents a task that is worthy of doing for a lifetime. Relax. You're in no rush. What matters is that you learn to practice good eating, sensible exercise and a healthy lifestyle the right way, so you never have to learn it again.

• Start with the most important part: Steps one and two, which focus on healthy eating. Learn the diet plan. Work out how to make it a reality for you. Try out the recipes and cooking techniques in this book. Learn how to order a healthy restaurant meal or choose a snack that's good for you.

• Begin implementing some of the next steps We recommend that you start the aerobic exercise step, which calls for you to walk for 30 minutes a day, five days a week. Perhaps you can also work in some breathing and stretching exercises. Stay with these until they have become a routine, natural part of your day.

• Start making the anti-stress choices we recommend If things are progressing well, then perhaps it's a good time to work on issues of stress and anxiety. Take your time. Make a habit out of having a positive, peaceful attitude.

• Strength training (if appropriate) may be the last big step While it's far more fun and rewarding than many non-exercisers think, it's also the step that's hardest to make a habit.

• Along the way, write, write, write Make enough copies of the logs we've provided for six weeks of writing and put them in a notebook. Each evening before bed, fill one out. We're talking about 30 seconds of work. Merely thinking each day about your desire to lower your blood pressure will help you to succeed.

• Look for encouragement It's helpful to follow this programme with someone else – and it's great for your family and anyone else in your life. Together you can compare progress, hold contests (who ate the most vegetables this week, for example), and, best of all, walk together. If you don't have a partner at home or in your neighbour-hood, how about inviting a long-distance friend or relative to follow the plan with you? Send your friend a copy of this book to get started, then follow each other's progress via email and phone.

• It gets easier Understand that the longer you do this and the lower you see your blood pressure go, the easier it will be for you to continue. Nothing feeds success like success.

The rest of your life

Just as we may never again live in a world without terrorism, you will never again live in a world without high blood pressure. There is no cure for hypertension. Nevertheless, you can learn to live with your blood pressure, all the while controlling it so it does no real damage to your body.

Eating and living for healthy blood pressure should provide loads of pleasure. Healthy meals should and can be utterly delicious, as the recipes in this book prove! Exercising and achieving a calm spirit can make you feel young and vibrant. Follow the healthy eating plan, and the benefits won't be merely statistical. You will feel healthier, more upbeat and more alive than ever!

There's more good news: researchers are becoming even more aggressive in their hunt for the causes and effects of, as well as treatments for, high blood pressure. You can expect announcements of better drugs and other treatments for years to come. If you work in close conjunction with your doctor, you'll realise that there has never been so much hope for managing high blood pressure easily and effectively.

So try to keep on with this plan. Eat healthily and enjoy every meal. Visit your doctor regularly for checkups, and monitor your blood pressure carefully (get a home monitor if you can).Your health – and your life – are worth it.

Four weeks of great eating

To help you understand the DASH approach to eating, we've prepared sample menus for four weeks, using several of the recipes in this book but also including several (healthy) fast food meals. The meals for each day in this sample plan provide roughly 1,800 to 2,000 calories – a level appropriate for a woman to maintain or slowly lose weight.

If you actually want to eat according to this plan, we're sure you will be delighted by the mix of flavours. If you want to try it for just one day, that's great, too. But even if you have no interest in following such a meal plan, read through it. Having good intuition about how much food to eat in a day is crucial to mastering the diet and to using food to its best effect for lowering blood pressure.

In addition to the meals listed below, plan on having two snacks a day. Try to choose snacks that combine complex carbohydrates with protein and add up to roughly 100 calories. Some choices:

- A handful of unsalted peanuts with a sliced pear
- A cube of reduced-fat cheese with a cut-up apple
- 200ml (7fl oz) fat-free vanilla yoghurt with cut-up grapes and cherries added
- 200ml (7fl oz) low-fat, low-sugar frozen yoghurt with 1 banana
- 5 ready-to-eat dried apricots
- Pecan biscuits (page 262) and 1 orange

Four weeks
of great eating

WEEK ONE

Day 1

Breakfast

High-vitality milk shake
(page 10)

1 slice of **wholemeal toast**
thinly spread with **margarine**
and reduced-sugar **jam** or
marmalade

Lunch

**Fresh artichoke and crab
salad** (page 176)

150g (5½oz) sliced **strawberries**

Dinner

125g (4½oz) grilled **pork chop**
brushed with **Dijon mustard**

**Noodles with roast
vegetables** (page 149)

small bunch of **grapes** or **fresh
fruit** of your choice

1 piece of **fresh fruit** (extra)

25g (1oz) **plain chocolate**

Day 2

Breakfast

40g (1½oz) **wholegrain cereal**
with 125ml (4fl oz) skimmed
milk

1 **pear** or fresh **fruit** of your
choice

1 slice of **wholemeal toast**
thinly spread with **margarine**
and reduced-sugar **jam** or
marmalade

Lunch

chicken salad sandwich
made with:

    2 slices toasted **wholemeal
bread** spread with 1tbsp
reduced-fat **mayonnaise**

    100g (3½oz) skinless roast
chicken breast

    handful **watercress**

    1 sliced **tomato**

4tbsp canned **fruit** in natural
juice

Dinner

75g (2¾oz) **lean roast beef**

2 tbsp low-fat **gravy**

**Sesame stir-fried asparagus
and peas** (page 196)

1 small **baked potato** with:

    2 tbsp natural **fromage frais**
mixed with 1 finely chopped
spring onion

1 small **wholemeal roll**

1 small **apple** or fresh fruit of
your choice

1 pot low-fat **yoghurt**

Day 3

Breakfast

Sweet couscous (page 16)

1 bowl of **fresh fruit salad**

1 scrambled **egg** on
1 slice of **wholemeal toast**

Lunch

roast beef sandwich
made with:

    2 slices **wholemeal bread**

    1 tsp **Dijon mustard**

    mixed with 2 tbsp low-fat
mayonnaise

    50g (1¾oz) lean **roast beef**

    lettuce

    sliced **tomato**

1 **apple** or fruit of your choice

Dinner

Spaghettini with seafood
(page 108)

**spinach salad
(baby spinach,** grated **carrot,
cherry tomatoes** and sliced
mushrooms) with 1 tbsp
low-fat **dressing**

1 bowl canned **pears** in natural
juice or **fresh fruit** of your
choice

Day 4

Breakfast

1 medium bowl of **porridge** made with equal quantities of semi-skimmed **milk** and water. Add a small **banana** and a pinch of **cinnamon**

225ml (8fl oz) skimmed **milk**

1 slice of **wholemeal toast** thinly spread with **margarine** and reduced-sugar **jam**

Lunch

chicken sandwich made with:

- 2 slices **wholemeal bread**
- 1 tbsp reduced-fat **mayonnaise**
- 75g (3oz) skinless roast **chicken breast**
- **lettuce**
- sliced **tomato**

1 **peach** or fresh fruit of your choice

250ml (9fl oz) **apple juice**

Dinner

Crispy tuna steaks in citrus sauce (page 107)

Pan-roasted new potatoes with garlic (page 195)

steamed **carrots** sprinkled with **fresh herbs**

mixed green salad with 1 tbsp low-fat **dressing**

Day 5

Breakfast

Pecan waffles with maple, pear and blackberry sauce (page 24)

1 **orange** or **fresh fruit** of your choice

225ml (8fl oz) skimmed **milk**

Lunch

Greek chicken pitta pockets (page 83)

carrot sticks with **tomato salsa** for dipping

1 pot low-fat **yoghurt**

Dinner

Speedy two-bean chilli (page 240)

pear and walnut salad (mix 1 sliced **pear** with **watercress** and a handful of toasted **walnuts**, add 40g (1½oz) diced reduced-fat **Cheddar** and 1tbsp low-fat **dressing**)

1 small **wholemeal roll**

Day 6

Breakfast

1 low-fat **cereal bar**

1 **banana**

1 pot low-fat **yogurt**

225ml (8fl oz) skimmed **milk**

Lunch

turkey sandwich made with:

- 2 slices **wholemeal bread**
- 2 tsp low-fat **mayonnaise** mixed with 1 tbsp **Dijon mustard**
- 75g (2¾oz) **turkey breast**
- 1 slice reduced-fat **Cheddar cheese**
- **lettuce, cucumber** and **tomato**

1 medium **orange**

250ml (9fl oz) **apple juice**

Dinner

Seared sirloin with garden vegetables (page 66)

175g (6oz) cooked **brown rice**

75g (2¾oz) steamed **carrots** sprinkled with **fresh herbs**

1 small **wholemeal roll** spread with 1 teaspoon **margarine**

1 pot low-fat **yoghurt**

Day 7

Breakfast

1 **hard-boiled egg** mashed with 1 tbsp reduced-fat **mayonnaise**

2 slices **wholemeal bread**

1 bowl **fruit salad** or fruit canned in its own juices

225ml (8fl oz) skimmed **milk**

Lunch

Cream of leek and potato soup (page 227)

1 **wholemeal roll** with 1 tsp **margarine**

spinach salad with sliced **tomatoes** sprinkled with 25g (1oz) toasted **pine nuts** and 1 tbsp fat-free **dressing**

1 pot low-fat **yoghurt**

Dinner

Classic grilled Dover sole (page 110)

steamed **green beans** sprinkled with 1 tbsp toasted **almonds**

4 small boiled new **potatoes**

steamed **sugar snap peas** with **lemon juice**

50g (1¾oz) fresh **strawberries**

WEEK TWO

Day 8

Breakfast

1 pot low-fat **yoghurt** mixed with 1 small sliced **banana**, 50g (1¾oz) fresh **strawberries** and 1 tsp **honey**

1 slice **wholemeal toast** spread with 1 tsp **peanut butter**

1 **orange** or **fresh fruit** of your choice

Lunch

tuna sandwich made with:

- 2 slices **wholemeal bread**
- 100g (3½oz) **tuna** canned in water, mixed with 2 tbsp reduced-fat **mayonnaise**
- 1 finely chopped stick of **celery**
- 1 handful of **watercress**
- 1 sliced **tomato**

100g (3½oz) **grapes** or **fresh fruit** of your choice

225ml (8fl oz) skimmed **milk**

Dinner

Chicken with apples (page 80)

75g (2¾oz) steamed **broccoli**

200g (7oz) cooked wholemeal **pasta** with 2 tbsp fat-free **dressing**

1 pot low-fat **yoghurt**

Day 9

Breakfast

Potato, sweetcorn and pepper frittata (page 20)

1 **orange** or **fresh fruit** of your choice

225ml (8fl oz) skimmed **milk**

Lunch

grilled chicken salad made with:

- 75g (2¾oz) skinless roast **chicken breast**
- 1 sliced **tomato**
- 1 diced **apple**
- 1 handful mixed **salad leaves**
- 2 tbsp **fat-free dressing**

1 small **wholemeal roll** spread with low-fat soft **cheese**

1 **banana** or **fresh fruit** of your choice

Dinner

Sauté of king prawns (page 112)

180g cooked **brown rice**

pepper, courgette garlic and **spring onions** stir-fried in 2 tsp **olive oil**

Day 10

Breakfast

200ml (⅓ pint) **fruit juice**

1 bowl **porridge** made with equal quantities of semi-skimmed **milk** and water, topped with 25g (1oz) **raisins** or **dried apricots**

1 slice **melon** or **fresh fruit** of your choice

Lunch

roast beef sandwich made with:

- **wholemeal pitta**
- 1 tsp **Dijon mustard** mixed with 1tbsp reduced-fat **mayonnaise**
- 75g (2¾oz) lean **roast beef**
- **tomato**
- **lettuce**

1 pot low-fat **yoghurt**

1 bowl canned **fruit** in natural juice or **fresh fruit** of your choice

Dinner

200g (7oz) cooked **wholemeal pasta** with 150g (5½oz) low-sodium tomato-based **pasta sauce**

salad made with:

- 75g (2¾oz) grated **carrot**
- 75g (2¾oz) sliced **red cabbage**
- 1 tbsp **raisins**
- 2 tbsp reduced-fat **mayonnaise**

2 **plums** or **fresh fruit** of your choice

Day 11

Breakfast

40g (1½oz) wholegrain **cereal** with 125ml (4fl oz) skimmed **milk** topped with 1 sliced **banana**

2 slices **wholemeal toast**, thinly spread with **margarine** and reduced-sugar **jam** or **marmalade**

Lunch

cheese on toast, made with 2 slices **wholemeal bread** topped with 50g (2oz) grated reduced-fat **cheese** topped with 1 sliced **tomato**

mixed green **salad** with low-fat **dressing**

1 pot low-fat **yoghurt**

Dinner

Turkey escalopes with fruity sauce (page 98)

Nutty lemon barley (page 132)

steamed **broccoli** with **lemon juice**

1 pot low-fat **yoghurt**

Day 12

Breakfast

1 **wholemeal banana muffin**

1 slice **melon** or **fresh fruit** of your choice

1 pot low-fat **yoghurt**

Lunch

Turkey salad with red cabbage (page 175)

carrot sticks with **tomato salsa** for dipping

1 pot low-fat **yoghurt** with 75g (2¾oz) fresh **raspberries**

Dinner

Linguine with no-cook sauce (page 154)

salad made with:
    25g (1oz) baby **spinach**
    1 chopped **tomato**
    1 chopped hard-boiled **egg**
    25g (1oz) chopped **cucumber**
    2 tbsp fat-free **dressing**

1 bowl fresh **fruit salad**, or canned fruit in its own juice

Day 13

Breakfast

Whole-grain griddle cakes with fruit and yoghurt (page 23)

225ml (8fl oz) skimmed **milk**

Lunch

tuna sandwich made with:
    wholemeal pitta
    100g (3½oz) **tuna** canned in water
    2 tbsp reduced-fat **mayonnaise**
    2 stalks **celery**, thinly sliced

spinach salad made with 25g (1oz) baby **spinach** and 2 tbsp crumbled **feta cheese**

50g (2oz) fresh **strawberries** with 1 pot low-fat **yoghurt**

Dinner

75g (2¾oz) lean **steak**

1 medium **baked potato** with 2 tbsp **fromage frais**

Lemony sugarsnap peas (page 198)

steamed **broccoli**

2 **kiwi fruit** or 1 piece of **fresh fruit** of your choice

Day 14

Breakfast

200ml (⅓ pint) **orange juice**

1 bowl **porridge** made with equal quantities of skimmed **milk** and water, sweetened with 1 sliced **banana**

1 slice **wholemeal bread** thinly spread with **margarine** and reduced-sugar **jam** or **marmalade**

Lunch

Falafel pitta (page 140)

1 bowl of **fruit salad** with 1 pot low-fat **yoghurt**

Dinner

Salmon with pepper and sweetcorn relish (page 114)

steamed **green beans** sprinkled with 1 tbsp toasted **almonds**

Wild rice with walnuts (page 131)

celery spread with low-fat **soft cheese** and sprinkled with **fresh herbs**

1 pot low-fat **yoghurt**

WEEK THREE

Day 15

Breakfast

Banana and apricot smoothie (page 11)

2 slices **wholemeal toast** thinly spread with **margarine** and reduced sugar **jam** or **marmalade**

apple

Lunch

Warm sesame chicken salad (page 159)

1 small **wholemeal roll** with 1 tsp **margarine**

150g (5½oz) fresh **pineapple**

Dinner

125g (4½oz) **salmon** brushed with mixture of **maple syrup** and **wholegrain mustard** and baked

150g (5½oz) boiled **brown rice**

French beans and **carrots**

1 pot low-fat **yoghurt**

Day 16

Breakfast

200ml (⅓ pint) **fruit juice**

40g (1½oz) **wholegrain cereal** with 125ml (4fl oz) skimmed **milk**

1 slice **wholemeal toast** thinly spread with **margarine** and reduced-sugar **jam** or **marmalade**
1 boiled **egg**

Lunch

hummus with wholemeal **pitta bread** (recipe for hummus is on page 57)

vegetable crudités

low-fat fruit **yoghurt**

Dinner

1 **cod steak**, grilled

Sweet-and-sour cabbage (page 206)

1 **wholemeal roll**

2 **oatcakes** with low-fat **soft cheese**

1 **apple** or **fresh fruit** of your choice

Day 17

Breakfast

1 bowl of **porridge** made with equal quantities of **milk** and water

Add handful of fresh **blueberries**

1 slice of **wholemeal toast** thinly spread with **margarine** and reduced sugar **jam** or **marmalade**

Lunch

200ml (⅓ pint) **fruit juice**

egg and cress sandwich made with:

   2 slices **wholemeal bread** spread with 2 small boiled **eggs** mixed with 1 tbsp of reduced fat **mayonnaise** and **mustard** and **cress**

fresh fruit salad

Dinner

Basmati chicken pilaf (page 81)

mixed salad with 1 tbsp low-fat **dressing**

low-fat **fruit yoghurt**

Day 18

Breakfast

3 tbsp canned **prunes** in natural juice

2 slices **wholemeal toast** thinly spread with **margarine** and reduced-sugar **jam** or **marmalade**

225ml (8fl oz) skimmed **milk**

Lunch

200ml (⅓ pint) **apple juice**

Mediterranean roasted vegetable soup (page 228)

3 **oatcakes** spread with reduced fat **soft cheese**

1 **peach** or **fresh fruit** of your choice

Dinner

Curried mushrooms, peas and potatoes (page 200)

mixed **green salad** with 1 tbsp low-fat **dressing**

Raspberry frozen yoghurt (page 248)
with fresh **raspberries**

Day 19

Breakfast

200ml (⅓ pint) **fruit juice**

40g (1½oz) **wholegrain cereal** with 225ml (8fl oz) skimmed **milk**

1 slice of **wholemeal toast**, topped with mashed **banana**

Lunch

Roast beef and rice salad (page 170)

1 pot low-fat **yoghurt**

Dinner

100g (3½oz) roast **chicken**

4 boiled baby **new potatoes**, skin on

steamed **green beans** and **broccoli**

large slice of **melon** or **fresh fruit** of your own choice

2 **oatcakes** spread with low-fat **soft cheese**

Day 20

Breakfast

200ml (⅓ pint) **cranberry juice**

3 tbsp sugar free **muesli**, 225ml (8fl oz) skimmed **milk**, with small chopped **banana**

fresh **raspberries**

1 slice of **wholemeal toast** thinly spread with **margarine**

Lunch

tuna sandwich made with
2 slices **wholemeal bread**
100g (3½oz) canned **tuna** in water mixed with 2 tsp reduced fat **mayonnaise**, 1 tbsp canned **sweetcorn**

1 medium **orange** or **fresh fruit** of your own choice

Dinner

Spaghetti with chickpeas and spicy tomato sauce (page 153)

1 pot low-fat **yoghurt**

Day 21

Breakfast

Strawberry-yoghurt smoothie (page 13)

2 slices of **wholemeal toast** thinly spread with **margarine** and reduced-sugar **jam** or **marmalade**

Lunch

Old-fashioned chicken noodle soup (page 230)

1 **wholemeal roll** with 1 tsp of **margarine**

1 **chewy granola bar** (page 269)

Dinner

grilled **tuna steak**

tomato salsa

4 small boiled **new potatoes**, skin on

steamed **mangetout** and **courgettes**

fruit salad made from fresh **strawberries** and **kiwi fruit**

WEEK FOUR

Day 22

Breakfast

1 pot of low-fat **yoghurt** mixed with 1 small sliced **banana**, 50g (1¾oz) fresh **blueberries**, 2 tbsp **muesli** and 1 tsp of **honey**

1 slice **wholemeal toast** thinly spread with **margarine** and reduced sugar **jam** or **marmalade**

Lunch

scrambled eggs on toast made with 2 **eggs** and 2 slices of **wholemeal toast**

Grilled **tomatoes**

100g (3½oz) **grapes** or **fresh fruit** of your choice

1 pot low-fat **yoghurt**

Dinner

Tagliatelle with mushroom medley (page 150)

steamed **broccoli**

fresh fruit salad

Day 23

Breakfast

200ml (⅓ pint) **fruit juice**

1 bowl of **porridge** made with equal quantities of **milk** and water and topped with 2 tbsp canned **prunes**

1 slice of **wholemeal toast** thinly spread with **margarine**

Lunch

Cream of courgette soup (page 223)

1 **wholemeal roll**

1 **peach** or **fresh fruit** of your choice

Dinner

Steamed fish with ginger and sesame (page 111)

175g (6oz) cooked **brown rice**

baby carrots and petit pois

1 low-fat **fruit yoghurt** with 50g (2oz) fresh **strawberries**

Day 24

Breakfast

200ml (⅓ pint) **fruit juice**

1 bowl of **porridge** made with equal quantities of semi-skimmed **milk** and water, sweetened with pinch of **cinnamon** and small sliced **banana**

Lunch

1 medium **baked potato**, 100g (3½oz) **tuna** canned in water mixed with 1 tbsp of **mayonnaise** and 2 tbsp of **sweetcorn**

1 slice of **melon** or **fresh fruit** of your choice

Dinner

Turkey Stroganoff (page 99)

mixed **green salad** with 1 tbsp low-fat **dressing**

fruit salad made from **kiwi**, **melon** and **passion fruit**

Day 25

Breakfast

200ml (⅓ pint) **fruit juice**

1 boiled **egg**

2 slices **wholemeal toast** thinly spread with **margarine** and reduced sugar **jam** or **marmalade**

Lunch

baked beans on 2 slices of **wholemeal toast** (choose reduced salt beans)

1 low-fat **yoghurt**

1 **pear** or **fresh fruit** of your choice

Dinner

Moroccan chicken with couscous (page 90)

steamed **broccoli** sprinkled with **lemon juice**

fresh fruit salad made with fresh **pineapple** and **strawberries**

Day 26

Breakfast

200ml (⅓ pint) **fruit juice**

1 **Blueberry muffin with lemon glaze** (page 30)

Lunch

chicken sandwich made with **wholemeal pitta**, 100g (3½oz) **tuna** canned in water, 2 tbsp reduced fat **mayonnaise** and 2 thinly sliced sticks of **celery**, **cherry tomatoes**

1 pot low-fat **yoghurt** with 75g (2¾oz) fresh **raspberries**

Dinner

125g (4½oz) roast **chicken**

1 medium **baked potato** with 2 tbsp **fromage frais**

Asparagus with confetti vinaigrette (page 190)

steamed **spring greens**

2 **plums** or 1 piece of **fresh fruit** of your choice

Day 27

Breakfast

Banana and mango shake (page 12)

40g (1½oz) **wholegrain cereal** with 125ml (4fl oz) skimmed **milk**

Lunch

Lemony lentil and vegetable salad (page 174)

peach or **fresh fruit** of your own choice

low-fat **fruit yoghurt**

Dinner

Fish baked on a bed of broccoli, sweetcorn and red pepper (page 115)

1 scoop of reduced fat **ice-cream** with fresh **raspberries**

Day 28

Breakfast

200ml (⅓ pint) **fruit juice**

40g (1½oz) **wholegrain cereal** with 125ml (4fl oz) skimmed **milk** topped with 1 sliced **banana**

1 slice of **wholemeal bread** thinly spread **margarine** and reduced-sugar **jam** or **marmalade**

Lunch

Soup of leafy greens and herbs (page 233)

wholemeal roll thinly spread with **margarine**

1 pot low-fat **yoghurt**

Dinner

Poached chicken breasts in vegetable and herb sauce (page 82)

steamed **green beans** sprinkled with 1tbsp toasted **almonds**

4 boiled baby **new potatoes**

1 low-fat **yoghurt**

Portion tracker

Wholemeal foods
1 2 3 4 5 6 **7** **8** 9 10

Vegetables
1 2 3 **4** **5** 6 7 8

Fruit
1 2 3 **4** **5** 6 7 8

Low-fat dairy foods
1 **2** **3** 4 5

Meat/poultry/fish
1 **2** 3 4 5

Fats
1 **2** **3** 4 5

Nuts/seeds/legumes
0 **1** 2

Sweets
0 **1** 2

Water
1 2 3 4 5 6 **7** **8** 9 10

Alcohol
0 **1** **2** 3

Today's progress

Eating

Did I meet my diet portion targets?	Y N
Did I keep my overall food intake at a healthy level?	Y N
Did I do a good job of avoiding packaged foods?	Y N
Did I do a good job of avoiding salty foods?	Y N
Did I enjoy my food?	Y N

Lifestyle

Aerobic exercise?	Y N
Time:_____ Type: _____	
Strength exercise?	Y N
Time:_____	
5-minute morning break?	Y N
5-minute evening break?	Y N
Breathing exercises?	Y N

Anti-stress actions?

1 Y N   Action: _____

2 Y N   Action: _____

3 Y N   Action: _____

My energy rating for today:

1 2 3 4 5

My attitude rating for today:

1 2 3 4 5

My health rating for today:

1 2 3 4 5

Notes

Healthiest thing I did today:

_____

_____

_____

Happiest thing I did today:

_____

_____

_____

For tomorrow:

_____

_____

_____

_____

_____

_____

Health glossary

Words and terms related to diet, high blood pressure and its treatment

allicin The chemical responsible for garlic's odour and health effects.

angina Pain that occurs when insufficient oxygen-carrying blood reaches the heart.

angiotensin converting enzyme (ACE) inhibitors Drugs that stop production of ACE, a chemical that makes blood vessels narrow.

antioxidant A substance that protects cells from the damaging effects of free radicals. Some are made by the body; others, such as vitamins C and E, can be obtained only from food or supplements.

atherosclerosis A process in which fatty substances build up inside the walls of blood vessels and/or blood components stick to the insides of vessel walls. The vessels narrow and 'harden', becoming less flexible (atherosclerosis literally means 'hardening of the artery').

beta-blockers Drugs that lower adrenaline levels.

beta-carotene One of a group of nutrients known as carotenoids.

calcium The most plentiful mineral in the body and a major component of bones, teeth and soft tissues. It is needed for nerve and muscle function, blood clotting and metabolism.

calcium channel blockers Drugs that relax blood vessels and are prescribed for high blood pressure and chest pain.

calorie The basic unit of measurement for the energy value of food and the energy needs of the body.

carbohydrates Simple carbohydrates, such as table sugar, plain flour and white rice, are foods that are easily digested and converted into glucose. Complex carbohydrates, which make up the bulk of whole grains and vegetables, are starches made up of complex sugars, fibre and other nutrients. They take longer to digest and have more beneficial components.

carotenes Yellow and red pigments that colour yellow-orange fruits and vegetables and most dark green vegetables. They are among the antioxidants that may protect against the effects of ageing and disease.

coronary heart disease A disease of the blood vessels of the heart that, if untreated, can cause heart attacks.

diabetes A disorder of carbohydrate metabolism, characterised by inadequate production or utilisation of insulin and resulting in excessive amounts of glucose in the blood and urine. Also known as diabetes mellitus.

diastolic blood pressure The measurement of the pressure when the left ventricle of the heart relaxes; expressed as the bottom number in a blood pressure reading.

dietary fibre Indigestible material in food that stimulates peristalsis in the intestine.

diuretic A substance that causes the body to excrete excess fluid in the form of urine.

essential fatty acids The building blocks that the body uses to make fats.

fats A class of organic chemicals, also called fatty acids or lipids. When digested, they create nearly double the energy of the same amount of carbohydrates or protein.

flavonoids Plant pigments that are potent antioxidants.

free radicals Waste products of oxygen metabolism that can damage cell components.

glucose A simple sugar that the body converts directly into energy. Blood levels of glucose are regulated by several hormones, including insulin.

Glycaemic Index A scale of numbers that rates carbohydrate foods according to their effect on blood sugar. There are two scales. In one, 100 represents a glucose tablet, having the most rapid effect on blood sugar. In the other, 100 represents white bread.

heart attack An injury to the heart that occurs when blood flow to a part of the heart is suddenly cut off, causing permanent damage to the heart muscle.

hypertension A medical condition in which a person has abnormally high blood pressure, typically defined as 140/90 or higher.

insulin A hormone that regulates carbohydrate metabolism.

lysine An amino acid basic to human nutrition.

macronutrients Nutrients the body requires in large amounts for energy – specifically, carbo-hydrates, proteins and fats.

magnesium A trace mineral needed for healthy bones, the transmission of nerve signals, protein and DNA synthesis, and the conversion of glycogen stores into energy.

metabolism The body's physical and chemical processes, including conversion of food into energy, that are needed to maintain life.

micronutrients Essential nutrients that the body needs in only very small amounts.

monounsaturated fats Fats that are liquid at room temperature and semisolid or solid under refrigeration. They are believed to help to protect against heart disease.

oestrogen A female sex hormone produced in both sexes, but found in much greater quantities in women.

omega-3 fatty acids Polyunsaturated fatty acids essential for normal kidney function that influence various metabolic pathways, resulting in lowered cholesterol and triglyceride levels, inhibited platelet clotting and reduced inflammatory and immune reactions, as well as lowered blood pressure.

peristalsis Wavelike muscle contracts that help propel food and fluids through the digestive tract.

phosphorus A mineral needed for healthy bones, teeth, nerves and muscles, and for many bodily functions.

phytochemicals Compounds found in plants that have various health benefits.

polyphenols Organic compounds, including tannins, that combine with iron and can hinder its absorption. Found in a number of foods, tea and red wines.

polyunsaturated fats Fats containing a high percentage of fatty acids that lack hydrogen atoms and have extra carbon bonds. They are liquid at room temperature.

potassium A trace mineral needed to regulate fluid balance and many other functions.

pre-eclampsia A condition that may occur in women during the second half of pregnancy. Symptoms include high blood pressure, swelling that doesn't subside, and higher-than-normal amounts of protein in the urine. Also known as toxaemia.

protein Part of a large class of chemicals called amino acids. The body uses proteins to build and repair muscles and tissues. They occur in plant foods and are the main component of animal foods such as beef, poultry, seafood and dairy products.

quercetin A phytonutrient found in apples and onions that has been linked to healthy heart function.

renin. A hormone that kidney cells release into the blood as a result of sodium depletion or low blood volume. It converts a particular liver protein into angiotensin, which ultimately helps the body to decrease its sodium loss. Angiotensin also causes small blood vessels to constrict, increasing blood pressure.

saturated fats Lipids with a high hydrogen content; the predominant fat in animal products and other fats that remain solid at room temperature. A high intake of saturated fat is linked to an increased risk of heart disease, certain cancers, and other diseases.

sodium A trace mineral essential for maintaining fluid balance. It combines with chloride to form table salt.

soluble fibre Dietary fibre that becomes sticky when wet and dissolves in water.

sphygmomanometer A machine commonly used by doctors and nurses to measure blood pressure involving an inflatable arm cuff.

stenosis Narrowing of an artery due to the build-up of plaque on the inside wall of the artery.

systolic blood pressure A measurement of the pressure when the left ventricle of the heart contracts; expressed as the top number in a blood pressure reading.

tannins Astringent substance derived from plants that can cause contraction of blood vessels and body tissues.

triglycerides The most common form of dietary and body fat; high blood levels have been linked to heart disease.

uric acid The end product of protein when it is metabolised by the body. High uric acid levels contribute to high blood pressure because they can damage the kidneys.

vitamin C A water-soluble antioxidant vitamin found in citrus fruits and green vegetables.

vitamin E An important antioxidant found in vegetable oils, whole grain cereals, butter and eggs.

Index

Titles in *italics* are for recipes in 'Some More Ideas'

A

ACE inhibitors 296
Alcohol 289, 292, 299
Almonds
 peach soup with almonds 226
 rice pilaf with dried fruits and almonds 120
Alpha-blockers 296
Ambrosia 250
Angiotensin-II receptor blockers (ARBs) 296
Apnoea, sleep 278
Apples
 apple and date salad 186
 apple crumble 252
 apple upside-down cake 265
 braised cabbage, apple and caraway 213
 chicken with apples 80
 fruit with apricot-chocolate cream 253
 mangetout with apples and ginger 194
 multi-grain waffles with apple-raspberry sauce 25
 pork and apple salad with hazelnuts 168
 spicy apple muffins 33
Apricots
 apricot and coriander tagine 239
 apricot yoghurt smoothie 13
 banana and apricot smoothie 11
 chewy muesli bars 269
 chicken and apricot casserole 95
 fruit with apricot-chocolate cream 253
 mango, peach and apricot fizz 244
 rice pilaf with dried fruits and almonds 120
Arteries, high blood pressure 274–5, 279, 292
Artichokes, globe
 artichoke, mushroom and chicken salad 176
 fresh artichoke and crab salad 176
Asian-style fish casserole 116
Asparagus
 asparagus and pea soup 222
 asparagus with confetti vinaigrette 190
 Cheddar cheese and asparagus soup 229
 chickpea soup with asparagus 238
 sesame stir-fried asparagus and peas 196
 sesame vegetable pasta 196
 summer salmon and asparagus 116
 zesty Cheddar and asparagus quiche 21
Atherosclerosis 279
Aubergines
 aubergine and pearl barley salad 146
 aubergine dip 57
 aubergine with millet and sesame seeds 127
 squash and aubergine casserole 203

Avocados
 avocado and prawn cups 184
 avocado, potato and tofu salad 184
 avocado salad with raspberries 216
 barley, black bean and avocado salad 158
 guacamole with a kick 52
 Italian-style avocado and mozzarella salad 216
 tropical avocado and mango salad 216

B

Balsamic baked tomatoes with Parmesan crumbs 197
Bananas
 banana and apricot smoothie 11
 banana and mango shake 12
 banana custard tart 257
 high-vitality milk shake 10
 strawberry and banana smoothie 11
Barley
 aubergine and pearl barley salad 146
 barley and egg salad 182
 barley, black bean and avocado salad 158
 barley pilaf with herbs 125
 beefy mushroom and barley soup 236
 nutty lemon barley 132
 pearl barley risotto 130
Basmati chicken pilaf 81
Bean sprouts
 oriental sprouted salad 219
Beans 287
 barley, black bean and avocado salad 158
 black-eyed beans with sweet peppers 208
 Boston baked beans 207
 butter bean eggah 137
 green pasta with white beans 145
 Mexican-style bean and sweetcorn salad 138
 refried bean burritos 134
 refried bean quesadillas 134
 speedy two-bean chilli 240
 spicy turkey chilli with spaghetti 100
 tagliatelle with cannellini beans 153
 three beans and rice 138
Beef
 beef satay with ginger dipping sauce 43
 beefy mushroom and barley soup 236
 beefy mushroom and brown rice soup 236
 fusilli and meatballs 67
 roast beef and rice salad 170
 roast beef hash 63
 seared sirloin with garden vegetables 66
 sizzling beef fajitas 60
 steakhouse salad 179
 stir-fried beef salad with mango 64
 succulent meat loaf 62
 tropical beef and rice salad 173

Beetroot
 chunky borscht 70
Berry granita 224
Berry shake 10
Beta-blockers 296
Biscuits
 chocolate biscuits 262
 oaty chocolate chip cookies 260
 pecan biscuits 262
Black bean, barley and avocado salad 158
Blackberries
 pecan waffles with maple, pear and blackberry sauce 24
Black-eyed beans
 black-eyed beans with sweet peppers 208
 three beans and rice 138
Blood pressure see **High blood pressure**
Blood vessel damage 280
Blueberries
 berry granita 224
 blueberry Bavarian 268
 blueberry muffins with lemon glaze 30
 blueberry swirl brunch cake 26
 cool blueberry soup 224
 turkey and blueberry salad 164
Borlotti beans
 Mexican-style bean and sweetcorn salad 138
 Tuscan-style baked polenta 136
Borscht, chunky 70
Boston baked beans 207
Bread
 corn bread 38
 garlic bread 76
 Lebanese flat bread 57
 maple and toasted-walnut bread 35
 orange, sultana and walnut bread 28
 peaches and cream bread 34
Breadcrumbs 201
Breadsticks, Parmesan 51
Breakfast 9–38, 290
 menu plans 301–9
Breakfast sausage burgers 22
Breathing exercises 299
Broccoli
 Cheddar cheese and broccoli soup 229
 fish baked on a bed of broccoli, sweetcorn and red pepper 115
Brunch and breakfast 9–38
Brussels sprouts and potatoes with caraway-mustard sauce 215
Buckwheat grains see **Kasha**
Bulghur wheat
 bulghur wheat pilaf with tomato, onions and basil 133
 bulghur wheat with spring vegetables 122

marinated duck salad with bulghur wheat 167
spicy tabbouleh with chicken 172
tabbouleh with goat's cheese 172
Burgers
  breakfast sausage burgers 22
  vegetarian chilli burgers 240
Burritos, refried bean 134
Butter bean eggah 137
Buttermilk
  cherry and oat muffins 32
  peach soup with almonds 226
Butternut squash
  Persian-style squash couscous 146
  squash and aubergine casserole 203

C

Cabbage
  braised cabbage, apple and caraway 213
  crunchy nut coleslaw 220
  hot cabbage and grape coleslaw 218
  sweet-and-sour cabbage 206
  see also Red cabbage
Caffeine 289
Cakes
  apple upside-down cake 265
  blueberry swirl brunch cake 26
  cappuccino cake 259
  chocolate snacking cakes 263
  daffodil cake 258
  ginger and pear upside-down cake 265
  lemon angel cake with strawberries 264
  old-fashioned glazed gingerbread 270
  vanilla chiffon cake 259
Calcium channel blockers 296
Calories 286
Cannellini beans
  green pasta with white beans 145
  speedy two-bean chilli 240
  tagliatelle with cannellini beans 153
Cappuccino cake 259
Cardiovascular disease (CVD) 275, 276, 279
Carrots
  chicken en papillote with carrots and
    courgettes 87
  chilled cream of carrot soup 223
  mackerel and carrots 116
  orange-glazed carrots 192
  sunny risotto with carrots 124
Cashew nuts
  chicken and cashew pancakes 86
Casseroles *see* **Stews**
Cauliflower
  crispy cauliflower with Parmesan and almonds
    201
  lamb curry 71

Celeriac coleslaw 220
Cereals 286, 287
Cheddar cheese and broccoli soup 229
Cheese
  baked rice with wild mushrooms and cheese
    118
  Cheddar cheese and asparagus soup 229
  Cheddar cheese and broccoli soup 229
  crispy cauliflower with Parmesan and almonds
    201
  double-cheese pizza bites 40
  herb and Cheddar scones 36
  hot crab dip 53
  Italian-style avocado and mozzarella salad 216
  Parmesan and spring onion puffs 29
  Parmesan breadsticks 51
  Parmesan waffles 24
  peachy cottage cheese salad 180
  refried bean burritos 134
  refried bean quesadillas 134
  tabbouleh with goat's cheese 172
  zesty Cheddar and asparagus quiche 21
Chequerboard cherry pie 256
Cherries
  chequerboard cherry pie 256
  cherry and oat muffins 32
  quinoa pilaf with cherries and walnuts 126
Chicken
  artichoke, mushroom and chicken salad 176
  basmati chicken pilaf 81
  chicken and apricot casserole 95
  chicken and cashew pancakes 86
  chicken dumplings with sesame dipping sauce
    50
  chicken en papillote with carrots and
    courgettes 87
  chicken jamboree 94
  chicken, peach and rice salad 170
  chicken with apples 80
  chicken with rosemary and orange sauce 92
  Chinese-style chicken salad 159
  citrus-grilled chicken breasts with melon
    salsa 78
  Coronation chicken 160
  country captain chicken 88
  creamy chicken mushroom casserole 94
  Greek chicken pitta pockets 83
  little chicken salad rolls 44
  mango chicken salad 164
  Middle Eastern chicken sandwich 83
  Moroccan chicken with couscous 90
  old-fashioned chicken noodle soup 230
  orange-roasted chicken 91
  oriental chicken salad 156
  poached chicken breasts in vegetable and
    herb sauce 82

sausage-stuffed chestnut mushrooms 48
sautéed chicken with caramelised onions 84
spicy tabbouleh with chicken 172
warm sesame chicken salad 159
Chickpeas
  braised vegetables with falafel and yoghurt
    sauce 144
  chickpea and vegetable eggah 137
  chickpea soup with asparagus 238
  falafel pittas 140
  Moroccan chicken with couscous 90
  pitta crisps with hummus 57
  roast pepper pinwheels 42
  spaghetti with chickpeas and spicy tomato
    sauce 153
  three beans and rice 138
Chilli
  chilli and herb dip 56
  guacamole with a kick 52
  speedy two-bean chilli 240
  spicy turkey chilli with spaghetti 100
Chinese-style cabbage parcels 210
Chinese-style chicken salad 159
Chocolate
  chocolate biscuits 262
  chocolate-nut meringues 271
  chocolate snacking cakes 263
  fruit with apricot-chocolate cream 253
  oaty chocolate chip cookies 260
Chutney, tomato 72
Cidered pork with red cabbage 70
**Citrus-grilled chicken breasts with melon
  salsa** 78
Clams
  Manhattan clam chowder 232
  New England clam chowder 232
Cod
  Asian-style fish casserole 116
Coffee
  cappuccino cake 259
Cold remedies 289
Coleslaw
  celeriac coleslaw 220
  crunchy nut coleslaw 220
  hot cabbage and grape coleslaw 218
Contraception 277
Corn bread 38
Coronary heart disease (CHD) 279
Coronation chicken 160
Country captain chicken 88
Country-style mashed potatoes 191
Courgettes
  chicken en papillote with carrots and
    courgettes 87
  cream of courgette soup 223
  fennel and courgette frittata 20

Couscous
Moroccan chicken with couscous 90
Persian-style squash couscous 146
prawn and bean couscous 90
saffron couscous with peppers 142
sweet couscous 16
Crab
crab and grapefruit salad 163
fresh artichoke and crab salad 176
hot crab dip 53
Cranberries
turkey escalopes with fruity sauce 98
Crudités with three dips 54
Crumble, apple 252
Cucumber
chilled cucumber soup 222
citrus-grilled chicken breasts with melon salsa 78
pasta salad with cucumber salsa 187
poached salmon with cucumber and dill sauce 102
Curries
Coronation chicken 160
curried mushrooms, peas and potatoes 200
lamb curry 71
prawn curry 71
spicy lentil dhal 139

D
Daffodil cake 258
Daily Tracker 310
DASH trials 285–6
Date and apple salad 186
Dementia 280
Depression 292–3
Diabetes 277
Diet, and high blood pressure 282–9
Dinner, menu plans 301–9
Dips
aubergine dip 57
chilli and herb dip 56
fresh herb dip 54
hot crab dip 53
Italian-style tomato dip 54
pesto-yoghurt dip 54
spiced root vegetable wedges with creamy mustard dip 56
Diuretics 296
Dried fruit
spiced fruits, nuts and seeds 58
sweet-spiced fruits, nuts and seeds 58
Drinks 291
apricot yoghurt smoothie 13
banana and apricot smoothie 11
banana and mango shake 12
gazpacho quencher 245

high-vitality milk shake 10
mango, peach and apricot fizz 244
peach and cinnamon smoothie 11
strawberry and banana smoothie 11
strawberry yoghurt smoothie 13
tomato and citrus blush 245
Drugs 289, 294–6
Duck
duck and pumpkin salad 162
grilled duck, sweet potato and apple salad 178
marinated duck and kasha salad 162
marinated duck salad with bulghur wheat 167
sesame duck pancakes 86
sweet-and-sour duck salad 178
Dumplings, chicken 50

E,F
Eggs
barley and egg salad 182
heavenly devilled eggs 47
see also Frittata; Omelettes
Energy density, foods 291
Exercise 291, 293–4, 299, 300
Eye damage 280
Fajitas, sizzling beef 60
Falafel
braised vegetables with falafel and yoghurt sauce 144
falafel pittas 140
Far Eastern fruit salad 247
Fats 286, 287, 289, 290
Fennel
chicken and apricot casserole 95
fennel and courgette frittata 20
Fibre 288
Fish 286, 287
fish baked on a bed of broccoli, sweetcorn and red pepper 115
see also individual types of fish
Frittata
fennel and courgette frittata 20
pepper and potato frittata 20
potato, sweetcorn and pepper frittata 20
Fritters, sweetcorn 204
Fruit 286, 287
ambrosia 250
Far Eastern fruit salad 247
fruit boats with orange glaze 246
summer fruit slush 242
tropical slush 242
see also individual types of fruit
Fruity muesli 14
Fusilli
creamy turkey salad with grapes and pecans 185
fusilli and meatballs 67

G
Garden pasta salad 169
Garlic 288
garlic bread 76
pan-roasted new potatoes with garlic 195
roasted garlic and cherry tomato filling 214
veal escalopes with lemon garlic sauce 76
vegetable stir-fry with spicy garlic sauce 209
Gazpacho quencher 245
Ginger
ginger and pear upside-down cake 265
mangetout with apples and ginger 194
old-fashioned glazed gingerbread 270
steamed fish with ginger and sesame 111
Ginger ale
mango, peach and apricot fizz 244
Goat's cheese, tabbouleh with 172
Grains 286, 287
Granita, berry 224
Grapefruit and crab salad 163
Grapes
creamy turkey salad with grapes and pecans 185
hot cabbage and grape coleslaw 218
Indian-style rice with turkey 166
Greek chicken pitta pockets 83
Green beans
seared sirloin with garden vegetables 66
steakhouse salad 179
three beans and rice 138
Griddle cakes, whole-grain 23
Guacamole with a kick 52

H
Haricot beans
Boston baked beans 207
Heart attack 275, 279
Heart disease 275, 279, 294–5
Heart failure 275, 279
Heavenly devilled eggs 47
Herbs
fresh herb dip 54
herb and Cheddar scones 36
High blood pressure 273–81
causes 275
classification 276–7
clinical studies 280–1
dangers of 279–80
diet and 282–9
measuring 273, 275–6, 278, 298
weight loss and 290–1
Hummus, pitta crisps with 57
Hypertension *see* **High blood pressure**

I,K&L

Indian-style okra with potatoes 212
Indian-style rice with turkey 166
Insulin resistance 290
Italian roasted potatoes 195
Italian-style avocado and mozzarella salad 216
Italian-style tomato dip 54
Kasha (buckwheat grains)
    kasha with onions and mushrooms 128
    marinated duck and kasha salad 162
    warm kasha and seafood salad 188
Kidney disease 277, 280
Lamb
    fragrant lamb with spinach 72
    lamb curry 71
    leg of lamb with double mint sauce 74
Lebanese flat bread 57
Leek and potato soup 227
Lemon
    lemon angel cake with strawberries 264
    lemon-glazed plaice fillets 103
    lemon mousse with strawberries 266
Lentils
    lemony lentil and vegetable salad 174
    lentil risotto 130
    lentils with macaroni 141
    spicy lentil dhal 139
    spicy red cabbage parcels 210
    tomato and lentil soup 237
Lifestyle changes 292–3
Linguine
    cold sesame noodles and vegetables 152
    linguine with no-cook sauce 154
Liquorice 289
Lunch, menu plans 301–9
Lychees
    oriental chicken salad 156

M

Macaroni, lentils with 141
Mackerel and carrots 116
Mangetout with apples and ginger 194
Mangoes
    banana and mango shake 12
    mango chicken salad 164
    mango frozen yoghurt 248
    mango muesli 14
    mango, peach and apricot fizz 244
    stir-fried beef salad with mango 64
    tropical avocado and mango salad 216
Maple syrup
    maple and toasted-walnut bread 35
    pecan waffles with maple, pear and blackberry
        sauce 24
Meat 59–76, 286, 287
Meat loaf, succulent 62

Meatballs
    fusilli and meatballs 67
    minestrone with meatballs 234
Medicines 289, 294–6
Mediterranean roasted vegetable soup 228
Melon
    citrus-grilled chicken breasts with melon salsa 78
    fruit boats with orange glaze 246
Menu planning 301–9
Meringues, chocolate-nut 271
Mexican-style bean and sweetcorn salad 138
Middle Eastern chicken sandwich 83
Middle Eastern leafy green soup 233
Milk
    banana and mango shake 12
    high-vitality milk shake 10
Millet
    aubergine with millet and sesame seeds 127
    millet with spinach and pine nuts 127
Minestrone with meatballs 234
Mint sauce, leg of lamb with 74
Moroccan chicken with couscous 90
Moroccan vegetable tagine 239
Mousse, lemon with strawberries 266
Moxonidine 296
Muesli
    chewy muesli bars 269
    fruity muesli 14
    mango muesli 14
Muffins
    blueberry muffins with lemon glaze 30
    cherry and oat muffins 32
    spicy apple muffins 33
Multi-grain waffles with apple-raspberry
    sauce 25
Mushrooms
    artichoke, mushroom and chicken salad 176
    baked rice with wild mushrooms and cheese
        118
    basmati chicken pilaf 81
    beefy mushroom and barley soup 236
    creamy chicken mushroom casserole 94
    curried mushrooms, peas and potatoes 200
    kasha with onions and mushrooms 128
    lentil risotto 130
    mushroom and herb omelette 18
    portobello pizzas 46
    sausage-stuffed chestnut mushrooms 48
    Spanish rice 119
    stuffed jacket-baked potatoes 214
    tagliatelle with mushroom medley 150
    turkey stroganoff 99
    Tuscan-style baked polenta 136
    veal Marsala 75
Mustard dip, spiced root vegetable wedges
    with 56

N,O

Nectarines
    sweet-and-sour duck salad 178
New England clam chowder 232
Noodles
    cold sesame noodles and vegetables 152
    linguine with no-cook sauce 154
    noodles with roast vegetables 149
    old-fashioned chicken noodle soup 230
    pesto-coated pork chops 68
Nuts 286, 287
    spiced fruits, nuts and seeds 58
Nutty lemon barley 132
Oats
    apple crumble 252
    cherry and oat muffins 32
    chewy muesli bars 269
    fruity muesli 14
    oaty chocolate chip cookies 260
Oils 286, 287
Okra, Indian-style with potatoes 212
Omega-3 fatty acids 288
Omelettes
    butter bean eggah 137
    chickpea and vegetable eggah 137
    mushroom and herb omelette 18
    pepper and potato omelette 17
    tomato and basil soufflé omelette 18
Onions
    bulghur wheat pilaf with tomato, onions and
        basil 133
    kasha with onions and mushrooms 128
    sautéed chicken with caramelised onions 84
Orange
    chicken with rosemary and orange sauce 92
    crispy tuna steaks in citrus sauce 107
    marinated duck salad with bulghur wheat 167
    orange-glazed carrots 192
    orange-glazed poussins 91
    orange mousse 266
    orange-roasted chicken 91
    orange, sultana and walnut bread 28
Oriental chicken salad 156
Oriental sprouted salad 219
Overweight 282, 283, 290

P

Painkillers 289
Pancakes, chicken and cashew 86
Papillote, sole en 104
Parmesan and spring onion puffs 29
Parmesan breadsticks 51
Parmesan waffles 24
Pasta
    cidered pork with red cabbage 70
    cold sesame noodles and vegetables 152

creamy turkey salad with grapes and pecans 185

fusilli and meatballs 67

garden pasta salad 169

green pasta with white beans 145

lentils with macaroni 141

linguine with no-cook sauce 154

noodles with roast vegetables 149

old-fashioned chicken noodle soup 230

pasta salad with cucumber salsa 187

penne primavera 148

pesto-coated pork chops 68

sesame vegetable pasta 196

spaghetti with chickpeas and spicy tomato sauce 153

spaghettini with seafood 108

spicy turkey chilli with spaghetti 100

tagliatelle with cannellini beans 153

tagliatelle with mushroom medley 150

turkey stroganoff 99

Peaches
chicken, peach and rice salad 170

mango, peach and apricot fizz 244

peach and cinnamon smoothie 11

peach soup with almonds 226

peaches and cream bread 34

peachy cottage cheese salad 180

strawberry-peach Bavarian 268

Pearl barley see **Barley**

Pears
fruit with apricot-chocolate cream 253

ginger and pear upside-down cake 265

pecan waffles with maple, pear and blackberry sauce 24

pork and pear salad with pecans 168

Peas
pea fritters 204

sesame stir-fried asparagus and peas 196

see also Mangetout; Sugarsnap peas

Pecan nuts
pecan biscuits 262

pecan waffles with maple, pear and blackberry sauce 24

Penne
green pasta with white beans 145

penne primavera 148

Peppers
asparagus with confetti vinaigrette 190

basmati chicken pilaf 81

beef satay with ginger dipping sauce 43

black-eyed beans with sweet peppers 208

fish baked on a bed of broccoli, sweetcorn and red pepper 115

pepper and potato frittata 20

pepper and potato omelette 17

potato, sweetcorn and pepper frittata 20

roast pepper pinwheels 42

saffron couscous with peppers 142

salmon with pepper and sweetcorn relish 114

sizzling beef fajitas 60

Spanish rice 119

steakhouse salad 179

Persian-style squash couscous 146

Pesto
pesto-coated pork chops 68

pesto-yoghurt dip 54

Pets 295

Pie, chequerboard cherry 256

Pilaf
barley pilaf with herbs 125

basmati chicken pilaf 81

bulghur wheat pilaf with tomato, onions and basil 133

gingery turkey pilaf 81

herbed rice pilaf 120

quinoa pilaf with cherries and walnuts 126

rice pilaf with dried fruits and almonds 120

Pine nuts, millet with spinach and 127

Pineapple
flamed pineapple 251

frozen pineapple and berry slush 242

turkey escalopes with fruity sauce 98

Pinto beans
portobello pizzas 46

refried bean burritos 134

Pitta breads
falafel pittas 140

Greek chicken pitta pockets 83

Middle Eastern chicken sandwich 83

pitta crisps with hummus 57

Pizzas
double-cheese pizza bites 40

portobello pizzas 46

Plaice
lemon-glazed plaice fillets 103

poached fish in vegetable and herb sauce 02

Plum tartlets 254

Polenta 203
Tuscan-style baked polenta 136

Pork
cidered pork with red cabbage 70

pesto-coated pork chops 68

pork and apple salad with hazelnuts 168

pork and pear salad with pecans 168

Portion sizes 290

Portobello pizzas 46

Potassium 282, 283, 288

Potatoes
avocado, potato and tofu salad 184

Brussels sprouts and potatoes with caraway-mustard sauce 215

classic grilled Dover sole 110

country-style mashed potatoes 191

cream of leek and potato soup 227

curried mushrooms, peas and potatoes 200

Indian-style okra with potatoes 212

Italian roasted potatoes 195

mango chicken salad 164

mashed potatoes with herbs 110

New England clam chowder 232

pan-roasted new potatoes with garlic 195

pepper and potato frittata 20

pepper and potato omelette 17

pork and pear salad with pecans 168

potato and carrot purée 203

potato, sweetcorn and pepper frittata 20

roast beef hash 63

seared sirloin with garden vegetables 66

stuffed jacket-baked potatoes 214

zesty Cheddar and asparagus quiche 21

Poultry 77–100, 286, 287

Poussins, orange-glazed 91

Prawns
avocado and prawn cups 184

prawn and bean couscous 90

prawn and cherry tomato sauté 106

prawn curry 71

prawns with dill dressing 181

sauté of king prawns 112

Pregnancy 277

Prunes
sweet couscous 16

Pumpkin
duck and pumpkin salad 162

Q,R

Quesadillas, refried bean 134

Quiche, zesty Cheddar and asparagus 21

Quinoa pilaf with cherries and walnuts 126

Raisins
sweet couscous 16

Raspberries
avocado salad with raspberries 216

multi-grain waffles with apple-raspberry sauce 25

raspberry frozen yoghurt 248

whole-grain griddle cakes with fruit and yoghurt 23

Ratatouille 144

Red cabbage
cidered pork with red cabbage 70

spicy red cabbage parcels 210

turkey salad with red cabbage 175

Red kidney beans
speedy two-bean chilli 240

spicy turkey chilli with spaghetti 100

three beans and rice 138

Refried bean burritos 134

Refried bean quesadillas 134
Relish, pepper and sweetcorn 114
Retinopathy 280
Rice
    baked rice with wild mushrooms and cheese 118
    beefy mushroom and brown rice soup 236
    breakfast sausage burgers 22
    chicken, peach and rice salad 170
    Coronation chicken 160
    herbed brown rice salad with salmon 166
    Indian-style rice with turkey 166
    prawns with dill dressing 181
    roast beef and rice salad 170
    Spanish rice 119
    sweet-and-sour duck salad 178
    three beans and rice 138
    tropical beef and rice salad 173
    see also Pilaf; Risotto; Wild rice
Risotto
    lentil risotto 130
    pearl barley risotto 130
    sunny risotto with carrots 124

S

Saffron couscous with peppers 142
Salads 155–88
    apple and date 186
    artichoke, mushroom and chicken 176
    aubergine and pearl barley 146
    avocado and prawn cups 184
    avocado, potato and tofu 184
    avocado with raspberries 216
    barley and egg 182
    barley, black bean and avocado 158
    celeriac coleslaw 220
    chicken, peach and rice 170
    Chinese-style chicken 159
    Coronation chicken 160
    crab and grapefruit 163
    creamy turkey with grapes and pecans 185
    crunchy nut coleslaw 220
    duck and pumpkin 162
    fresh artichoke and crab 176
    garden pasta 169
    grilled duck, sweet potato and apple 178
    herbed brown rice with salmon 166
    hot cabbage and grape coleslaw 218
    Indian-style rice with turkey 166
    Italian-style avocado and mozzarella 216
    lemony lentil and vegetable 174
    little chicken salad rolls 44
    mango chicken 164
    marinated duck and kasha 162
    marinated duck with bulghur wheat 167
    Mexican-style bean and sweetcorn 138
    oriental chicken 156

oriental sprouted 219
pasta salad with cucumber salsa 187
peachy cottage cheese 180
Persian-style squash couscous 146
pork and apple with hazelnuts 168
pork and pear with pecans 168
prawns with dill dressing 181
roast beef and rice 170
saffron couscous with peppers 142
spicy tabbouleh with chicken 172
steakhouse salad 179
stir-fried beef with mango 64
summer turkey 175
sweet-and-sour duck 178
sweetcorn and whole grain 182
tabbouleh with goat's cheese 172
tropical avocado and mango 216
tropical beef and rice 173
turkey and blueberry 164
turkey with red cabbage 175
warm kasha and seafood 188
warm sesame chicken 159
Salmon
    herbed brown rice salad with salmon 166
    poached salmon with cucumber and dill sauce 102
    salmon with pepper and sweetcorn relish 114
    summer salmon and asparagus 116
Salsas
    cucumber 187
    melon 78
    tomato 134
Salt 282, 283–6, 290, 298, 299
Saturated fats 289, 290
Sausage-stuffed chestnut mushrooms 48
Scallops
    sauté of scallops 112
    scallop and cherry tomato sauté 106
Scones, herb and Cheddar 36
Seafood 102–16
    spaghettini with seafood 108
    warm kasha and seafood salad 188
Seeds, spiced fruits, nuts and 58
Sesame oil
    cold sesame noodles and vegetables 152
    sesame duck pancakes 86
Sesame seeds
    sesame stir-fried asparagus and peas 196
    sesame vegetable pasta 196
    warm sesame chicken salad 159
Sleep 278, 293
Smoking 292, 297
Smoothies
    apricot yoghurt smoothie 13
    banana and apricot smoothie 11
    peach and cinnamon smoothie 11

strawberry and banana smoothie 11
strawberry yoghurt smoothie 13
Snacks and starters 39–58, 290–1, 301
Sodium 283–6, 299
Sole
    classic grilled Dover sole 110
    sole en papillote 104
Soups 221–38
    asparagus and pea 222
    beefy mushroom and barley 236
    beefy mushroom and brown rice 236
    Cheddar cheese and asparagus 229
    Cheddar cheese and broccoli 229
    chickpea with asparagus 238
    chilled cream of carrot 223
    chilled cucumber 222
    chunky borscht 70
    cool blueberry 224
    cream of courgette 223
    cream of leek and potato 227
    leafy greens and herbs 233
    Manhattan clam chowder 232
    Mediterranean roasted vegetable 228
    Middle Eastern leafy green 233
    minestrone with meatballs 234
    New England clam chowder 232
    old-fashioned chicken noodle 230
    peach soup with almonds 226
    tomato and lentil 237
    tomato and yellow split pea 237
Spaghetti
    spaghetti with chickpeas and spicy tomato sauce 153
    spaghettini with seafood 108
    spicy turkey chilli with spaghetti 100
Spanish rice 119
Spinach
    classic grilled Dover sole 110
    fragrant lamb with spinach 72
    millet with spinach and pine nuts 127
    sole en papillote 104
Squash *see* **Butternut squash**
Starters and snacks 39–58
Steakhouse salad 179
Stews
    apricot and coriander tagine 239
    Asian-style fish casserole 116
    chicken and apricot casserole 95
    chicken jamboree 94
    creamy chicken mushroom casserole 94
    Moroccan vegetable tagine 239
    squash and aubergine casserole 203
Strawberries
    berry shake 10
    frozen pineapple and berry slush 242
    lemon angel cake with strawberries 264

lemon mousse with strawberries 266
strawberry and banana smoothie 11
strawberry-peach Bavarian 268
strawberry yoghurt smoothie 13
Stress 294, 299–300
Stroke 275, 279–80
Sugarsnap peas
asparagus and pea soup 222
lemony sugarsnap peas 198
Moroccan chicken with couscous 90
summer salmon and asparagus 116
Sunny risotto with carrots 124
Sweet-and-sour cabbage 206
Sweet-and-sour duck salad 178
Sweet potatoes
grilled duck, sweet potato and apple salad 178
Sweetcorn
corn bread 38
fish baked on a bed of broccoli, sweetcorn
and red pepper 115
Mexican-style bean and sweetcorn salad 138
potato, sweetcorn and pepper frittata 20
roast beef hash 63
salmon with pepper and sweetcorn relish 114
sweetcorn and whole grain salad 182
sweetcorn fritters 204
Tex-Mex sweetcorn bake 202
Sweets 286, 287

T

Tabbouleh
spicy tabbouleh with chicken 172
tabbouleh with goat's cheese 172
Tagines
apricot and coriander tagine 239
Moroccan vegetable tagine 239
Tagliatelle
tagliatelle with cannellini beans 153
tagliatelle with mushroom medley 150
turkey stroganoff 99
Tarts
banana custard tart 257
fresh plum tartlets 254
Tex-Mex corn bread 38
Tex-Mex sweetcorn bake 202
Three beans and rice 138
Tilapia
steamed fish Italian style 111
steamed fish with ginger and sesame 111
Tofu
avocado, potato and tofu salad 184
Tomatoes
balsamic baked tomatoes with Parmesan
crumbs 197
bulghur wheat pilaf with tomato, onions and
basil 133

country captain chicken 88
double-cheese pizza bites 40
fusilli and meatballs 67
gazpacho quencher 245
Italian-style tomato dip 54
lamb curry 71
lentils with macaroni 141
linguine with no-cook sauce 154
prawn and cherry tomato sauté 106
roasted garlic and cherry tomato filling 214
salsa 134
scallop and cherry tomato sauté 106
spaghetti with chickpeas and spicy tomato
sauce 153
speedy two-bean chilli 240
spicy turkey chilli with spaghetti 100
succulent meat loaf 62
tomato and basil soufflé omelette 18
tomato and citrus blush 245
tomato and lentil soup 237
tomato and yellow split pea soup 237
tomato chutney 72
Tortillas
refried bean burritos 134
refried bean quesadillas 134
roast pepper pinwheels 42
sizzling beef fajitas 60
Tropical beef and rice salad 173
Tuna steaks in citrus sauce 107
Turkey
breakfast sausage burgers 22
country-style mashed potatoes 191
creamy turkey salad with grapes and pecans 185
gingery turkey pilaf 81
Indian-style rice with turkey 166
minestrone with meatballs 234
spicy red cabbage parcels 210
spicy turkey chilli with spaghetti 100
summer turkey salad 175
turkey and blueberry salad 164
turkey escalopes with fruity sauce 98
turkey piccata 96
turkey salad with red cabbage 175
turkey stroganoff 99
Tuscan-style baked polenta 136

V

Vanilla chiffon cake 259
Vasodilators 296
Veal
veal escalopes with lemon garlic sauce 76
veal Marsala 75
Vegetables 286, 287
braised vegetables with falafel and yoghurt
sauce 144
bulghur wheat with spring vegetables 122

chicken jamboree 94
chickpea and vegetable eggah 137
cold sesame noodles and vegetables 152
crudités with three dips 54
Mediterranean roasted vegetable soup 228
Middle Eastern leafy green soup 233
Moroccan vegetable tagine 239
noodles with roast vegetables 149
penne primavera 148
poached chicken breasts in vegetable and
herb sauce 82
ratatouille 144
soup of leafy greens and herbs 233
spiced root vegetable wedges with creamy
mustard dip 56
spicy lentil dhal 139
vegetable dumplings 50
vegetable stir-fry with spicy garlic sauce 209
*see also individual types of vegetable and
Salads*
Vegetarian chilli burgers 240
Vegetarian recipes 117–54
Vinaigrette
asparagus with confetti vinaigrette 190
Vitamins 288

W,Y

Waffles
multi-grain waffles with apple-raspberry sauce
25
Parmesan waffles 24
pecan waffles with maple, pear and blackberry
sauce 24
Walnuts
chocolate-nut meringues 271
maple and toasted-walnut bread 35
quinoa pilaf with cherries and walnuts 126
wild rice with walnuts 131
Watermelon
tomato and citrus blush 245
Weight 282, 290–1
**Whole-grain griddle cakes with fruit and
yoghurt** 23
Wholewheat grains
sweetcorn and whole grain salad 182
Wild rice with walnuts 131
Wonton wrappers
chicken dumplings with sesame dipping sauce
50
Yoghurt
apricot yoghurt smoothie 13
high-vitality milk shake 10
mango frozen yoghurt 248
pesto-yoghurt dip 54
raspberry frozen yoghurt 248
strawberry yoghurt smoothie 13

Reader's Digest Project Team
Project editor Rachel Warren Chadd
Designer Jane McKenna
Recipe editor Norma Macmillan
Nutritionist Fiona Hunter
Recipe tester Susanna Tee
Proofreader Ron Pankhurst
Indexer Hilary Bird

Reader's Digest General Books
Editorial director Julian Browne
Art director Anne-Marie Bulat
Managing editor Nina Hathway
Picture resource manager Sarah Stewart-Richardson
Pre-press account manager Dean Russell

Printed and bound in Europe by Arvato Iberia

Beat High Blood Pressure Cookbook published by The Reader's Digest
Association Limited, London.

First edition copyright © 2005
The Reader's Digest Association Limited, 11 Westferry Circus,
Canary Wharf, London E14 4HE
www.readersdigest.co.uk

Reprinted 2009

We are committed both to the quality of our products and the service we
provide to our customers. We value your comments, so please do contact us
on 08705 113366 or via our web site at www.readersdigest.co.uk

If you have any comments or suggestions about the content of our books,
you can contact us at: gbeditorial@readersdigest.co.uk

PHOTOGRAPHERS
Sang An, Sue Atkinson, Martin Brigdale,
Beatriz DaCosta, Mark Ferri, Gus Filgate, Michael Grand,
Amanda Heywood, Martin Jacobs, Graham Kirk,
Lisa Koening, William Lingwood, David Murray,
Sean Myers, Simon Smith, Jules Selmes, Elizabeth Watt

Additional images courtesy of Photodisc

Beat High Blood Pressure Cookbook was adapted
from Eat to Beat High Blood Pressure published by
The Reader's Digest Association, Inc., USA
First edition © 2004

Book code 400-241 UP0000-4
ISBN 978 0 276 44039 7
Oracle code 250009337H.00.24